To Hunter Hancock — and Chris too,
with best regards —
Frank Cross.

Handbook of

FISHES of KANSAS

Frank B. Cross

STATE BIOLOGICAL SURVEY &
THE UNIVERSITY OF KANSAS MUSEUM OF NATURAL HISTORY

University of Kansas
Museum of Natural History

Miscellaneous Publication No. 45

The Handbook of Fishes of Kansas results from a continuation of the work of the State Biological Survey of Kansas and is a response to many requests for a booklet of this kind.

Cover Illustration—The white crappie, *Pomoxis annularis* Rafinesque. Watercolor by Eugene Pacheco.

PRINTED BY
ROBERT R. (BOB) SANDERS, STATE PRINTER
TOPEKA, KANSAS
1967

31-6169

HANDBOOK OF FISHES OF KANSAS

By

Frank B. Cross

Contribution from The State Biological Survey of Kansas

MUSEUM OF NATURAL HISTORY
UNIVERSITY OF KANSAS
LAWRENCE, KANSAS

University of Kansas
Museum
of Natural History

Editor: E. Raymond Hall

Miscellaneous Publication No. 45, pp. 1-357, 4 colored plates, 20 numbered figures and other illustrations
Published April 24, 1967

University of Kansas
Lawrence, Kansas

PRINTED BY
ROBERT R. (BOB) SANDERS, STATE PRINTER
TOPEKA, KANSAS
1967

31-6169

CONTENTS

INTRODUCTION

The purpose of this handbook is to provide means for identifying fishes found in Kansas, information about their distribution within the State, and general accounts of their habits. It is hoped that publication of the handbook will summon new records of fishes from sources that I have overlooked, that the references cited will lead students into further study of the literature on fishes and into investigations that answer some of the many remaining questions about the natural history of fishes in Kansas, and that the information summarized will facilitate assessment of future changes in the composition and distribution of our fish-fauna.

Approximately 130 kinds (species) of fish are thought to inhabit Kansas, the exact number depending on whether doubtful reports of a few species are accepted as valid records. Most of the Kansas species occur widely in the Mississippi River Basin. Kansas has no endemic species, although one catfish in the Neosho River approaches that status, as does one darter in the Arkansas River System. Our native fishes are mainly fluviatile kinds, because the State had no lakes of consequence prior to the construction of impoundments in the last several decades. Oxbows or "horseshoe lakes" existed, of course, owing to natural shortening of stream-channels. Oxbows added diversity to the natural habitat, but their effect on the composition of the native fish-fauna was minor because of their temporary nature and frequent inundation by floodwaters of the parent streams.

Several factors, both natural and artificial, account for the kinds of fishes that we now have, and their present distributions. Obviously access of fishes to the area is fundamental; secondarily, characteristics of the physical environment are important, as are adaptive reactions by the animals to different environments. Access is dependent primarily on continuity of stream-systems, but environmental conditions also affect the dispersal of fishes. Stream-environments vary according to soil-type, local relief, and climate.

Surface-water in Kansas flows into the Mississippi River by way of two major river-basins (Figure 1). The Missouri Basin, comprising all tributaries of Kansas River and several streams tributary to Osage River (Marais des Cygnes, Little Osage, and Marmaton rivers), occupies approximately the northern half of Kansas. Streams south of the Kansas and Osage river systems discharge into the

Arkansas River. The two major basins are now so well separated that interchange of their fishes is unlikely, but these basins have not always been isolated. Western segments of the Kansas and Arkansas rivers once formed part of the same Plains drainage system, and connections between them persisted through much of the Pleistocene (Frye and Leonard, 1952; Metcalf, 1966). The separation of the two basins is relatively recent in terms of geologic time. The effect of their separation on the present composition of the fish-fauna seems minor. Of the 130 species now known from Kansas, 110 occur in the Arkansas System, and 97 have been reported from tributaries of the Missouri River within the State. Hence, a majority of our native fishes occupy both basins.

Whereas the divide between major drainageways splits Kansas into north and south halves, aquatic environments vary most from east to west in Kansas. These differences in habitats for fishes are associated with physiographic and climatic differences that affect the nature of stream-bottom materials, the amount of runoff, the strength of subsurface aquifers, and the permanency of streams. If, then, the State is divided arbitrarily into eastern and western halves, a rough measure of the effect of environmental factors on fish-distribution can be obtained.

All species of fish known from Kansas are found in the eastern half of the State. None is now restricted to the western half, although two species (the plains killifish and the Arkansas River shiner) are mainly western in occurrence. Records of only 51 species have been obtained west of 98°30′ longitude—38 from the Arkansas River System and 48 from the Kansas River System. Omitting species the distributions of which have been affected by introductions, only 24 fishes are known from the western half of the Arkansas System, and 32 from the western Kansas River Basin. Twenty-one species are common to both systems. Therefore, the present distribution of fishes in Kansas depends more on local environments than on isolation in different stream-systems.

The Spring and Neosho rivers harbor more kinds of fishes than do other rivers in Kansas. Faunal diversity in the Spring-Neosho drainage is enhanced by proximity to the Ozark region, which extends into Cherokee County (Fig. 3), and by the dissected terrain and numerous small aquifers of the Flint Hills, which extend north-south as a narrow exposure of resistant limestones in eastern Kansas. Southeastern streams benefit also from greater annual precipitation than occurs elsewhere in Kansas. The gradient

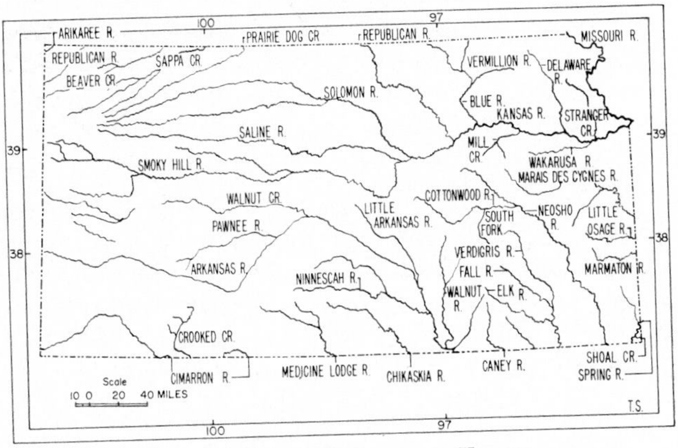

FIG. 1. Principal streams in Kansas.

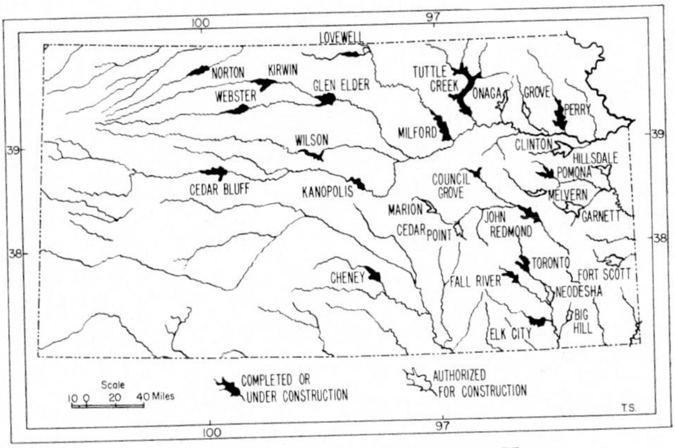

FIG. 2. Principal impoundments in Kansas

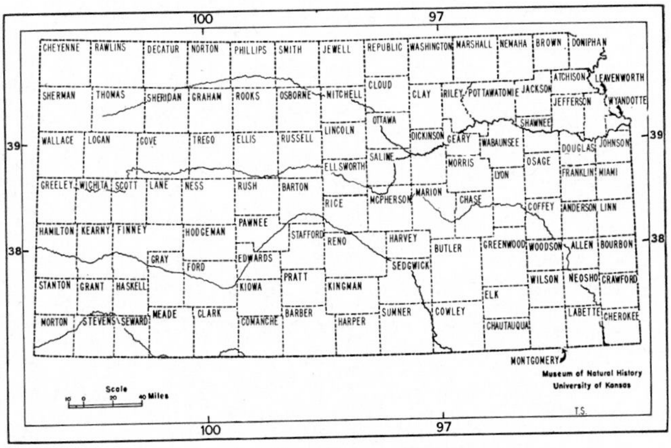

FIG. 3. Counties in Kansas.

of these streams is comparatively steep; their turbidity and their fluctuation in volume of flow are less than elsewhere. The southeastern streams provide diverse and persistent habitats or "niches" for occupancy by many kinds of fish. In contrast, most western streams are now intermittent, or flow over shallow, sandy beds characterized by uniformity of habitat. Furthermore, most western streams fluctuate more, and their waters are muddier, than streams draining the dissected uplands of eastern Kansas. The fauna of the western streams is not diverse, consisting principally of those species, also present farther east, that withstand erratic variation in their habitat.

Natural factors that control the distribution of fishes, as discussed above, are subject to alteration by man. Artificial changes in habitats for fishes, and in the distribution and abundance of fishes, can result from: intensive land-use for agricultural, industrial, and residential purposes; consumption of water or its pollution; construction of impoundments that modify the depth, width, and rate of discharge of streams; and introductions of fishes into places where the same species did not occur naturally. The effects of these modifications are seldom abrupt and obvious; rather, the resultant faunal changes are often so gradual that they escape notice, or grow vague in the memory of those who witnessed the transition. Consequently, one hears contradictory descriptions of the "original" appearance of various streams in Kansas, and conflicting opinions as to the kinds and abundance of fishes that originally occupied those streams.

Reliable information about changes in the fish-fauna that are caused by man's activities is useful. Because fishes are a valuable resource, the nature and extent of our own effect on that resource has direct importance to us. Indirectly, knowledge of changes in the fish-fauna may have importance as an index whereby man can recognize environmental changes that have broad significance to our own welfare.

Major, artificial changes in the fish-faunas of some areas eastward and westward from Kansas have been reported by Trautman (1957) and Miller (1961). In Kansas, the historical record seems good enough to permit an appraisal of man's influence on native fishes and their habitats, if the beginnings of white settlement are taken as a point of departure. Indians occurred in such low density, and made so little use of fish in the region including Kansas (Rostlund, 1952), that they probably had scant effect on the natural fish-populations. Thus, the fish-fauna that existed when Indians were displaced by immigrants to Kansas in the mid-nineteenth century probably was truly "natural."

Knowledge of fishes in Kansas began to accumulate as early as did agricultural and industrial activity that may have altered the fish-fauna. A few kinds of fish were mentioned in journals of the earliest exploring expeditions that crossed the Plains. In the mid-nineteenth century, several kinds of fishes from the region of Kansas were made known by exploring parties seeking westward routes for railroads (Girard, 1856, 1858; Abbott, 1860a, 1860b; Cope, 1864, 1865a, 1865b, 1871, and others); regrettably, the precise localities of capture were not indicated for most species. Numerous fish-collections were made in subsequent decades, as settlement progressed westward across Kansas. These surveys culminated in the 1880's, permitting publication of comprehensive lists of fishes in Kansas by Cragin (1885b) and Graham (1885b), as well as a valuable report by Evermann and Cox (1896) concerning fishes of the whole Missouri River Basin. Increasingly well-documented literature on the regional fish-fauna has appeared in the past half-century. A recent review of the fishes of the Kansas River Basin by one of my students, A. L. Metcalf (Metcalf, 1966), deserves special mention. His publication should be read by all who are seriously interested in the origin and historical record of species that inhabit the central Plains region.

Apart from records of the fishes themselves, early descriptions of Plains streams are useful in interpreting changes in the natural fish-fauna. Metcalf (1966) quoted from accounts by many early occupants of the Kansas River Basin who recorded their impressions of primeval stream-conditions. Similar observations are available on the pristine Arkansas River and its tributaries. Examples are in the journals and reports of G. C. Sibley, leader of a party that established the route of the Santa Fe Trail in 1825-1827 (Gregg, 1952). Although Sibley's writings indicate that several clear creeks having rather deep channels were crossed, the elation evident in his remarks quoted below indicate to me that strong springs and constant streams were few; the quotation is from Gregg (1952:60) and pertains to Diamond Springs, in what is now Morris County.

> ". . . a very fine Spring . . . uncommonly large and beautiful, and the Water very pure & cold. I have Seldom seen so fine a Spring any-where. After so hot a day [11 August 1825], this fine Water was a luxury to us all."

The channel of the Arkansas River was described repeatedly by

Sibley as being broad, shallow, and sand-filled. In a report to the Secretary of War, he and others summarized their impression of that river in central and western Kansas as follows:

". . . the character of the River varies but very little indeed. It bears a uniform width of from 400 to 500 yards, a depth of from 18 inches to 4 feet—velocity of current, 2¼ miles an hour—its bed sand—banks, low and loose—Water turbid, Sometimes filthy—channel crowded with Sand banks and Islets . . .

"Its annual floods occur in June, and frequently inundate much of the adjacent flat land. In its ordinary Stages, it may be crossed by carriages without the least difficulty, or a moment's delay." (Gregg, 1952:208.)

The Cimarron River where it traverses the area now in Grant, Stevens, and Morton counties evoked these comments by Sibley:

"The Semerone Creek or River exhibits so far but a poor Stream, if that can be called a stream which is only to be seen here & there in Puddles at intervals of from ½ to 1½ mile, which intervals are of loose dry Sand.

"Where we Struck it today [1 October 1825] however, find a small *rivulet* of clear running *brackish* Water. The Stones, grass & earth adjacent encrusted with a kind of Saline Substance . . ." (Gregg, 1952:90.)

On the previous day, Sibley wrote that the Cimarron had surface-flow at latitude 37°14′17″, but that the party nevertheless "Dug in the Sand about 18 Inches deep & got pretty good Water, that which stands or runs on the surface is sulpherous & brackish & strongly *seasoned* with Buffalo Urine." (Gregg, 1952:89.)

Sibley's descriptions seem fitting even today, except that domestic stock has replaced the bison, and Diamond Springs has lost much of its appeal. His writings and those of other observers persuade me that most habitats of fishes in Kansas have not suffered conspicuous modification since settlement.

If descriptive accounts of prairie streams provide insight into the probable composition of their fish-fauna, inferences in the reverse direction are equally valid and meaningful. The structural adaptations of fishes reveal much about the environment in which they evolved. Several species indigenous to Kansas are morphologically adapted for life in shallow, sandy, turbid rivers. Examples of such adaptations are (1) reduced size of scales, especially on the nape, and embedding of those scales in a thickened epidermis—presumably as an adjustment to molar effects of drifting sand; (2) reduced size of the eyes, or partial shielding of them by surrounding tissue; and (3) increased development of other sensory structures such as taste-buds in the skin on the head, body, and fins, compensating for reduced vision (Hubbs, 1940:202; Moore, 1950; Metcalf, 1966:

82-85). Also, the life histories of some of our commonest fishes show adaptations to fluctuating waterlevels and unstable stream-bottoms, especially in modes of reproduction. These characteristics evolve slowly. Their occurrence in native fishes adds evidence that Plains streams—the major ones, at least— have been shallow, sandy, and erratically variable in flow for many thousands of years.

The above generalizations do not mean that no changes have occurred in local stream-conditions and local fish-faunas within the single century in which "civilized" man has been at work on the land in Kansas. The lowermost part of the Kansas River once had pools deeper than any there now, judging from early records of deep-water species no longer obtainable from the Kansas River. On the other hand, the western sectors of some rivers provide deeper water than in the past, because of recent construction of large impoundments in their floodplains and tens of thousands of smaller lakes on their watersheds. Consequently, some species that are ill-adapted for life in sandy rivers or intermittent creeks have become established far to the west of their original ranges.

A few kinds of fish that were known to inhabit streams of Kansas in the late 1800's have been extirpated, or their populations have been decimated locally. Many of these species live in small streams that have permanent flow and clear pools with aquatic vegetation. To date, the effects of civilization probably have been more pronounced on small, upland streams than on large rivers in Kansas. The adverse effects seem attributable to recession of watertables, siltation originating from nearby croplands, and diversion of springs for domestic use. In all instances where declining abundance of a species is suspected, attention is directed to that trend in the appropriate species-account.

EXPLANATION OF SPECIES-ACCOUNTS

Accounts of the 130 species of fishes for which plausible records exist in Kansas comprise the major part of this handbook. Most accounts contain an illustration of the fish, a map of its known distribution, a list of literature-references, a descriptive characterization, and a general discussion of the status of the species in the State. The initial reference-list includes all literature, known to me, that contributes original data about the species in Kansas. The list is organized as a chronological synonymy, correlating names that have been used for each species with the name recommended here. The scientific and vernacular names that I accept are those used in "*A list of common and scientific names of fishes from the United States and Canada*" (Amer. Fish. Soc., Spec. Publ. 2, second edition, 1960), with this exception: Some vernacular names given in the publication cited are changed slightly for grammatical reasons (*e. g.*, "shovelnose sturgeon" emended to "shovel-nosed sturgeon").

The symbols used on distributional maps have the following meaning: Circles represent records prior to 1915, whereas discs (solid black dots) represent records obtained since 1915; circles and discs bearing short vertical lines represent literature-records for which I have not seen specimens. Triangles represent records from impoundments. The distributional records shown were compiled mainly from collections obtained by personnel of the State Biological Survey and the Museum of Natural History, at The University of Kansas. Catalogue numbers of important specimens are indicated in a few accounts. Museums in which these specimens are deposited are The University of Kansas Museum of Natural History (KU), the University of Michigan Museum of Zoology (UMMZ), the United States National Museum (USNM), and the zoological collections of Kansas State University (KSU).

The sequence in which the several families of fishes appear in the text follows the arrangement proposed by Greenwood, Rosen, Weitzman, and Myers (1966).

METHODS FOR IDENTIFICATION OF SPECIES

Identification of an unknown fish requires an understanding of descriptive terminology that may be unfamiliar to some users of this book. Therefore, a glossary of terms employed in the keys and species-accounts is provided on pages 20-23. The glossary is supplemented by illustrations that depict some of the characteristics on which identifications are based.

Several of the characters useful for identification pertain to counts of scales, fin-rays, or other structures; additional characters pertain to the relative size (or shape) of body-parts, and are expressed as proportional measurements. For characters that are used most often, and for the terms relating to them, a more detailed explanation than that in the glossary is given below.

Lateral-line scales refers to the total number of scales in the distinctive lateral-line row (see glossary) apparent on the mid-sides of most fish. The count begins with one scale that is in contact with the bony shoulder-girdle, at the back of the head of the fish, and terminates with the scale that lies at the structural base of the caudal fin (see Fig. 4). That base can be located by flexing the caudal fin from side to side and noting the point at which a crease appears on the body immediately before the fin. Scales posterior to this crease overlie rays and membranes of the fin itself and are *not* counted.

Scale rows around body refers to the number of longitudinal rows of scales, counted at the point of greatest body-depth. Most fishes in which this character is used have their greatest depth immediately before the dorsal and pelvic fins. In making the count, the lateral line is taken as the point of departure. Scale rows dorsal to the lateral line are enumerated separately from those ventral to the lateral line. The count is begun with the first row of scales above the lateral line on one side of the fish, and continues by tallying all scale rows over the crest of the back and downward to the lateral line on the opposite side. The process is repeated ventrally. A count given as 11—2—13 means that the fish has 11 rows of scales dorsal to its lateral lines, and 13 rows ventral to the lateral-line rows; because the lateral-line row on each side is omitted from the count, a "2" is inserted to permit accurate expression of the total number of rows, or *circumferential* scale-count.

Scale rows around caudal peduncle are counted in the same manner as scale rows around the body; but, the count is made at the narrowest point on the peduncle (see Fig. 4 and glossary).

Predorsal scale rows are defined as the total number of rows ot scales that cross the midline of the back, obliquely, between the occiput and the origin of the dorsal fin.

Fin-rays (*spines* and *soft-rays*) refer to the rodlike structures that support membranes in the fins. In soft-rayed fins that are angular in shape and have a relatively straight leading edge, only the *principal rays* are counted, as shown in Figure 6B. In fins that curve gradually away from the body-wall, the *total rays* must be enumerated, including all anterior rudiments (Fig. 6A). In either case, the last two soft-rays, at the posterior end of the fin, are counted as one ray if their bases are notably closer together than are the bases of other rays anterior to these two (Fig. 6). The counts given (in keys) for the dorsal and anal fins of minnows and suckers are of principal rays; counts given for the same two fins in topminnows, and for the anal fin in catfishes, are of total rays. All rays are counted in the pectoral and pelvic fins in all fishes. Fin-spines are counted separately from soft-rays. Means for distinguishing soft-rays from spines are indicated in the glossary.

Pharyngeal teeth are conical structures projecting from the fifth (pharyngeal) gill arch (Fig. 9); its location is indicated in the glossary. A tool useful for removing the pharyngeal arch from minnows and suckers can be made by heating the tip of an ordinary dissecting-needle and bending the tip into a minute hook. The hooked tip is inserted alongside the dorsal and ventral arms of the pharyngeal arch, which can then be torn free of their ligamentous attachments. Fine-tipped forceps also are useful in separating the arch from the soft tissue in which it is embedded, but the operation must be performed gently to avoid breaking the teeth. In minnows, the teeth are situated in one or two rows on the crescent-shaped arch (three rows in the introduced carp). The primary row consists of four or five teeth; the secondary "row," if present, contains one or two teeth situated within the curve of the primary row. A count given as 2,5—4,2 means that 2 teeth exist in the secondary row of each arch, and that the pharyngeal arch on the left side of the fish has a primary row of five teeth whereas the right pharyngeal arch has but 4 teeth in the primary row. A count of 0,4—4,0 indicates that the 4 teeth present on each arch all lie in the same plane or row. The central portion of the arch must be examined carefully, under magnification, for evidence of broken or lost teeth; a well-defined pit adjacent to other teeth (or the broken base of a tooth) constitutes such evidence, which should be incorporated in the count.

Vertebral counts given in descriptive paragraphs were obtained by means of X-rays, and are total counts inclusive of the hypural vertebra. In counting vertebrae of cypriniform fishes (minnows, suckers, and catfishes), it was assumed that four centra are represented in the fused Webberian group anteriorly. Vertebral counts are not essential for identification of any species discussed.

Proportional measurements are expressed either in integers or as fractions—for example, "head length 4.0-5.0 in standard length," or "head length 1/4 to 1/5 of standard length." The distances represented by terms such as "head length" and "standard length" are indicated in Figure 4 or in the glossary. The smaller dimension can be established conveniently by means of an implement called dividers, which can then be rotated step-wise along the larger dimension. If the length of the head stepped into the standard length of a specimen proved to be 4.5, the head length would be "more than 4.0 in" or "less than 1/4" the standard length of that specimen.

Use of Keys

The keys form a sequence of numbered couplets (paired, contrasting statements) beginning on page 24. Both parts of each couplet should be read carefully before deciding which of the two statements best describes the fish at hand. Use of the keys proceeds as follows, from couplet number 1 on page 24:

(1) If your fish lacks jaws, has a mouth that resembles a suction-cup, and has a line of seven gill-pits rather than a single slotlike gill-opening, you are

fortunate to have found a lamprey (Family Petromyzontidae) and you may turn to page 30 for further information about it. If, on the other hand, your specimen does have jaws and a single gill-opening, continue use of the key with couplet number 2.

(2) Read both alternatives in couplet 2, and refer to Figure 5. Then, if you conclude that the caudal fin of your fish is symmetrical and has a vertical base (homocercal), go to the couplet numbered 6 (otherwise go to couplet 3).

(3) In couplet 6, if the first statement accurately describes your specimen, it is an American eel (Family Anguillidae, page 49). If the second statement better fits the fish at hand, proceed to couplet number 7, and continue as above until specific identification has been made. Often, the identification will require use of a second set of keys, to the kinds of fishes within families that are represented by more than one species in Kansas.

As a precautionary measure, you should check the characteristics of several individual fish that you believe to be alike, while utilizing the keys to identify them. Most kinds of fish have a wide range of individual variation, as is implied by the range in scale-count or fin-ray count that is cited in each half of many couplets. The range of variation given is inclusive of most (but not necessarily all) individuals of a species; therefore, failure of a specimen to "fit the key," or its misidentification, may result from unusual features of that specimen relative to others of its kind. Examination of several specimens (if available) will minimize this problem. For the same reason, namely because of intraspecific variation, some species are "keyed out" in more than one way, accounting for duplicate appearance of the names of those species in different parts of the same key.

Most difficulties encountered in identifying particular fish will reflect unusual but still "normal" characteristics of the species. Nevertheless, users of this handbook should remember that knowledge of our fish-fauna is incomplete. Additional species are likely to be found within the State, and extensions of the known distributions of other species are certain. Therefore, "unidentifiable" specimens command real interest, as do specimens caught outside the areas of known occurrence as given in the species-accounts. Such specimens, preserved in formalin or alcohol, can be packaged as directed on page 329 and sent to the Museum of Natural History at The University of Kansas for identification.

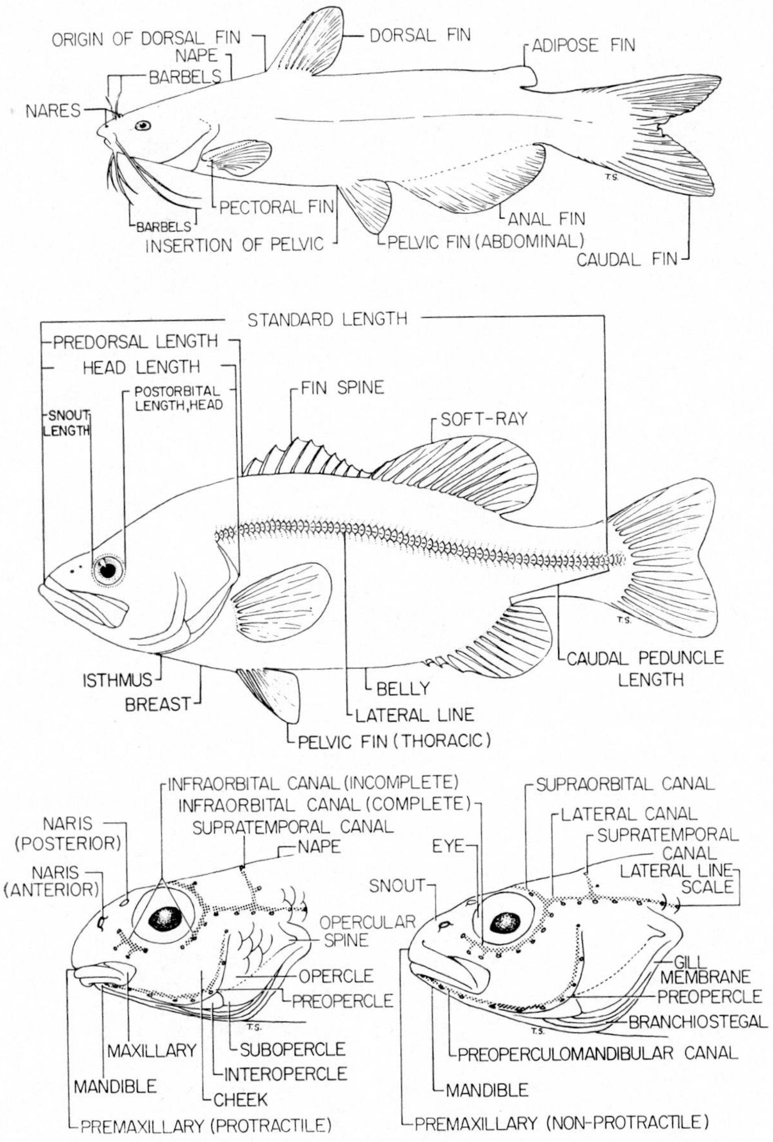

FIG. 4. Structural features of fishes that are used often for identification. Species shown are channel catfish (top), largemouth (center), johnny darter (lower left), and stippled darter (lower right).

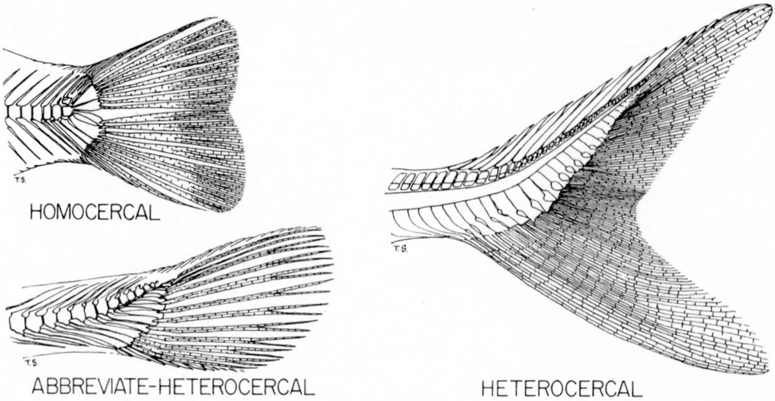

FIG. 5. Kinds of caudal fins in fishes. Homocercal fin shown is that of black crappie; abbreviate-heterocercal, short-nosed gar; heterocercal, paddlefish.

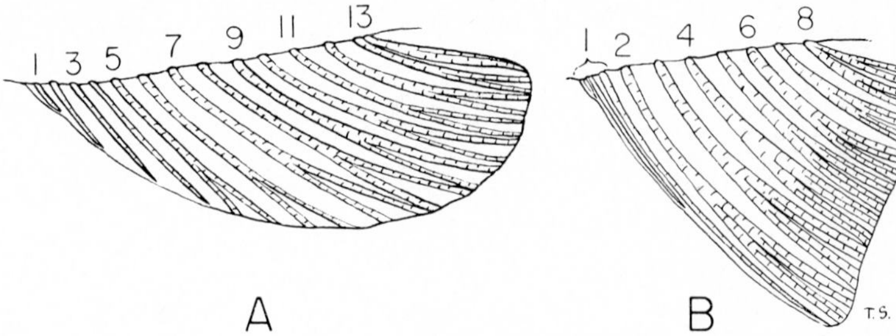

FIG. 6. Hypothetical anal fins (or, in effect, inverted dorsal fins) showing how fin-rays are counted. (Redrawn from Bailey, 1956: Fig. 7.)

A. Total ray-count, as taken in fins that slope gradually away from the body contour.

B. Principal ray-count, as taken in fins that have a straight leading edge (rudimentary [procurrent] rays contiguous anteriorly).

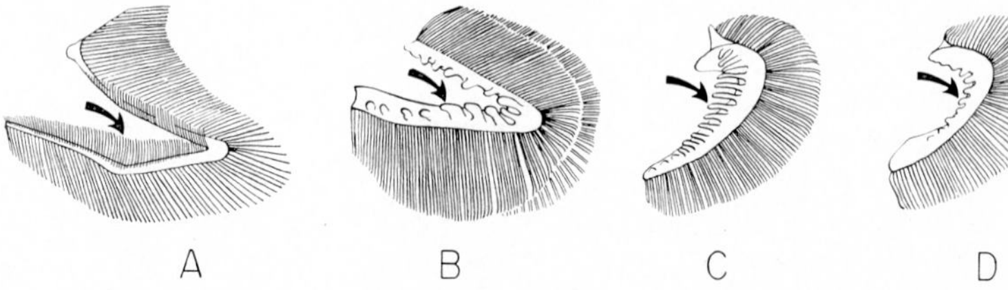

FIG. 7. First gill arches of four fishes, showing differences in number and shape of gill rakers (on left or concave side of each arch, see arrows).

A. Rakers numerous and slender, as in Clupeidae. Gizzard shad illustrated.

B. Rakers short and knoblike, as in Hiodontidae. Goldeye illustrated.

C. Rakers slender, as in species of *Lepomis* other than the longear and the redear. Green sunfish illustrated.

D. Rakers short and knoblike, as in the longear (illustrated) and the redear.

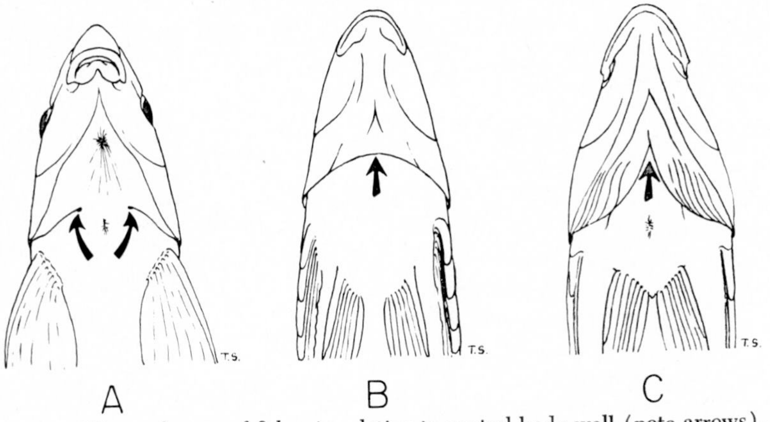

FIG. 8. Gill membranes of fishes in relation to ventral body wall (note arrows).

A. Right and left membranes bound down to isthmus, as in minnows and suckers (carpsucker illustrated); a needle-tip slipped into the gill cleft on one side cannot be moved freely across to the opposite side. Gill membranes free from isthmus in B and C.

B. Gill membranes broadly joined across isthmus, as in banded darter.

C. Gill membranes separate (right and left sides not conjoined), as in stippled darter.

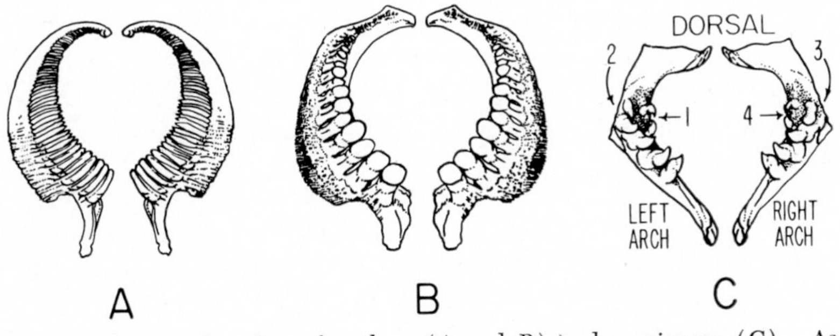

FIG. 9. Pharyngeal arches of suckers (A and B) and a minnow (C). As shown, arches have been laid on a horizontal surface with teeth projecting upward. (Redrawn from Bailey, 1956:Fig. 5.)

A. Golden redhorse; Teeth numerous and slender, in a single row (comblike).

B. River redhorse; Lower teeth stumplike or molariform, but numerous and uniserial.

C. Creek chub; Teeth few, confined to central part of arch, often hooked (two-rowed in this species). The sequence in which rows are counted is indicated by numerals 1, 2, 3, 4. The count of number of teeth therefore is 2,5—4,2. See p. 15 for additional explanation.

GLOSSARY

abdominal (adj.): pertaining to the belly; pelvic fins abdominal when inserted far behind the bases of pectoral fins (Fig. 4).

acute (adj.): sharply pointed.

adipose fin: fleshy, rayless fin on the midline of the back between the dorsal and caudal fins (Fig. 4).

adnate (adj.): grown together (united). See Fig. 17.

air bladder (n.): membranous, gas-filled sac in the upper part of the body cavity.

anal fin: ventral unpaired fin (Fig. 4).

barbel (n.): slender, flexible process located near the mouth; tactile and gustatory in function (Figs. 4, 11D, 12A).

basioccipital (n., adj.): hindmost bone on the underside of the skull. In *Hybognathus*, the basioccipital can be exposed by cutting across the isthmus (throat) and bending the head upward. The posterior process of the basioccipital is then seen as a posterior projection into the anterior part of the body cavity; the bone and its attached muscles pivot downward as the head is bent back (Fig. 14).

belly (n.): ventral surface posterior to the base of the pelvic fins, anterior to the anal fin (Fig. 4).

bicuspid (adj.): having two points (applicable especially to teeth).

branchiostegal (n., adj.): one of the bones supporting the gill membranes, ventral to the operculum (Fig. 4).

breast (n.): ventral surface anterior to the insertion of the pelvic fins (Fig. 4).

caducous (adj.): readily shed (as belly-scales in genus *Percina*, Fig. 20).

caecum (n.): blind pouch or other saclike evagination, especially at the pylorus (junction of stomach and small intestine).

canine teeth: in fishes, conical teeth, in the front part of the jaws, that project beyond the others.

caudal fin: tail fin (Fig. 4).

caudal peduncle: narrow region of the body in front of the caudal fin (from the posterior end of the base of the anal fin to the base of the caudal fin; Fig. 4).

cheek (n.): area between the eye and the preopercle bone (Fig. 4).

circumoral teeth: horny teeth that surround the esophagus in lampreys.

circumorbital (n., adj.): any one of a series of thin dermal bones behind, below, and in front of the eye (preorbital anterior, suborbitals below, postorbitals behind).

cleithrum (n): major bone of the pectoral girdle, extending upward from the fin-base and forming the posterior margin of the gill chamber.

compressed (adj.): narrow from side to side (flattened laterally).

concave (adj.): curved inward (hollowed).

convex (adj.): curved outward (arched).

ctenoid scales: scales that bear a patch of spinelike prickles on the exposed (posterior) field.

cycloid scales: more or less rounded scales that bear no ctenii or prickles.

depressed (adj.): flattened from top to bottom; wider than deep.

distal (adj.): remote from point of attachment (free edge of fins, farthest from their bases).

dorsal (adj., n.): pertaining to the back; often used as an abbreviation for dorsal fin.

dorsal fin (n.): median unpaired fin (or fins, exclusive of adipose) atop the back (Fig. 4, 10).

emarginate (adj.): having the distal margin notched.

entire (adj.): having an edge (as of a spine or bone) that is smooth rather than serrate.

falcate (adj.): sickle-shaped (with a concave margin).

fin-ray (n.): a bony or cartilaginous rod supporting the fin-membrane. *Soft-rays* usually are segmented (cross-striated), often branched, and flexible near their tips (Figs. 4, 5, and 6), whereas *spines* are not segmented, never branched, and usually are stiff to their sharp distal tips (Fig. 4).

fontanelle (n.): aperture or opening in a bony surface.

frenum (n.): ridge or fold of tissue that binds or restrains any part; as the tissue that binds the upper jaw to the snout.

ganoid (adj.): pertains to thick, strong scales with a covering of ganoin, as in gars.

gape (n., v. int.): refers to the mouth. In fishes, width of gape is the transverse distance between the two ends of the mouth cleft, when the mouth is closed; length of gape is the diagonal distance from the anterior (median) end of the lower lip to one end of the mouth cleft.

genital papilla: fleshy projection adjacent to anus, as in darters.

gill filaments: respiratory structures projecting posteriorly from gill arches.

gill membranes (n.): membranes that close the gill cavity ventrolaterally, supported by the branchiostegals (Fig. 8).

gill rakers: projections (knobby or comblike) from the concave anterior surface of the gill arches (Fig. 7).

gonopodium (n.): modified anal fin of *Gambusia* and other poeciliid fishes, used in transfer of sperm to genital pore of female.

gular fold (n.): transverse fold of soft tissue across the throat.

gular plate (n.): large, median, dermal bone on the throat, as in the bowfin.

heterocercal (adj.): the caudal fin is heterocercal if the vertebral column turns upward into the dorsal lobe (Fig. 5).

homocercal (n.): the caudal fin is homocercal if the posterior vertebra (with its hypural plate) is modified to support the entire fin; neither lobe is invaded by the vertebral column (Fig. 5).

humeral "scale" (n.): scalelike bone, often dark colored, behind the gill opening and above the base of the pectoral fin (in darters).

hypurals (n.): expanded last vertebral processes in fishes having a homocercal tail (Fig. 5).

infraorbital canal: segment of the lateral-line canal that curves beneath the eye and extends forward onto the snout (Fig. 4).

insertion (of fins) (n.): anterior end of the bases of the paired fins (Figs. 4, 10).

intermuscular bones: fragile, branched bones that are isolated in the connective tissue between body-muscles (myomeres).

interopercle (n.): small bone of the gill cover situated between the preopercle and the subopercle (Fig. 4).

interradial membranes (n.): membranes between fin-rays.

isthmus (n.): contracted part of the breast that projects forward between (and separates) the gill chambers (Figs. 4 and 8).

jugular (adj.): pertaining to the throat; pelvic fins jugular when inserted in front of bases of pectoral fins.

lateral line: system of sensory tubules communicating to the body-surface by pores; refers most often to a longitudinal row of scales that bear tubules and pores. *Incomplete* if only the anterior scales have pores; *complete* if all scales in that row (to base of caudal fins) have pores (Fig. 4).

lingual lamina: horny ridge on the "tongue" of a lamprey.

mandible (n.): principal bone of the lower jaw (Fig. 4).

mandibular pores: pores along a tube that traverses the underside of each lower jaw (part of the lateral line system) (Fig. 4).

maxilla (maxillary) (n.): bone of each upper jaw that lies immediately above (or behind) and parallel to the premaxilla (Fig. 4).

melanophore (n.): black pigment cell.

myomere (n): muscle segment.

nape (n.): dorsal part of the body from the occiput to the origin of the dorsal fin (Fig. 4).

nares (n.): nostrils; in fishes, each nostril usually has an anterior and a posterior narial opening, located above and in front of the eyes (Fig. 4).

non-protractile (adj.): not protrusible; premaxillaries non-protractile if they are not fully separated from the snout by a continuous groove (Fig. 4).

nuchal (adj.): pertaining to the nape.

nuptial tubercles: hardened, often thornlike projections from the skin, seen in adult males of many fishes during their breeding season; also called pearl organs.

occiput (n.): in fishes, the posterior dorsal end of the head, often marked by the line separating scaly and scaleless portions of the skin.

opercle (n.): large posterior bone of the gill cover (Fig. 4).

opercular flap: posterior extension of the operculum, especially in sunfishes ("ear" flap in *Lepomis* spp.).

oral valve: thin membranes, one near the front of each jaw, which function in respiration.

orbit (n.): eyesocket; orbital diameter is measured from the anterior to the posterior bony rim of the eyesocket, whereas eye diameter is measured across the cornea only (and is slightly less than orbital diameter).

origin (of fins) (n.): anterior end of the base of a dorsal fin or anal fin (Figs. 4, 10).

palatine teeth (n.): teeth borne by the paired palatine bones, which lie on the roof of the mouth behind the median vomer and mesial to the upper jaw.

papilla (n.): in fishes, any small, blunt, soft, and rounded protuberance on the skin.

papillose (adj.): covered with papillae (as contrasted with *plicate* when applied to lips of suckers) (Fig. 11C).

pectoral fin: paired fin on the side, or on the breast, behind the head (Fig. 4); corresponding to forelimb of a mammal.

pelvic fin: ventral paired fin, lying below the pectoral fin or between it and the anal fin (Fig. 4).

peritoneum (n.): membranous lining of the body cavity (Fig. 13).

pharyngeal teeth: bony projections from the fifth gill arch, which is non-respiratory and is embedded in tissues behind the gill-bearing arches, mesial to the cleithrum (Fig. 9).

plicate (adj.): having parallel folds or soft ridges; grooved lips (Fig. 16).

premaxilla (premaxillary) (n.): paired bone at the front of the upper jaw. The right and left premaxillae join anteriorly and form all or part of the border of the jaw (Figs. 4, 18).

preopercle (n.): sickle-shaped bone that lies behind and below the eye (Fig. 4).

preoperculomandibular canal: branch of the lateral-line system which extends along the preopercle and mandible (Fig. 4).

preorbital (adj., n.): bone forming the anterior rim of the eyesocket, and extending forward on side of snout; see circumorbital.

principal rays: fin-rays that extend to the distal margin of median fins, especially if those fins have a straight leading edge; enumerated by counting only one unbranched ray anteriorly, plus subsequent branched rays; see page 15 and Fig. 6B).

procurrent ("rudimentary") rays: small, contiguous rays at the anterior bases of the dorsal, caudal, and anal fins of many fishes; excluded from the count of *principal* fin-rays.

protractile (adj.): capable of being thrust out. Said of the upper jaw if it is completely separated from the face by a continuous groove (absence of a *frenum*) (Fig. 4).

pseudobranchium (n.): accessory gill on the inner surface of the operculum.

ray (n.): see fin-ray.

serrate (adj.): notched or toothed on the edge, like a saw; opposed to *entire*.

snout (n.): part of the head anterior to the eye (but not including the lower jaw) (Fig. 4).

soft-ray (n.): see fin-ray.

spine (n.): see fin-ray.

spiracle (n.): orifice on the back part of the head (above and behind the eye) in some fishes (paddlefish and some sturgeons), representing a primitive gill cleft.

standard length: distance from the tip of the snout to the structural base of the caudal fin (point at which central caudal rays originate) (Fig. 4).

subopercle (n.): bony plate immediately below the opercle in the gill cover (Fig. 4).

suborbitals (n.): thin bones forming the lower part of the orbital rim.

subterminal mouth: mouth that opens slightly ventrally, rather than straight forward from the front of the head; lower jaw closing within the upper jaw rather than equal to it in its anterior extent.

supramaxilla (n.): small, movable bone adherent to the upper edge of the maxilla near its posterior tip.

supraorbital canal: paired branch of the lateral-line system that extends along the top of the head between the eyes and forward onto the snout (Fig. 4).

supratemporal canal: branch of the lateral-line system that crosses the top of the head at the occiput, connecting the lateral canals (Fig. 4).

symphysis (n.): articulation of two bones in the median plane of the body, especially that of the two halves of the lower jaw (mandibles) at the chin.

terete (adj.): cylindrical and tapering with circular cross-section; having a rounded body form, the width and depth about equal.

thoracic (adj.): pertaining to the thorax, including especially the chest in fishes; pelvic fins thoracic when inserted below the pectoral fins (Fig. 4).

tuberculate (adj.): having, or characterized by, a tubercle or tubercles; see nuptial tubercles.

turgid (adj.): distended; swollen or inflated with fluid.

KEY TO FAMILIES OF FISHES

1. Jaws absent, mouth an oval suction-cup; seven small gill-openings in a line behind head .... Petromyzontidae, page 30

   Jaws present, mouth not cuplike; gill-opening single, slotlike, at back of head 2

2. Caudal fin at least slightly asymmetrical, its base slanting downward and forward (heterocercal, Fig. 5) 3

   Caudal fin symmetrical, its base vertical (usually homocercal, Fig. 5) 6

3. Body naked or with 5 rows of bony plates; caudal fin forked, strongly heterocercal 4

   Body completely scaled; caudal fin rounded, abbreviate-heterocercal, 5

4. Body naked (except for a small patch of scales on tail); mouth opening forward, beneath paddlelike snout; gill cover long, flexible, pointed posteriorly .... Polyodontidae, page 38

   Body with 5 rows of bony plates; mouth protrusible downward; gill cover short, rounded posteriorly .... Acipenseridae, page 32

5. Jaws prolonged into a toothed beak; scales diamond-shaped, hard; dorsal fin far back on body, with fewer than 12 rays, Lepisosteidae, page 40

   Jaws short, snout blunt; scales rounded, flexible; dorsal fin extending most of length of back, with more than 45 rays .... Amiidae, page 46

6. Body form snakelike; dorsal, caudal, and anal fins united; pelvic fins absent .... Anguillidae, page 49

   Body form not snakelike; dorsal, caudal, and anal fins separate; pelvic fins present 7

7. Adipose fin present (sometimes as a low fleshy ridge joined to caudal fin) (Figs. 4, 17) 8

   Adipose fin absent 10

8. Body naked; each pectoral fin with a strong spinous ray; 8 barbels on front of head .... Ictaluridae, page 196

   Body scaled; pectoral fins entirely soft-rayed; no barbels 9

9. Scales minute, cycloid (more than 100 in lateral line); anal fin with 10-12 soft-rays, lacking spines .... Salmonidae, page 60

   Scales large, ctenoid (about 52 in lateral line); anal fin with 6 or 7 soft-rays and an anterior spine .... Percopsidae, page 226

10. A single barbel on middle of chin; base of pelvic fins anterior to base of pectoral fins; two dorsal fins, both entirely soft-rayed; more than 50 rays in second dorsal fin and anal fin .... Gadidae, page 227

    No barbel on chin; base of pelvic fins not anterior to base of pectoral fins; one or two dorsal fins, the first spinous if present; fewer than 35 rays in anal and second dorsal fins 11

Family Petromyzontidae

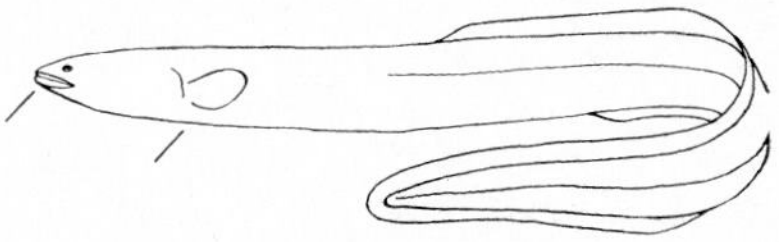

Family Anguillidae

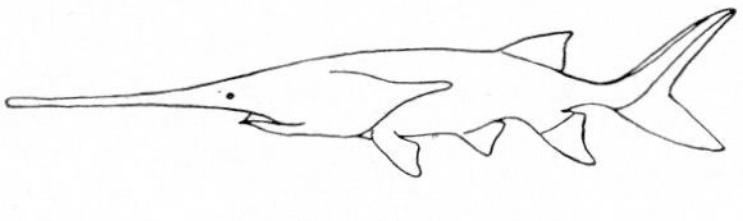

Family Polyodontidae

Family Ictaluridae

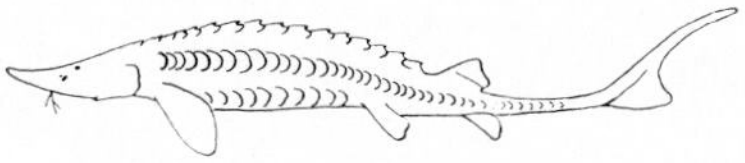

Family Acipenseridae

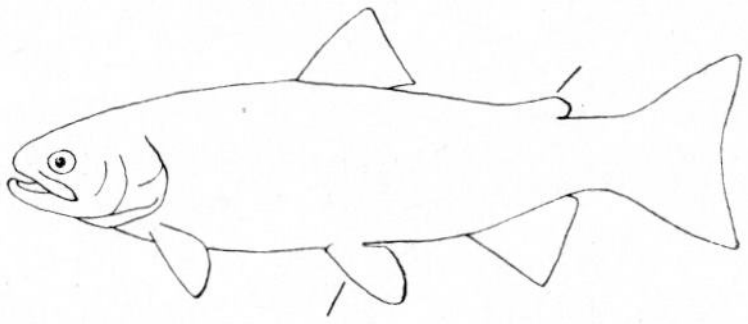

Family Salmonidae

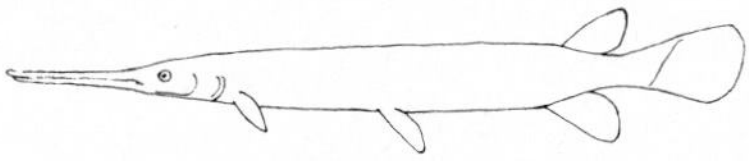

Family Lepisosteidae

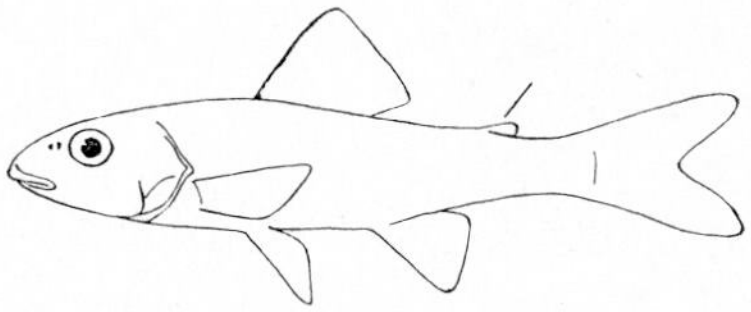

Family Percopsidae

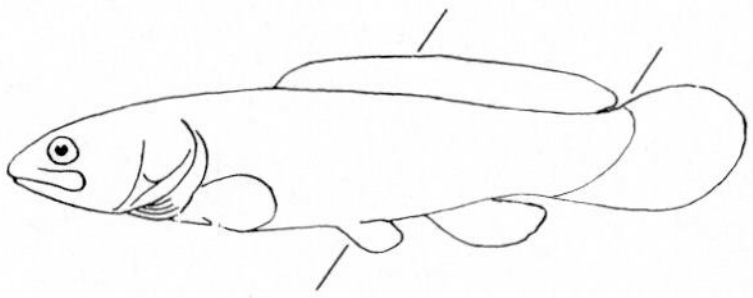

Family Amiidae

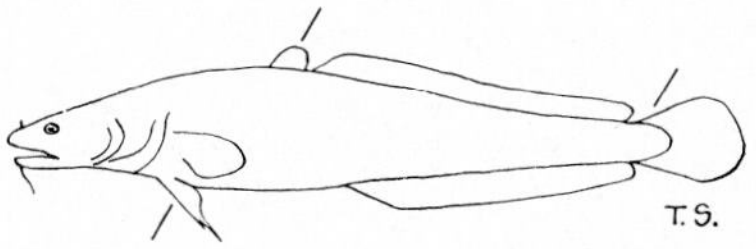

Family Gadidae

11. Pelvic fins abdominal (their base nearer tip of pectoral fin than base of pectoral fin when pectoral fin is laid straight back along body, see Fig. 4); dorsal fin never with more than one spine, except in Atherinidae (one species, see 12) 12

Pelvic fins thoracic (their base nearer base of pectoral fin than tip of pectoral fin when pectoral is laid back along body, see Fig. 4); dorsal fin with several spines 19

12. A small dorsal finlet, containing 4 or 5 spines, in front of and well separated from the large soft-dorsal fin .... Atherinidae, page 240

Dorsal fin single, without true spines (first ray sometimes hardened and spinelike) 13

13. Anal fin with 18 or more rays; longest ray in anal fin only about half, or less than half, length of fin base (Fig. 6B) 14

Anal fin with fewer than 18 rays; longest ray in anal fin more than half length of fin base (Fig. 6B) 15

14. Lateral line absent; belly with modified, sharp-edged scales that catch or tear when rubbed forward; gill rakers numerous and slender (Fig. 7A) .... Clupeidae, page 51

Lateral line well developed; belly smooth, with ordinary scales; gill rakers few and knoblike (Fig. 7B) .... Hiodontidae, page 56

15. Jaws produced into a flattened, ducklike bill; teeth large, Esocidae, page 62

Jaws not produced into a ducklike bill; teeth inconspicuous or absent 16

16. Head scaleless; gill membranes joined to isthmus (opercular clefts terminating ventrally at a point behind level of eye, the membranes not overlapping each other anteriorly, see Fig. 8A); caudal fin forked 17

Head partly scaled, or with scaly plates; gill membranes free from isthmus (opercular clefts extending forward below eye, the membranes usually overlapping anteriorly, see Fig. 8C); caudal fin not forked 18

17. Dorsal fin with 8 or 9 principal rays, *or*, if longer, containing a single spinelike, saw-edged ray at origin; pharyngeal arch with 1-3 rows of teeth, never more than 6 teeth in primary row (Fig. 9C); lips thin (Figs. 11, 12) .... Cyprinidae, page 64

Dorsal fin with 10 or more principal rays; first dorsal ray flexible at tip, never saw-edged posteriorly; pharyngeal arch with single row of more than 20 teeth (Fig. 9A); lips usually thick and fleshy (Figs. 15, 16) .... Catostomidae, page 164

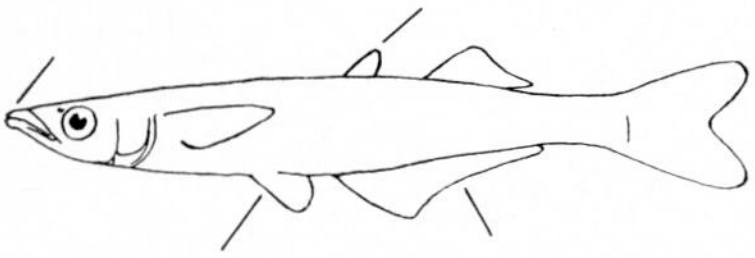

Family Atherinidae

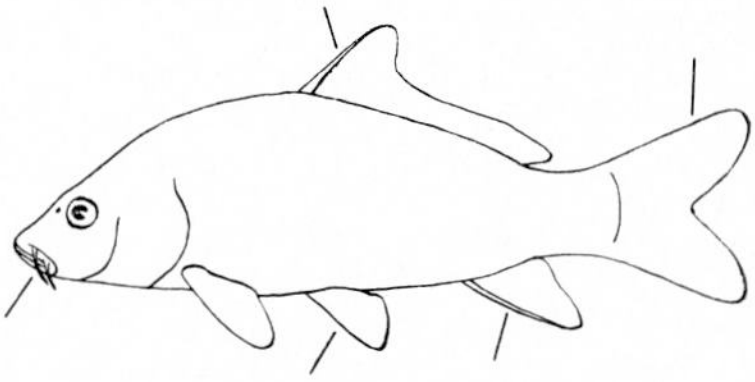

Family Cyprinidae

Family Clupeidae

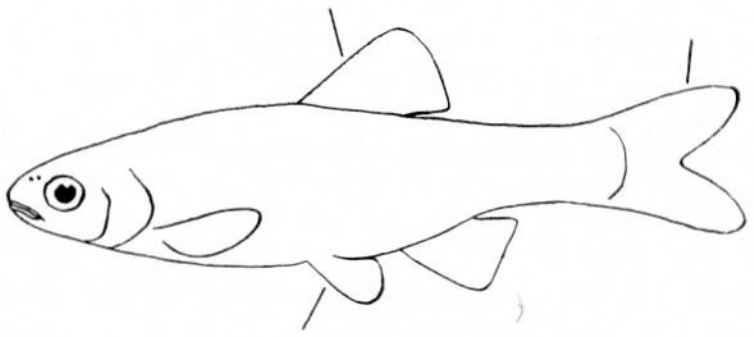

Family Cyprinidae

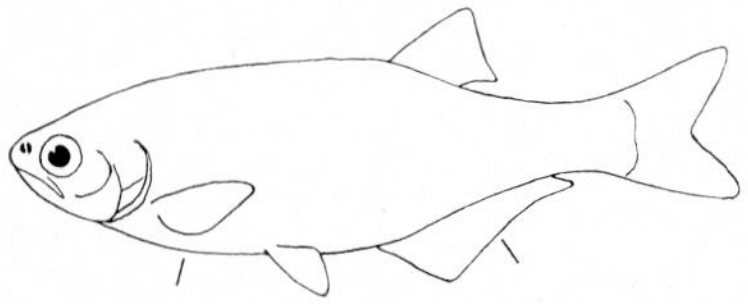

Family Hiodontidae

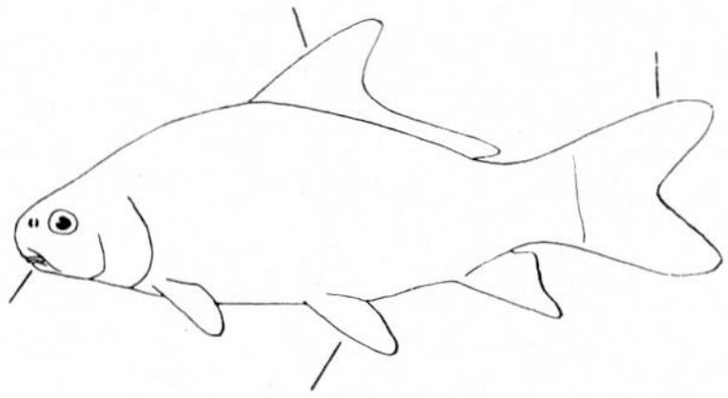

Family Catostomidae

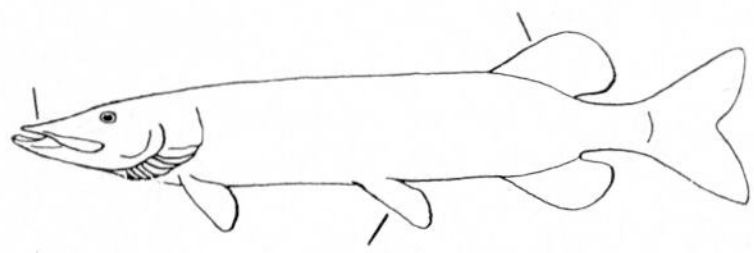

Family Esocidae

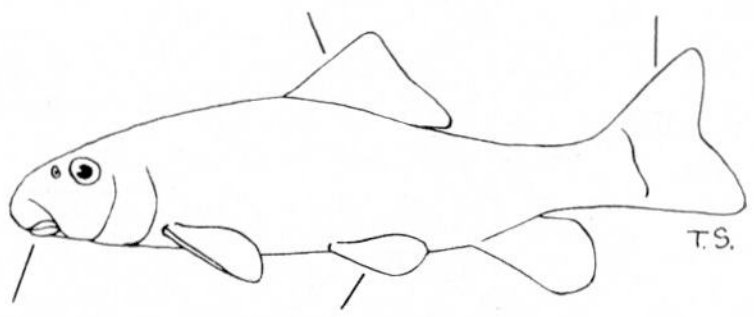

Family Catostomidae

18. Dorsal fin with 9 or more rays; anal rays 12 or more (Fig. 6A); anal fin of males large, not rodlike; egg-laying . . Cyprinodontidae, page 229

Dorsal fin with 7 or 8 rays; anal rays fewer than 10; anal fin of males a slender, rodlike organ (gonopodium); livebearing, Poeciliidae, page 238

19. Body nearly naked; head width more than ⅔ predorsal length (see Fig. 4); pelvic fin with fewer than 5 soft-rays . . . . Cottidae, page 241

Body scaled; head width less than ⅔ predorsal length (see Fig. 4); pelvic fin with 5 soft-rays 20

20. Anal fin with 3 or more spines 21

Anal fin with 1 or 2 spines 22

21. Spinous and soft-rayed parts of dorsal fin separate or scarcely joined (shortest spine in notch between dorsal fins not more than ⅓ length of longest dorsal spine); sides with several narrow, longitudinal stripes; pseudobranchia well developed . . Serranidae, page 243

Spinous and soft-rayed parts of dorsal fin continuous (if fin is notched, next-to-last dorsal spine more than ⅓ length of longest dorsal spine); sides not marked by several distinct longitudinal stripes; pseudobranchia absent or inconspicuous . . . . Centrarchidae, page 246

22. Lateral line not extending onto caudal fin; dorsal fin divided into two parts, the second with fewer than 25 soft-rays; second anal spine weak if present; species mostly small and mottled or barred with color . . . . Percidae, page 279

Lateral line extending onto caudal fin; dorsal fin single, with 25 or more soft-rays; second anal spine long and stout; plain silvery, deep-bodied species of large size . . . . Sciaenidae, page 324

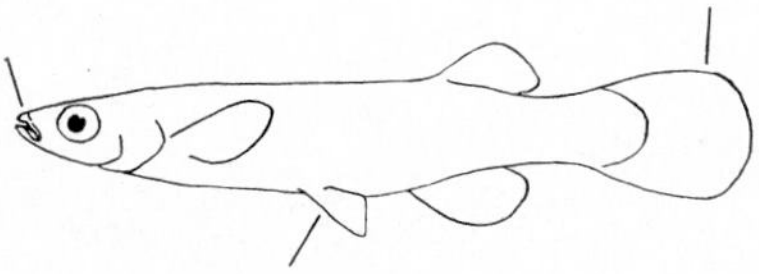

Family Cyprinodontidae

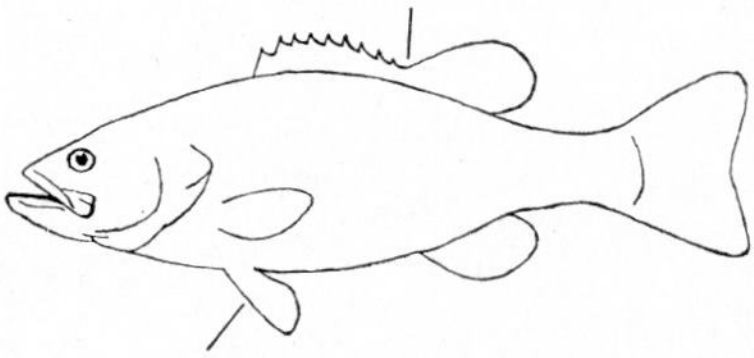

Family Centrarchidae

Family Poeciliidae

Family Centrarchidae

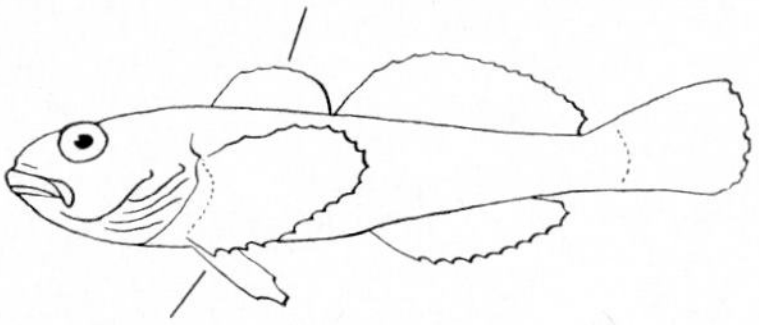

Family Cottidae

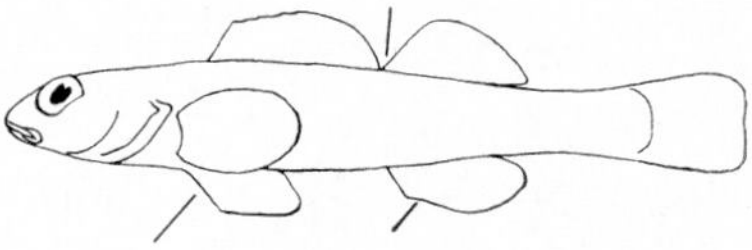

Family Percidae

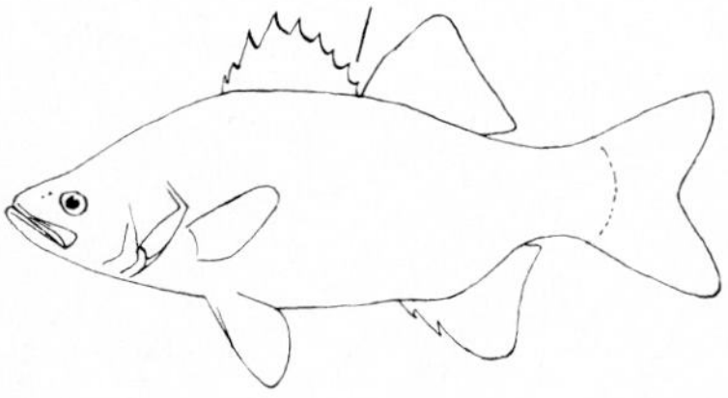

Family Serranidae

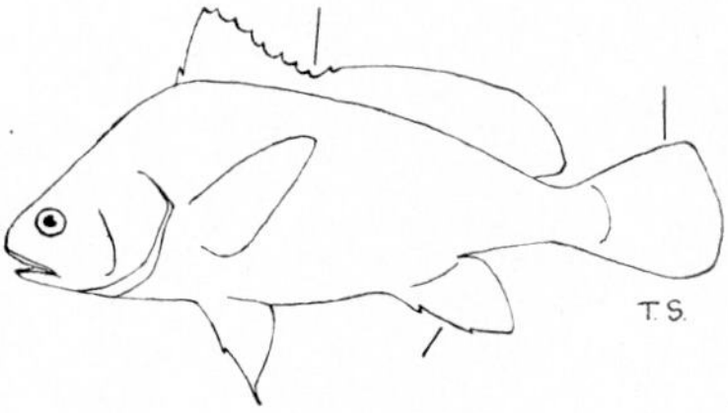

Family Sciaenidae

Lampreys

FAMILY PETROMYZONTIDAE

Chestnut lamprey

Ichthyomyzon castaneus Girard

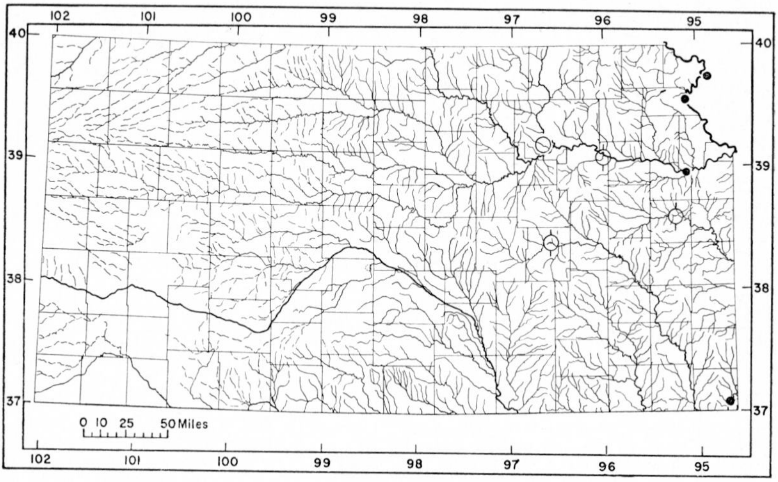

Petromyzon argenteus, Wheeler (1879:34); Cragin (1885b:106); Graham (1885b:70).

Petromyzon castaneus, Cragin (1885a:100, 1885b:106).

Ammocoetes niger, Cragin (1885b:106); Graham (1885b:70).

Ichthyomyzon castaneus, Hubbs and Trautman (1937:44, 72); Cross and Metcalf (1963:187); Metcalf (1966:91).

Paired fins absent; 7 porelike external gill openings; mouth oval, jawless, lined with horny teeth; circumoral teeth usually 19-23, 4-9 of them bicuspid; usually 4 or 5 teeth in anterior row, 7-9 in lateral row; transverse lingual lamina nearly linear rather than prominently bilobed; myomeres usually 50-56; length of oral disc 1/11 to 1/17 of total length.

Coloration plain, dark gray to olivaceous, lighter ventrally.

Maximum length approximately 14 inches, average about 9 inches.

A century ago, the chestnut lamprey may have occurred throughout eastern Kansas. Wheeler (1879:34) recorded a lamprey that I assume was this species from the Marais des Cygnes at Ottawa. Graham (1885b:70) reported lampreys as far west as Manhattan in the Kansas River Basin, and in the Cottonwood River of the Neosho System. Cragin (1885b:106) found lampreys in the Kansas

River System, and listed them from the Osage Drainage. To my knowledge, the only recent records and extant specimens (KU 2740 and KU 11091) are from the Missouri River. Since 1952, I have heard reports of lampreys found by anglers on fish from the Kansas River in Wyandotte County and the Spring River in Cherokee County.

Adult chestnut lampreys are parasitic on such fishes as carp, buffalofish, redhorse, paddlefish, and the larger sunfishes. By means of their funnellike mouths, they attach themselves to the sides of large fishes, and use the toothed tongue to rasp a shallow wound, through which they obtain body-fluids of the host as food. The lamprey detaches when satiated. Because some fish caught by commercial fishermen in the Missouri River bear scars of attacks by lampreys, it is evident that many of the hosts survive.

After an unknown period of parasitic existence (probably about 15 months), the lampreys mature and move upstream to suitable spawning-grounds. In Oklahoma, chestnut lampreys in spawning-migrations have been collected below dams in mid-April.

Although the spawning habits of chestnut lampreys have not been described, these habits are almost certainly like those of other known species. The males select nest-sites in swift, shallow riffles, where the bottom is composed of clean gravel. In preparing the nest the males remove small stones, by mouth or by dislodging them by vigorous swimming motions, thus creating a shallow depression. In the spawning act, both males and females attach by mouth to stones at the upper end of the nest, and eggs and sperm are extruded while the bodies of the fish extend downstream over the nest-depression. The eggs fall into crevices in the gravel, and develop there without attention from the parent fish, which die after completion of spawning. Well-oxygenated water, essential for survival of the eggs throughout their development, is provided by flow through crevices in the gravel.

On hatching, the young lamprey (called an ammocoete) emerges from the gravel and drifts downstream. Arriving in an area of slack current, the ammocoete burrows into soft sediment. The sedentary larva protrudes its head from its burrow and feeds on minute organisms that are produced in the waters above the "lamprey beds," or are washed into the area by currents.

After an unknown period (one or more years), the ammocoete emerges permanently from its burrow in autumn, acquires the disc-like, strongly-toothed mouth and other characteristics of adulthood, and assumes the parasitic habit.

A suitable environment for lampreys must provide clear, flowing water over clean gravel for spawning; stable waterlevels over bottoms of soft silt, occupied by the ammocoetes; and an adequate population of large fishes acceptable as hosts for the adult lampreys. Commercial fishermen on the Missouri River have told me that they saw far fewer lampreys, and scarred fish, in the 1950's than in former years—especially than several decades ago. The records of lampreys in the 1800's in streams where none has been found in recent surveys also indicate a decline in the abundance of lampreys in Kansas. Probably most streams in which lampreys formerly spawned have been so modified by cultivation of their watershed, with attendant siltation and instability of flow, that neither riffles clean enough for survival of eggs, nor backwaters stable enough for survival of ammocoetes presently exist.

Other species that may occur in Kansas.—Two other lampreys, *Ichthyomyzon gagei* Hubbs and Trautman, and *I. unicuspis* Hubbs and Trautman, may occur in Kansas. *I. gagei,* a nonparasitic relative of *castaneus,* has been reported from several localities in the Neosho River System in northeastern Oklahoma. It differs from *castaneus* in smaller adult size (5 to 6 inches) and length of disc (1/16 to 1/30 of total length). *I. unicuspis,* a parasitic species, has been found in the Missouri River both above and below that part of the mainstream which borders Kansas. It differs from *castaneus* in: circumoral teeth unicuspid (one or two teeth rarely biscuspid); teeth in anterior row usually 3, in lateral row usually 7; transverse lingual lamina bilobed.

Sturgeons

FAMILY ACIPENSERIDAE

KEY

1. Caudal peduncle partly naked, its length (Fig. 4) much less than distance from origin of anal fin to insertion of pelvics; spiracle present
lake sturgeon, *Acipenser fulvescens,* p. 33

Caudal peduncle covered by scaly plates, its length greater than distance from origin of anal fin to insertion of pelvics; spiracle absent 2

2. Barbels arising near middle of snout length; distance from base of inner barbel to front of mouth contained 1.3-2.2 times in distance from base of outer barbel to tip of snout; length of inner barbels contained 1.2-1.5 times in length of outer barbels; breast (in front of pelvic fins) scaled except in young
shovel-nosed sturgeon, *Scaphirhynchus platorynchus,* p. 34

Barbels arising much nearer front of mouth than tip of snout; distance from base of inner barbel to front of mouth contained 2.3-3.3 times in distance from base of outer barbel to tip of snout; length of inner barbels contained 1.6-2.4 times in length of outer barbels; breast naked in front of pelvic fins
pallid sturgeon, *Scaphirhynchus albus,* p. 36

Lake sturgeon

Acipenser fulvescens Rafinesque

Acipenser maculosus, Snow (1875:140).
Acipenser rubricundus, Cragin (1885b:106); Graham (1885b:70).
Acipenser fulvescens, Breukelman (1960:29); Metcalf (1966:162).

Scutes (scales) on body arranged in five prominent longitudinal rows; snout short and conical; spiracle present; caudal peduncle short, stout, not fully scaled.

Coloration gray or olivaceous dorsally, white ventrally; young with dusky dorsal blotches.

Maximum weight more than 200 pounds.

All the listed records of the lake sturgeon in Kansas are indefinite, and may originate from the same report of occurrence in the Kansas River at Lawrence, by Francis H. Snow. Snow (1875:140) stated that this sturgeon was "Well known to our fishermen" and that "The largest specimen taken weighed 26 lbs." Snow listed shovel-nosed sturgeons in the same report, so confusion with that species seems unlikely.

Because no specimens from Kansas were preserved, and Lawrence is the southwesternmost locality from which lake sturgeons ever have been reported, Snow's record may be doubted. However, the abundance of *A. fulvescens* seems to have diminished greatly in the past century, over much of its original range. I think Snow's record is valid. Since 1952, I have seen photographs of two lake sturgeons that were said to have been caught near to Kansas by anglers: one in the Missouri River at Rulo, Nebraska, and one in the Osage River in Missouri. I have been told that a sturgeon weighing 35 pounds was caught in the Kansas River in the 1930's.

A. fulvescens inhabits large rivers and lakes. Some individuals weigh 200 pounds or more, and live 80 or more years. Females are not mature until 20 or more years old. Spawning occurs in late spring, over gravel-bottoms of streams or in the shallows of large lakes. Some individuals migrate many miles prior to spawning. The food of sturgeons consists mainly of aquatic insects, mollusks, and crayfish.

A widespread decline in abundance of lake sturgeons, near the beginning of this century, is thought to be attributable to several factors: Pollution and siltation of rivers, which adversely affected food-supplies (especially of mollusks) and spawning sites; construction of dams that restricted access to spawning sites; and over-exploitation by fishing.

Shovel-nosed sturgeon

Scaphirhynchus platorynchus (Rafinesque)

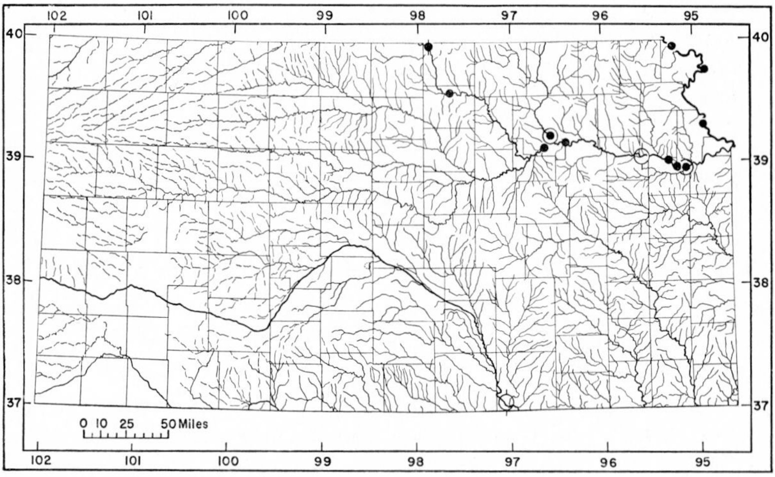

Scaphirhynchus platyrhynchus, Snow (1875:140); Breukelman (1940b:383).
Scaphirhyncho psplatyrhynchus, Graham (1885a:4).
Scaphirrhynchops platyrrhynchus, Cragin (1885b:106); Graham (1885b:70).
Scaphirhynchus platorhynchus, Jennings (1942:364).
Scaphirhynchus platorynchus, Bailey and Cross (1954); Cross and Hastings (1956:86); Minckley (1959:414-415); Breukelman (1960:29); Metcalf (1966:94).

Snout flat, broad, spadelike; spiracle absent; caudal peduncle long, slender, depressed, covered by large scales; venter covered by small scales; barbels inserted in straight line, their bases about equidistant from tip of snout and lower (hind) lip; inner barbels at least $\frac{2}{3}$ as long as outer barbels; anal fin-rays 18 to 23.

Coloration light brown dorsally, white ventrally.

The shovel-nosed sturgeon is common in the Missouri and lower Kansas rivers, diminishing in abundance westward, but occurring in the lower Blue River and in the Republican River to Nebraska. Although Graham (1885b:70) reported the species as "common over State," Hay (1887) did not record any sturgeon in the main branches of the Kansas River in western Kansas, nor did Jordan (1891) list any from the Arkansas River at Wichita. However, Bandel (1932:156) wrote of seining "a few buffalo, catfish, *sturgeons* (italics mine), and gars" in the Arkansas River near the Kansas-Oklahoma boundary on July 2, 1857. I have heard that fishermen still catch shovel-nosed sturgeons, rarely, in the lower mainstream of the Arkansas River in Kansas; the nearest published record represented by specimens is a few miles south of the State line.

Shovel-nosed sturgeons live near the bottom in large rivers, most often over firm, shallow, sandy bottoms in channels where the current is strong. Males become sexually mature at a length of about 20 inches, and females at a length of 25 inches. The maximum size normally attained is about 30 inches and 5 pounds, but specimens as large as 7 pounds have been reported.

Our meager knowledge of the spawning habits of the shovel-nosed sturgeon is summarized by Forbes and Richardson (1920:27) as follows: "It spawns between April and June, probably ascending smaller streams for that purpose." Specimens from which eggs and milt flowed freely have been found in Kansas in late April, and in the Mississippi River near Keokuk, Iowa, in mid-May. Reports from the latter area "indicate that spawning occurs on rocky bottom in swift water" (Coker, 1930:155).

Concentrations of this species in early spring, below a low dam on the Kansas River at Lawrence, indicate that migrations upstream precede spawning. These concentrations seem greatest in years when the river is high, and least in time of drought. At Keokuk, Iowa, Coker (1930:154) stated that runs of sturgeon in the Mississippi River are variable, best when the river is low in spring and poor when it is high. Perhaps the species seeks an optimal volume of flow, departing from the largest rivers to enter tributaries for spawning in years when streams are high.

The few reports published on the food of this species indicate that it is mainly insectivorous, but eats some algae and bits of higher aquatic plants. The stomachs of specimens from Kansas contain a wide variety of larval insects, plus organic detritus—the latter probably ingested coincidentally with insects. In aquaria under my observation food was found by raking the bottom by means of the sensitive barbels that project downward from the snout. The highly-protrusible lips are adapted for sucking.

Most shovel-nosed sturgeons caught by anglers are taken on worms. In the commercial fishery of the Missouri River, the largest numbers of sturgeons are caught in trammel nets, which are drifted with the current in winter. Although the species has long had significant commercial importance elsewhere, many of the fishermen on the Missouri River consider the sturgeon a nuisance. Sturgeons are highly vulnerable to drift-nets, regardless of mesh-size, because the hooked scutes of small sturgeons become entangled in threads of the nets. Most sturgeons caught are below marketable size, but some fishermen kill them, nonetheless. Depletion from this cause, coupled with modification of the habitat (dams; restriction of channels for purpose of navigation) may cause a decline of the species like that described by Coker (1930:152) in the Mississippi River.

Because of their ancient lineage, sturgeons command great biological interest, and merit preservation. Most Kansans proudly claim as their progenitors the hardy pioneer stock that settled here about a century ago; many can claim some ancestry from the Indians that occupied the region for several thousands of years; sturgeons, in contrast, have inhabited our rivers for hundreds of millions of years. Their severe depletion now would be tragically unnecessary.

Pallid sturgeon (or white sturgeon)

Scaphirhynchus albus (Forbes and Richardson)

Scaphirhynchus albus, Bailey and Cross (1954); Fisher (1962:427); Metcalf (1966:94).

Like the shovel-nosed sturgeon, except: venter naked; median (inner) barbels inserted slightly anterior to outer pair of barbels; bases of barbels much nearer lower (hind) lip than tip of snout; inner barbels less than ⅔ as long as outer barbels; anal fin-rays 24 to 28.

Coloration light brown dorsally, white ventrally.

In Kansas, the pallid sturgeon is known only from the mainstream of the Missouri River and the lower Kansas River. This sturgeon

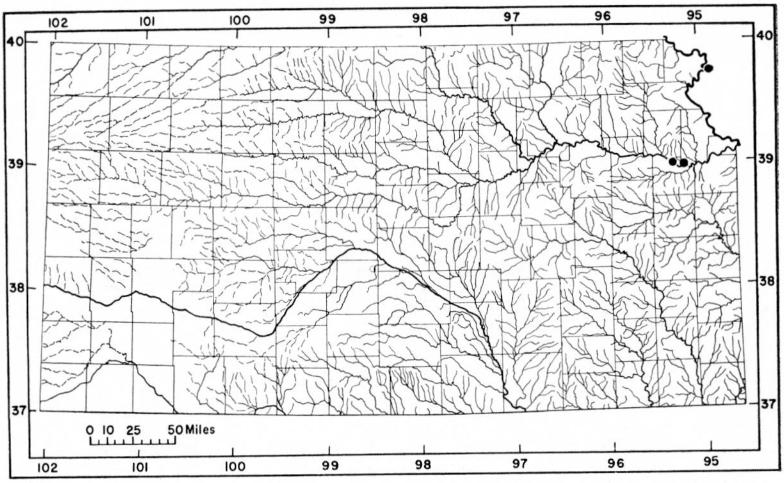

seems to live only in the largest, muddiest rivers of the Missouri-Mississippi System. Like the shovel-nosed sturgeon, the pallid sturgeon is found most often over firm sandy bottom in strong current. Unlike the shovel-nosed sturgeon, S. *albus* does not penetrate far into secondary streams of the Missouri System, nor does it inhabit the less turbid large rivers north and east of the mouth of the Missouri River. Seemingly, pallid sturgeons enter the lower Kansas River from the Missouri mainstream only in years of exceptionally high water. During the spring of 1952, following unprecedented floods on Kansas River, the ratio of pallid to shovel-nosed sturgeons at Lawrence was about 1 to 20. From 1953 to 1966, no pallid sturgeons were known to have been caught in the Kansas River. None was found among thousands of fish (including many shovel-nosed sturgeons) that washed ashore after an extensive fish-kill in the Kansas River near Eudora in 1955.

The pallid sturgeon sometimes grows large. Bailey and Allum (1962:28) mention a 68-pound example caught in North Dakota; and, a specimen from Montana that weighed 31.5 pounds was 58 inches long (Bailey and Cross, 1954:202). Nothing is known of the longevity, growth-rate, size at maturity, or reproductive habits. The stomach-contents of a few specimens from the Kansas River consisted of larval insects and small fishes.

Because of its restricted range and probable late attainment of maturity, the pallid sturgeon is more seriously threatened than the shovel-nosed sturgeon (see discussion of that species) by man's modification of river-channels and wasteful fishing practices.

Paddlefish

FAMILY POLYODONTIDAE

Paddlefish (Spoonbill, Spoonbill cat)

Polyodon spathula (Walbaum)

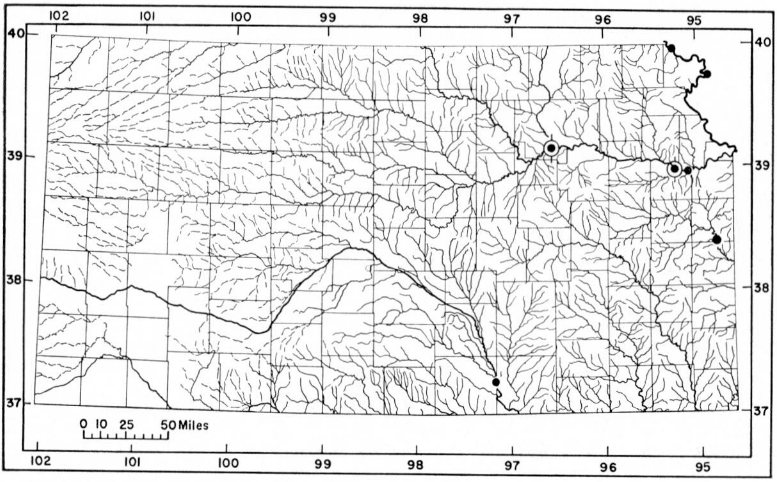

Polyodon folium, Snow (1875:140).

Polyodon spathula, Graham (1885a:4; 1885b:70); Cragin (1885b:106); Cross and Hastings (1956:86); Wilson (1957); Metcalf (1959:383; 1966:95); Breukelman (1960:29, 33).

Polydon spathula, Jennings (1942:364).

Body stout, naked except for patch of ganoid scales on upper lobe of caudal fin; snout long, spatula-shaped; caudal fin heterocercal; mouth large, opening straight forward beneath snout; barbels (2) minute, much nearer mouth than tip of snout; gill membranes continuous across isthmus, and with long posterior projections laterally; skeleton cartilaginous.

Coloration bluish-gray dorsally, white ventrally.

Maximum weight about 100 pounds.

In Kansas the paddlefish is confined to the Missouri River, where *Polyodon* remains common, and the lower mainstreams of the Kansas, Marais des Cygnes, and Arkansas rivers. Records from the Arkansas River (Metcalf, 1959:383) are unsupported by specimens, but several reports by anglers indicate occasional occurrence of paddlefish there. Authenticated records exist for several localities in the Arkansas System in northern Oklahoma, from Grand (Neosho) River westward to the Arkansas Mainstream.

The species is now rare in the lower Kansas River. A few juveniles were found dead on sandbars near Eudora, Douglas County, after pollution killed most fish in that part of Kansas River in September, 1955. On September 19, 1962, a 26-pound paddlefish was caught at Lawrence by John C. Huston [Kansas Fish and Game, 21(1):14, (1963)]. The Kansas Forestry, Fish and Game Commission recognized this fish as the largest of its kind taken on hook and line in the State; heavier paddlefish have been captured by other means in the Missouri and Marais des Cygnes rivers.

Reports by Graham (1885a:4) and Jennings (1942:364) suggest that paddlefish formerly occurred farther west in the Kansas River Basin than at present. In the lower Kansas River, Snow (1875:140) commented, "Previous to 1874 only two specimens of this curious fish had ever been taken at Lawrence, but since the building of the dam [a low-head dam for operation of a mill] several have been taken, varying in weight from 1 lb. to 20 lbs., and in length from 2 to 5 feet." I suspect that the dam caused temporary accumulations of migrant fish, accounting for the local increase of paddlefish that is implied by Snow's statement.

The reproductive habits of paddlefish were described by Purkett (1961), whose studies were based on migrant populations that support an important "snagging" fishery in the Osage River of Missouri. Spawning takes place in midstream, over submerged gravel-bars when the river is high and muddy in early spring. Under favorable conditions of rising waterlevels, at temperatures of about 60° F., adults move upstream into swift currents over large gravel-bars. The adhesive eggs stick to the first object they touch, normally stones on the stream-bottom, where their development is rapid. After hatching, the fry swim upward vigorously, then settle toward the bottom. Frequent repetition of this activity by the fry is significant in that it permits the strong currents to sweep the fry downstream, out of the shallows and into deep pools before the gravel-bars are exposed by receding waterlevels.

Large pools (or lakes) having silty bottoms are the principal feeding areas of paddlefish, which strain minute animals and plants from the water as their sole source of food. The fragile snout is not used for "rooting" in bottom-muds. It is profusely studded with taste-buds that may aid the fish in locating concentrations of food-organisms. Also, the wide lateral sweeping motion of the snout as the fish swims over the bottom may serve to swirl food-items up from the bottom, into the enormous mouth.

Polyodon is one of the largest, strangest, and most ancient of freshwater fishes—hence one of the most interesting of our native animals. Its sustained abundance is jeopardized by pollution, and by flowage-improvements on our major rivers (dredging for navigation, dams). Although large reservoirs provide the quiet water and abundant plankton that permit excellent growth of paddlefish, the dams obstruct reproductive migrations. For example, the Kaysinger Bluff Dam on the Osage River in western Missouri will block migrant paddlefish in that stream. The reservoir behind the dam will inundate the main spawning-grounds in Osage River where Purkett first revealed the reproductive requirements of the species only a few years ago.

Gars

FAMILY LEPISOSTEIDAE

KEY

1. Distance from front of eye to back of operculum less than half the distance from front of eye to tip of snout; least width of snout less than diameter of eye . . . . long-nosed gar, *Lepisosteus osseus*, p. 43

   Distance from front of eye to back of operculum more than half the distance from front of eye to tip of snout; least width of snout greater than diameter of eye 2

2. Fifty or more scales on midline of back, from occiput to dorsal fin; top of head and back plain greenish, unblotched
   short-nosed gar, *Lepisosteus platostomus*, p. 40

   Fewer than 50 scales on midline of back, from occiput to dorsal fin; top of head and back with dark blotches
   spotted gar, *Lepisosteus oculatus*, p. 42

Short-nosed gar

Lepisosteus platostomus Rafinesque

Cylindrosteus platystomus, Wheeler (1879:34).

Lepidosteus platystomus, Cragin (1885b:106); Graham (1885a:4, 1885b:71); Breukelman (1940b:383).

Lepisosteus platostomus, Breukelman (1940b:379, 1960:34); Jennings (1942:364); Clarke, Breukelman, and Andrews (1958:166); Metcalf (1959:363, 1966:95); Minckley (1959:415); Deacon (1961:373-374); Deacon and Metcalf (1961:315); Fisher (1962:427); Branson and Hartmann (1963:591).

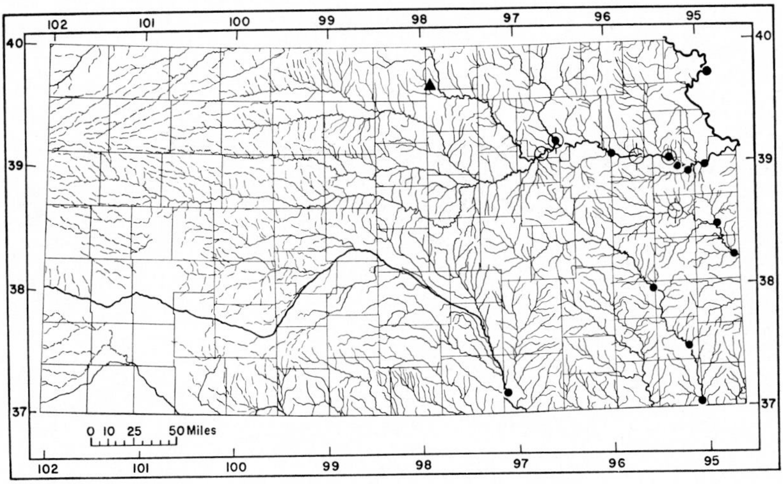

Snout short and moderately wide, its width at nostrils 0.7-1.0 in eye diameter, 4.6-7.1 in snout length; predorsal scales 50-53; scale rows from vent to midline of back 19-22; body uniformly slender, dorsal and ventral lines parallel from occiput to bases of dorsal and anal fins.

Olivaceous green dorsally shading to white ventrally; dark spots usually few, mostly confined to fins; head and back never mottled by dark blotches.

Size small, seldom exceeding two feet in length.

Most records of short-nosed gars in Kansas are from the mainstreams of the Blue, Kansas, Marais des Cygnes, Neosho, and Arkansas rivers. The species is common in the lower Kansas River, but is nowhere so abundant as the long-nosed gar. Short-nosed gars usually avoid the quiet backwaters, oxbows, and impoundments that often are inhabited by long-nosed gars, and that typically are occupied by spotted gars. Our westernmost record, from Republic County State Lake, is an exception.

In this species as in *L. osseus,* the average size of individuals in the upper Neosho River was considerably less than farther downstream in the same river (Deacon, 1961:373-374).

The food and reproductive habits of *L. platostomus* are generally like those of *L. osseus* (see account of that species). For the first few weeks after hatching, young gars live in shallow backwaters, where organic debris accumulates along the margins of eddies. There, they float near the surface, feeding mostly on small crustaceans and the fry of other fishes. The short-nosed gar later moves into the deeper water and stronger currents of the mainstream.

Spotted gar

Lepisosteus oculatus (Winchell)

Lepisosteus oculatus, Branson and Hartmann (1963:591).

Snout short, its width at nostrils 5.0 to 7.0 in snout length; predorsal scales 44-49; scale rows from vent to midline of back 17-20; body usually less terete than *L. platostomus* (thicker medially, rather than almost perfectly cylindrical).

Top of head mottled by large spots, underside of head freckled, body often profusely spotted.

Maximum size 44 inches, six pounds (Trautman, 1957:163).

When this account was written, the spotted gar was known only from the Neosho Waterfowl Management Area near St. Paul, Neosho County. Several specimens were captured there by Robert Hartmann of the Kansas Forestry, Fish and Game Commission in 1963, in a newly-created impoundment that communicates with Neosho River.

Probably *L. oculatus* occurs elsewhere in the Arkansas River System of southeastern Kansas, but has escaped notice because its preferred habitat, in large oxbows and other lakes, has been investigated less than the mainstreams of creeks and rivers in southern Kansas. Spotted gars were reported by Wallen (1958:29) from the Verdigris Drainage only three or four miles south of the Kansas line, and have been taken in reservoirs on other tributaries of the Arkansas River in western Oklahoma.

Long-nosed gar

Lepisosteus osseus (Linnaeus)

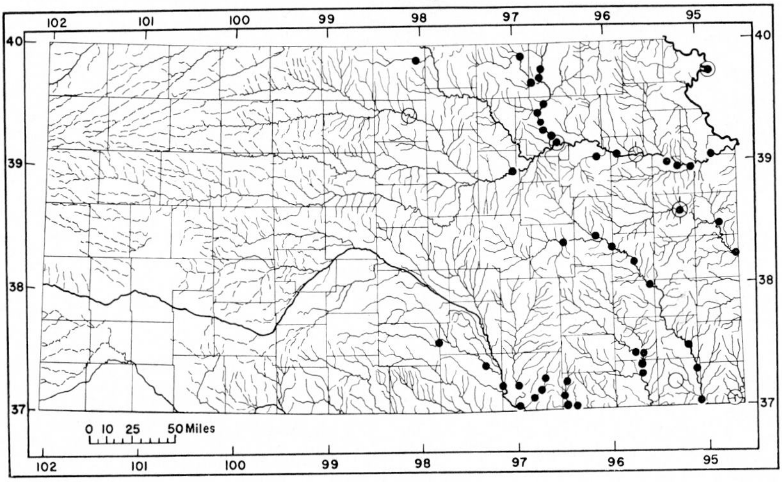

Lepidosteus otarius Cope (1865b:86 [orig. descr.], possibly from Platte River in Nebraska rather than from Kansas).

Lepidosteus osseus, Snow (1875:139); Wheeler (1879:34); Cragin (1885b: 106); Graham (1885a:4; 1885b:70); Jordan and Meek (1885:13); Hay (1887:247); Hall (1934:230); Breukelman (1940b:383).

Lepisosteus osseus, Hoyle (1937:285); Breukelman (1960:33); Cross and Hastings (1956:86); Schelske (1957:38-39); Clarke, Breukelman, and Andrews (1958:166); Minckley (1959:415); Deacon (1961:371-373); Fisher (1962:427); Metcalf (1966:95).

Lepisosteus osseus oxyurus, Breukelman (1940b:379); Jennings (1942:354); Cross (1954:307); Metcalf (1959:362-363); Deacon and Metcalf (1961: 315).

Jaws slender; snout width at nostrils 1.6-1.9 in eye diameter, 11.5-16.4 in snout length; predorsal scale rows 50-53; scale rows from vent to midline of back 19-21.

Brown or olivaceous dorsally, grading to white or yellowish ventrally; fins somewhat orange; dorsal, caudal, and anal fins usually with prominent, oval dark spots; body often having dark spots or streaks, their number variable in different specimens, and their intensity variable in the same live individual at different times (depending partly on water-clarity and color of background).

Largest Kansas specimen 56 inches long, weight 27½ pounds [Kansas Fish and Game 23(1):11, 14. 1966].

The long-nosed gar occurs commonly in large rivers of eastern Kansas, less frequently in tributaries, and rarely in intermittent creeks. Sometimes this species is abundant in oxbows and impoundments. Although long-nosed gars invade swift riffles, these gars are found more often in the less turbulent parts of streams—at the bases of riffles, the margins of eddies, or in quiet pools. When streams are high and currents are strong, gars often are distributed linearly alongshore.

In summer gars inhabit surface-waters where aerial respiration supplements or replaces gill-breathing. "Air-breathing" is accomplished by momentary projection of the jaws above the surface, for expulsion of gas in the air-bladder and its replacement by atmospheric air. Experiments at the University of Oklahoma Biological Station indicate that aerial respiration is essential when water-temperatures are high (Drs. Carl Riggs and George Moore, personal communication).

In winter in the Kansas River, long-nosed gars congregate at the bottoms of deep pools.

Long-nosed gars spawn in May and early June. Various reports indicate that the eggs are strewn over vegetation in calm water, or over silt-free, rocky bottom in shallow water having moderate current. The eggs adhere to the substrate and develop without benefit of parental care. On hatching, the larva attaches itself to a stone or other object by means of a "sucking disk" at the front of its blunt, short head. Subsequently, the organ of attachment is lost, the snout elongates, and the young acquires the body-form and habits of the adult.

Netsch and Witt (1962) suggest that, in Missouri, *L. osseus* migrates upstream for spawning. That suggestion is based partly on the common occurrence of young in small streams where adults rarely are found. Similar occurrences of young long-nosed gars in upland brooks, where no adults were in evidence in late summer, have been noted in Kansas. Deacon (1961:372) found that the average size of gars captured in the Neosho River increases downstream; but, young-of-the-year were taken in the lower mainstream of Neosho River as well as upstream.

According to Netsch and Witt (1962), some long-nosed gars live more than 20 years, females longer than males. Males probably mature at three or four years of age, and females at about six.

Gars eat mainly fish. Even small gars, 1¼ to 2 inches long, may be piscivorous, according to Forbes and Richardson (1920:33-34). Though voracious, gars are not active, aggressive fishes. A gar usually approaches its prey slowly, moving into a position in which the snout is close alongside the victim; it then grasps the prey with a quick, sideways jerk of the head. Often, rather than stalking prey, gars lie quietly in advantageous locations, awaiting the approach of schools of small fish within striking range of their beaks. The prey is pinioned on the needlelike teeth of the jaws and is gradually turned and swallowed. Little if any non-living food (carrion) is taken, although captive long-nosed gars in aquaria at the University of Kansas accepted mice that were killed before being put in the aquaria. These gars always touched the floating mouse with the side of the snout before grasping it, as if to test its edibility. Netsch and Witt (1962) discuss the rapid growth and highly-efficient food-conversion by young gars under laboratory conditions.

The long-nosed gar is one of the largest and most widespread predatory fishes in Kansas; as such, it serves an important and beneficial function. Like other predators, gars aid in cropping the surplus production of the prey-species, helping to stabilize their abundance at the moderate level that is most advantageous to the prey-species. For the most part, the kinds of fish eaten by gars are those that predominate in the area occupied by each individual gar.

Gars can be caught by angling. One effective kind of tackle consists of a thin stainless-steel wire that is threaded through the eye of a small, short-shanked hook and formed into a loop (lasso-fashion). Live minnows are satisfactory bait. When a gar strikes the baited hook, the wire loop is drawn tightly around the upper jaw by the same motion used in setting the hook on other fishes. In the Kansas River in winter, gars can be caught in deep pools by "snagging." The hooks used are single or treble, carefully sharpened, and may have the barbs removed. When the hook contacts a gar, its point slides over the bony scales, but readily penetrates the groove between rows of scales; the unique thickness and hardness of gar-scales help to hold the hook once it is embedded. Gars therefore seem especially vulnerable to snagging, which is, however, not a legal method of angling in Kansas at the present time.

The alligator gar, *Lepisosteus spatula* Lacépède, was reported by Cragin [1885b:106, as *Litholepis tristoechus* (Bloch and Schneider)]. Cragin wrote, "An unsuccessful attempt was made to harpoon a large 'Alligator Gar' that made its appearance just below the dam in the Kansas River at Junction City a few years since. The occurrence was related to me by a southern fisherman, familiar alike with the 'Alligator Gar' and with our two commoner species, and who described the Junction City specimen as green in color, like the true southern gar."

Reports like that above provide the only evidence of alligator gars in Kansas. All "alligator gars" from Kansas that I have heard about have proved to be long-nosed gars, if photographs or descriptions enabled specific identification. The nearest definite record of *L. spatula* is in the lower Missouri River in eastern Missouri, and the present distribution of the species is almost confined to the Gulf Coastal Plain. Past occurrences farther northwest are possible, but I suspect that large long-nosed gars account for all current reports by anglers. Cragin (1885b:106) likewise suggested this explanation in citing reports of alligator gars in the Neosho and Cottonwood rivers in the late 1800's.

Alligator gars have broader snouts than other gars, and have 23-25 rows of scales from the vent to the midline of the back.

Bowfin

FAMILY AMIIDAE

Bowfin

Amia calva Linnaeus

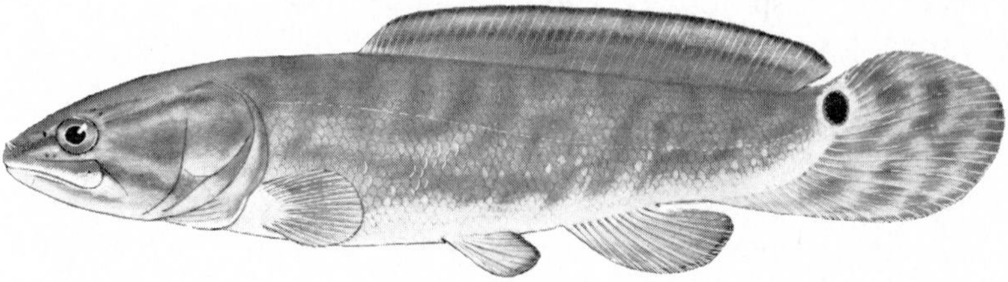

Amia calva, Cragin (1885b:106); Graham (1885b:71); Metcalf (1966:162).

Form elongate, moderately compressed; caudal fin rounded, slightly asymmetrical at base (abbreviate-heterocercal), with 25-28 rays; dorsal fin long and low, lacking spines but with more than 40 rays; mouth large, bordered by strong maxillae; underside of head with large bony (gular) plate; scales cycloid; lateral line complete, with 65-70 scales; anal fin with 11 or 12 rays; pelvic fins abdominal, with 7 rays; pectoral fins rounded, with 17 or 18 rays; air bladder joined to gut, partitioned (lung-like).

Dark olivaceous dorsally, lighter ventrally, lower fins greenish. Caudal fin with prominent dark spot at upper base, except in large females. Young with three dark stripes: one extending from anterior nostril through eye to upper end of gill-opening; second originating below eye near end of maxilla and extending backward across cheek; lowermost (third) stripe on mandible. Fins of young dark-outlined, often with dark central streak. Length to 30 inches, weight to eight pounds, rarely more than four pounds.

On August 22, 1965, an angler reportedly caught a bowfin in Independence Creek, Atchison County, where that stream flows across the floodplain of Missouri River in Sec. 30, T. 5S, R. 21E.

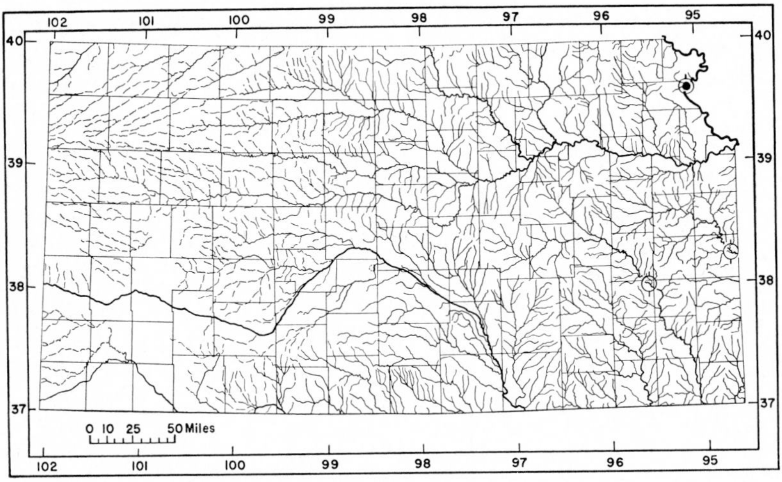

The fish was frozen and presented to Dr. Eugene Dehner of St. Benedict's College in Atchison on August 24. I have seen the specimen, and have talked with persons who stated that they witnessed its capture at the locality given above. These and other anglers told Dr. Dehner and me that another bowfin was caught near the mouth of Independence Creek earlier in 1965. I have heard previous reports that bowfins occur in oxbows and backwaters of the Missouri River, but most commercial fishermen whom I have interviewed along the river have never seen this species there. The specimen at St. Benedict's is 22¼ inches long and weighed 4 pounds, 1½ ounces when I saw it, still frozen, on September 1.

Apart from the above reports, all evidence for the occurrence of *Amia* in Kansas antedates 1900. Cope (1865b:86) included *Amia* in his list of fishes "brought from the Platte River, near Fort Riley." The fishes reported by Cope were taken at several localities, part of them in Kansas, but the place to which each species should be assigned seems indeterminable. Graham (1885b:71) reported the bowfin from "Branches of Missouri river, Osage river, etc." To my knowledge, no specimens substantiate his record. Cragin (1885b:106) stated, "Neosho R.; collected by Col. N. S. Goss, identified by Prof. E. D. Cope." Colonel Goss was a competent naturalist, principally an ornithologist, whose home was in Neosho Falls, Kansas. A brief biography of Goss, which mentions his correspondence with Spencer F. Baird and Robert Ridgway but not with Cope, has been published by Janes (1964). No specimen sent to Cope by Goss has been located in collections of the Academy of Natural Sciences of Philadelphia, which was Cope's headquarters.

Evermann and Cox (1896:418) found no bowfins in extensive surveys of the Missouri River Basin in 1892 and 1893, but cited the records mentioned above and stated, "This species doubtless occurs in all the bayous along the lower Missouri." In his map of the range of *A. calva*, Rostlund (1952:251) included the Missouri River System as far westward as Fort Riley, Kansas, and as far northward as eastern South Dakota. Bailey and Allum (1962:30) cite Churchill and Over (1933:22) to the effect that bowfins formerly were "found rather generally" in eastern South Dakota, and suggest that the species may have been extirpated there in the drought of 1933 to 1939. Nevertheless, Bailey and Allum qualified their acceptance of former records by stating, "We know of no firm evidence of the natural occurrence of the bowfin in the Missouri River Drainage." Bowfins still occur in the lower Arkansas River System, as far westward as east-central Oklahoma.

The habitat of the bowfin consists mainly of clear, calm waters in lowland areas, especially in backwaters of rivers and oxbows that have extensive growths of aquatic vegetation. A century ago, such habitat occurred in Kansas but little remains today. Drought and drainage of marshes, restriction of channels by means of dikes and dredging, and agricultural use of bottomlands have eliminated most natural pools alongside rivers.

As adults, bowfins feed mainly on other fishes. Spawning occurs in spring, when the males construct and defend nests having silt-free bottoms, often situated in beds of vegetation. The eggs adhere to sticks, vegetation, or stones on the floor of the nest. On hatching, young bowfin (like gars) have an adhesive organ at the tip of the snout, by means of which they anchor themselves to objects in the nest until the yolk-sac is absorbed. Thereafter, the schooled young gradually range farther from the nest, in search of food, which at this stage of their lives consists mainly of animal plankton. A few weeks after hatching, the young depart permanently from the area of the nest and from the influence of the attendant male parent.

Bowfin can be caught by anglers on some artificial lures, but more often on natural baits, especially at night. Where bowfins are abundant, dozens of them can sometimes be caught on trotlines. The species is an unusually strong and tenacious fighter, but is not a good food-fish.

Eels

FAMILY ANGUILLIDAE

American eel

Anguilla rostrata (LeSueur)

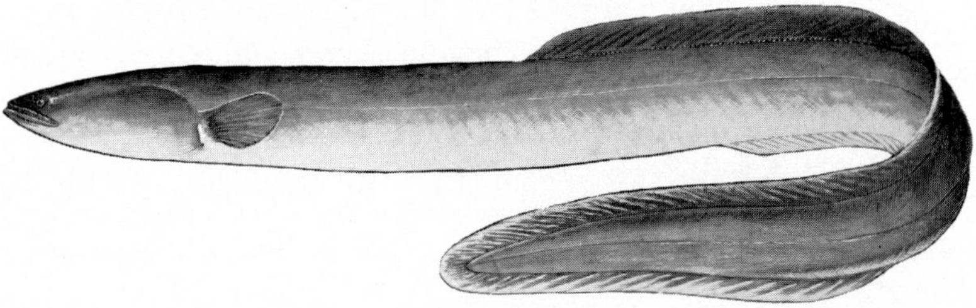

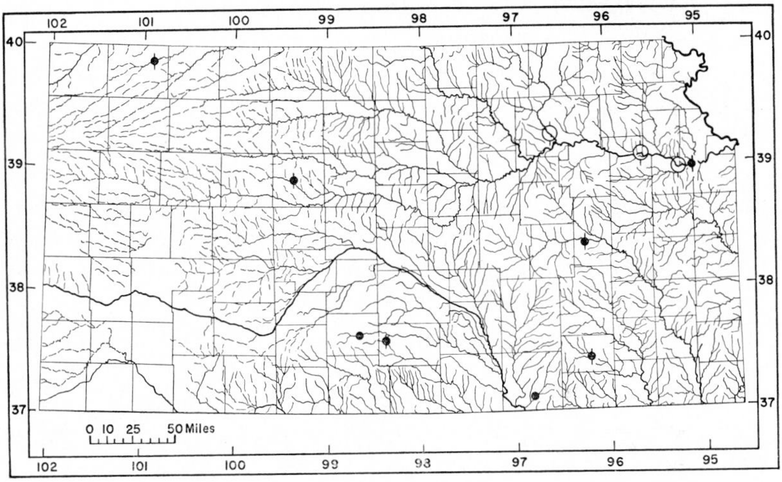

Anguilla Bostoniensis, Snow (1875:141).
Anguilla bostoniensis, Breukelman (1940a:372); Jennings (1942:365); Metcalf (1959:376); Minckley (1959:428).
Anguilla rostrata, Cragin (1885b:110); Graham (1885b:75); Clarke, Breukelman, and Andrews (1958:168); Breukelman (1960:34); Metcalf (1965:151).

Body extremely slender, slightly compressed; continuous median fin (dorsal, caudal, and anal fins united); pelvic fins absent; gill-cleft a short, membranous slot at base of small, rounded pectoral fin; jaws toothed; scales minute, scarcely evident, embedded in mosaic pattern.

Coloration brown, yellowish ventrally.

In 1875, Snow stated that eels were "occasionally taken by the hook, sometimes of 6 lbs. weight" in the Kansas River near Lawrence. Cragin (1885b:110) wrote that they were "reported by fishermen as not uncommon at Topeka," and Graham (1885b:75) believed eels to be "common throughout the State." According to Breukelman (1940a:372), "There is a specimen from Big Creek [Ellis County] in the museum at the Kansas State College at Hays, and a fisherman at Atwood [Rawlins County] reported having caught one in Beaver Creek." In the same account, Breukelman wrote that eels were "fairly common in eastern and central Kansas," but Clarke, Breukelman, and Andrews (1958:168) later listed *Anguilla* as "Scarce; only a few specimens from the Cottonwood R." in Lyon County. Records by Jennings (1942:365) and Minckley (1959:428) refer to a specimen still extant at Kansas State University (KSU 2916), caught by Graham from the Blue River, Riley County, in 1885.

The present rarity of eels in Kansas probably results from dams on rivers that impede inland migrations by this fish. A few eels still are caught. In 1965 two eels were in aquaria at the headquarters of the Kansas Forestry, Fish and Game Commission in Pratt, both of which were taken from the Ninnescah River by anglers. Mr. Roy Schoonover, Chief of Fisheries for the Commission, told me of other recent catches of eels from Painter Creek in Kingman County and the Ninnescah River below the dam that impounds Pratt County Lake. I have records of an eel caught in Elk River near Howard (Elk County) in 1955, one caught in Grouse Creek (Cowley County) by A. L. Metcalf in 1949, and one caught in the Kansas River near Eudora (Douglas County) in 1960.

Reproduction by *A. rostrata* occurs only in the Atlantic Ocean, in a limited area south of Bermuda. Thus, the fisherman who caught an eel near Atwood may have spared her a journey of more than 3000 miles—down Beaver Creek to the Republican River, the Kansas River, and the Missouri River, down the Mississippi to the Gulf of Mexico, thence eastward across the Gulf and hundreds of miles of ocean to breeding-grounds where she would have spawned and died. The eel surely was female, because only that sex occurs far inland. Her seaward journey would have begun in the autumn of the year before she attained reproductive maturity, and before her eggs developed. She might not have fed at all *en route*, although the journey required months to complete.

Her progeny, hatched after her death, would have drifted in the sea as leaflike (leptocephalus) larvae during their first summer. Some would have emerged along the American coastline, transformed to the slender adult shape, and entered rivers as yearlings.

In the several years of their life in streams they would have fed mainly on other fishes until their stage of growth, and the opportunity for escape downstream, permitted their return to the Sargasso Sea.

Shads

FAMILY CLUPEIDAE

KEY

Mouth terminal, lower jaw protruding beyond upper jaw anteriorly; last dorsal fin-ray not filamentous.........skipjack, *Alosa chrysochloris,* p. 51

Mouth subterminal, lower jaw shorter than upper jaw; last dorsal fin-ray greatly elongated into a filament
gizzard shad, *Dorosoma cepedianum,* p. 53

Skipjack

Alosa chrysochloris (Rafinesque)

Clupea chrysochloris, Graham (1885b:77).

Body thin, compressed; snout acute, with transparent membranes partly sheathing eye; mouth large, jaws weakly toothed, lower jaw projecting; dorsal fin with 15 or 16 rays, last ray not long or filamentous; caudal fin forked; anal fin low, with about 18 rays; pelvic fins abdominal, with 8 or 9 rays; scales along belly-line modified as sharp-edged scutes, their number 20 or more before pelvic fin-base, 13 or more behind base of pelvics; lateral line not externally apparent, approximately 53 scales in lateral series; vertebrae 53.

Bluish-gray dorsally, silvery or white laterally and ventrally; longitudinal row of small, dark spots dorsolaterally (sometimes obscure).

Length to 21 inches, weight to 3½ pounds, usually less than 16 inches and one pound (Trautman, 1957:177).

The skipjack was listed by Graham (1885b:77) as "Abundant in larger streams" of Kansas. Subsequent records by Evermann and Cox (1896:413), Forbes and Richardson (1920:49), and Rostlund (1952:254-255) probably are based on Graham's statement. A single skipjack in collections of the University of Michigan Museum of Zoology (UMMZ 146722) is the only specimen extant from Kansas, to my knowledge. Data associated with that specimen indicate that it was taken at Wellington, Sumner County, on October 27, 1942, by Dolf Jennings.

Few records of skipjacks exist in areas near to Kansas. Evermann and Cox (1896) list none from the Missouri River System except that of Graham. Bailey and Allum (1962:31) cite only one individual, taken at Fort Randall Dam, in their recent surveys of fishes in South Dakota. There are no published records from Nebraska, and those from Iowa are in streams tributary to the Mississippi rather than the Missouri River. The species may have been extirpated in Iowa (Harlan and Speaker, 1956:59) and in the upper Mississippi Basin generally (Bailey and Allum, *loc. cit.*). The skipjack occurs in the Ozark region of eastern Oklahoma, Arkansas, and Missouri; hence its habitation of streams in the Arkansas River System of southeastern Kansas is plausible, though Jennings' record from Wellington is surprisingly far to the west in that basin.

Skipjacks travel in schools and feed on crustaceans or small fishes. According to Trautman (1957:179), *A. chrysochloris* usually occupies deep, swift water in large streams, avoiding high turbidities. Carlander (1954:22) believed that dams in the upper Mississippi River impeded reproductive migrations of skipjacks, accounting for their decline in that river. She pointed out that, even though the skipjack itself was not utilized commercially, its decline had great economic import because the skipjack was the host for the larvae of a species of mussel which until then was highly valuable in the button industry.

Gizzard Shad

Dorosoma cepedianum (LeSueur)

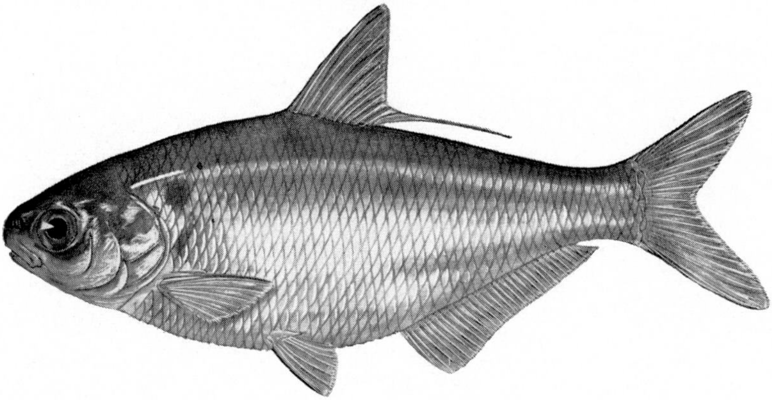

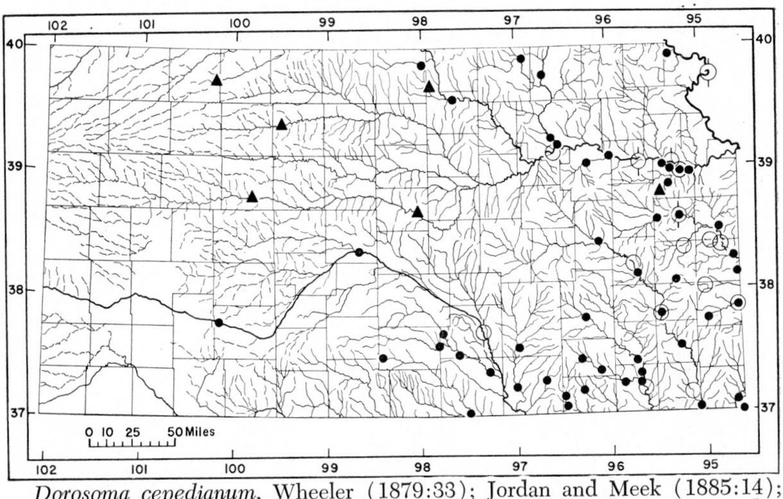

Dorosoma cepedianum, Wheeler (1879:33); Jordan and Meek (1885:14); Cragin (1885b:109); Graham (1885b:75); Gilbert (1889:40); Jordan (1891:17); Hall (1934:230); Breukelman (1940b:379, 1960:33); Jennings (1942:364); Moore and Buck (1955:21); Cross and Hastings (1956:86); Clarke, Breukelman, and Andrews (1958:166); Metcalf (1959:363, 1966:96); Minckley (1959:415); Deacon and Metcalf (1961:315); Fisher (1962:427).

Dorosoma cepidanum, Graham (1885a:4).

Shad—Schoonover and Thompson (1954:173).

Body thin, deeply compressed; snout blunt, with transparent membranes that partly sheath eye; mouth small, toothless in adults, subterminal (lower jaw closing inside upper jaw); dorsal fin usually 12-rayed, last ray prolonged and filamentous; caudal fin deeply forked; anal fin long and low, with 25-33 rays; pelvic fins abdominal, usually 8-rayed; pectoral fins 15-rayed; scales along belly-line modified as sharp-edged scutes, their number 17-19 before pelvic fins and 10-12 behind pelvics; lateral line not externally apparent, 59-67 scales in lateral series; vertebrae 48-51.

Gray to olivaceous or pale brown dorsally; sides bright silvery or creamy white; a distinctive dark "shoulder spot" (behind upper end of gill-cover); fins dusky.

Length to 19 inches, weight to three pounds, usually less than one pound.

The gizzard shad occurs in the larger streams of eastern Kansas, and in some reservoirs. Its abundance and possibly its range within the State have increased as a result of impoundment of rivers. There are no records of shad from the western half of Kansas prior to 1900. Mr. Frank Schryer, biologist for the Kansas Forestry, Fish and Game Commission, informs me that no shad occurred naturally in Webster, Kirwin, nor Cedar Bluff reservoirs. (Shad have been stocked in Cedar Bluff, Kanopolis, and some other lakes.) Schryer found shad in "sand pits" (excavations for construction-material) along Prairie Dog Creek in Norton and Decatur counties, Kansas, in 1964; whether these were introduced or were natural populations established by overflow of Prairie Dog Creek is uncertain.

Once established in reservoirs, *D. cepedianum* usually becomes the prevalent species. In samples from Fall River Reservoir, Schoonover and Thompson (1954:173) reported that gizzard shad comprised 97 per cent of all fish by number and 83 per cent by weight. They recovered 236,000 shad that weighed 3,300 pounds, following application of rotenone in coves having a total area of approximately three acres.

Gizzard shad are pelagic in habit, and seem to prefer relatively deep, calm water, although they are found occasionally in small creeks and in strong currents of rivers.

Dorosoma spawns pelagically, scattering its eggs without preparation of any nest-site, and without providing care of eggs or young. In streams of Kansas, spawning usually occurs in late May or in June. Two or more "peaks" of reproductive activity are sometimes indicated by a bimodal size-distribution of young obtained in July and August. Larval gizzard shad feed mainly on animal plankton. At this stage in life the young are slender, their mouths are large and toothed, and their alimentary tracts are short. After attaining a length of about an inch, usually in midsummer, the young become slab-sided in appearance. They develop the long gut and slender gill-rakers characteristic of "filter-feeders"; thereafter, they consume microorganisms (both plant and animal) that are strained indiscriminately from water as it passes over the gills.

Throughout late summer the young swim in open water, where vast schools of them may be seen near the surface of reservoirs on calm days. Large adults less often cruise at the surface. Seemingly, gizzard shad occupy progressively deeper water as they grow older, and tend increasingly to consume organisms associated with bottom-sediments rather than those found near the surface.

Gizzard shad cannot be caught on hook-and-line except by sheerest accident. Their food in no way resembles anything in the angler's tacklebox. Shad powerfully influence angling success for other species, however, because shad are the predominant food of game-fish in many lakes. Success in the establishment of some game-fish, notably the white bass (*Roccus chrysops*) in southwestern reservoirs, seems to be contingent on the prior establishment of high populations of *Dorosoma* in these lakes.

Gizzard shad are not hardy fish. They quickly succumb to abrupt changes in temperature of the water, or reduction in its dissolved-oxygen content. This vulnerability, coupled with great abundance of the species, sometimes results in "fish-kills" that are startling in terms of the number of dead shad that suddenly appear. These die-offs happen so often in autumn or winter that they may be considered a natural occurrence. Unless numerous fish of other kinds also are dying, high mortality of shad in the cold months should not alarm anglers.

A second species of *Dorosoma*, the threadfin shad *D. petenense* (Günther), was introduced (unsuccessfully) in Kansas in the 1950's. Mr. Robert Hiland, Superintendent of the U. S. Fish and Wildlife Service Hatchery at Farlington, told me that threadfins stocked in a pond at the hatchery reproduced abundantly but that the entire population died in winter. The threadfin is a southern species that probably cannot tolerate temperatures lower than 54° F. *D. petenense* differs from the gizzard shad in having a terminal mouth and in having fewer scales (less than 50 in lateral series), fewer ventral scutes (14-17 before pelvic fins), fewer anal fin-rays (20-25), and fewer vertebrae (40-45) (Miller, 1950:390, 1960:373).

Mooneyes

FAMILY HIODONTIDAE

KEY

Dorsal fin with 9 or 10 principal rays, originating posterior to origin of anal fin. . . . . goldeye, *Hiodon alosoides,* p. 56

Dorsal fin with 11 or 12 principal rays, originating anterior to origin of anal fin. . . . . mooneye, *Hiodon tergisus,* p. 58

Goldeye

Hiodon alosoides (Rafinesque)

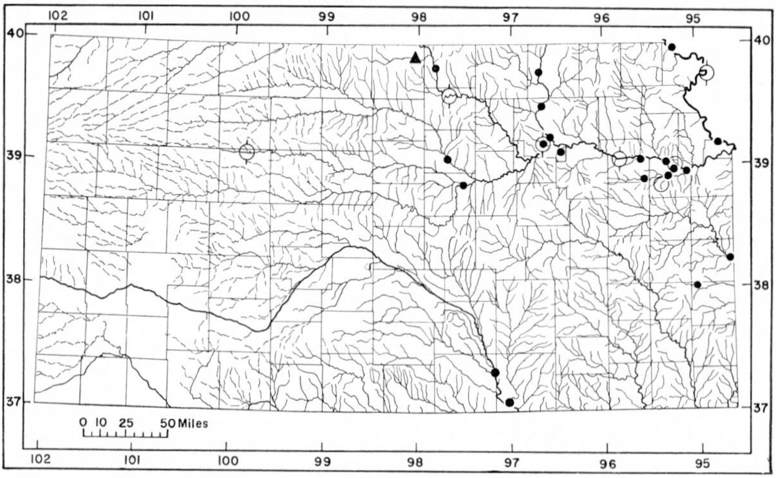

Hyodon alosoides, Jordan and Meek (1885:14); Graham (1885b:74); Hay (1887:242, 250).

Hyodon alveoides, Cragin (1885b:109).

Amphiodon alosoides, Breukelman (1940a:369, 1940b:379); Jennings (1942:364).

Hiodon alosoides, Cross and Hastings (1956:86); Metcalf (1959:383, 1966: 96); Minckley (1959:415-416); Breukelman (1960:33).

Body compressed; back nearly straight from occiput to dorsal fin; body depth less than half predorsal length of body; mouth large, terminal; jaws and tongue strongly toothed; eye large, its height less than half postorbital length of head in specimens more than 10 inches long; dorsal fin with 9 or 10 rays, its origin far back on body, behind origin of anal fin; caudal fin forked; anal fin long, with 30-32 rays; pelvic fins with 7 rays; pectoral fins with 11 or 12 rays; ventral keel smooth, without enlarged, sharp-edged scutes; pored scales in lateral line well-developed, numbering 55-58; vertebrae 58-60.

Green or gray along midline of back, silvery or white laterally; iris yellowish; fins usually colorless (sometimes yellowish-pink or dusky); no dark spot behind upper end of gill-cover.

Maximum weight three pounds, rarely exceeding one pound.

The goldeye is common in the lower Kansas River, but seems scarce elsewhere in the State. In addition to the localities mapped, *H. alosoides* has been reported from the Neosho River (precise location unspecified) by Jennings (1942:364). Most records are from rivers of moderate or large size; those from lesser streams, such as Wildcat Creek in Riley County and tributaries of Wakarusa River in Douglas County, probably result from migratory dispersal of goldeyes for spawning.

The abundance of goldeyes varies at Lawrence, being greatest in wet years (high volume of flow in Kansas River), and in the cool seasons. Goldeyes are active, vagile fish that sometimes congregate, suddenly and sporadically, below dams. At such times goldeyes provide interesting sport for anglers using minnows, spinning lures, or other small baits. I have heard of goldeyes being caught on small leopard frogs and on worms. The food of goldeyes consists mainly of insects, both larval aquatic stages and winged forms that fall on the water-surface. Large adults often consume other fishes.

Goldeyes spawn in early spring (usually April) in Kansas. I have no information as to the sites used for reproduction in this State, but reports from other parts of the range indicate that goldeyes deposit their eggs in shallow, flowing water over rocky or gravelly bottoms, perhaps after lengthy migrations upstream. The species also spawns in shoal-waters of lakes. Males are distinguishable from females by the curvature of the anal fin-margin, which is strongly sigmoid (convex anteriorly) in males but concave or nearly straight in females.

Goldeyes attain lengths of at least 16 inches, and ages of seven years, in Kansas.

Mooneye

Hiodon tergisus LeSueur

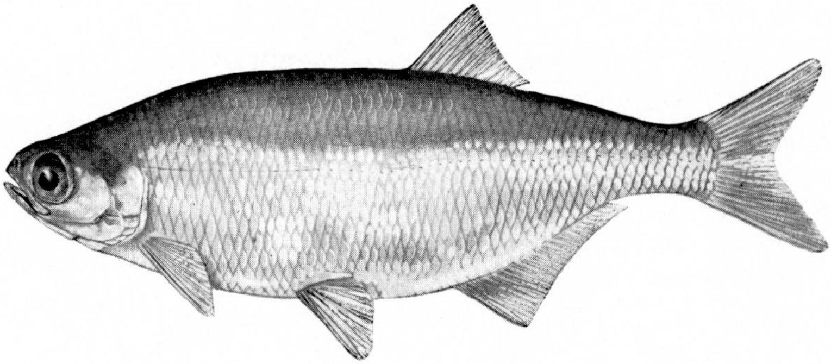

Hyodon tergisus, Cope (1865b:85); Graham (1885a:4, 1885b:74); Cragin (1885b:109).

Hyodon turgisus, Snow (1875:141).

Hiodon tergisus, Breukelman (1960:26, 33); Fisher (1962:427); Metcalf (1966: 97, 163).

Resembles *Hiodon alosoides* except as follows: body deeper, back gently arched rather than straight; greatest depth of body about half, or more than half, predorsal length of body in adults; dorsal fin with 11 or 12 rays, its origin anterior to origin of anal fin; eye larger, its height more than half postorbital length of head; vertebrae 56-58.

To my knowledge, no specimens of mooneyes from Kansas are extant, and most records in literature are indefinite as to the localities of capture. The fish reported by Cope (1865b:85) may have been taken in the Platte River (Nebraska), and may have been a goldeye rather than a mooneye; other *Hiodon* reported by Cope were misidentified, according to Johnson (unpublished doctoral dissertation, University of Michigan, 1942) and Bailey and Allum (1962:33). Snow (1875:141) failed to mention the goldeye in listing the mooneye among fishes that he observed in the Kansas River near Lawrence, although the former species is the only *Hiodon* now found commonly at this locality. Graham (1885a:4) likewise listed only the mooneye, from "Kansas river." Later, Graham (1885b:74) recorded both species, commenting that *H. tergisus* was "Common."

Cragin (1885b:109) provided the first record that inspires my confidence, in reporting *H. tergisus* from "Kansas R. at Topeka." In his adjacent account of the goldeye, Cragin stated, "This is the *Hyodon tergisus* of Girard . . . and probably of Cope (P. P. A. N. S. '65); but at the time when Cope's record was made *tergisus* and *alveoides* [= *alosoides*] had not been recognized and characterized as distinct." Breukelman (1960) indicated that both species occur uncommonly in eastern Kansas. The purposes of his popular report were such that no locality-records were given for any species. I found no specimens of *H. tergisus* in Breukelman's collections at the Kansas State Teachers College, Emporia, but his illustration (1960:27) clearly represents a mooneye rather than a goldeye. Fisher's report (1962:427), based on collections made in 1945, tabulates an abundance of mooneyes from the Missouri River near its mouth, one mooneye from the same river at St. Joseph, Buchanan County, Missouri, and 13 from Watson, Atchison County, Missouri.

I have seen many goldeyes but no mooneyes from the Kansas and Missouri rivers, although the latter name is often used by anglers for *H. alosoides*. If records of *H. tergisus* are valid, that species must have declined in this area in recent years. Trautman (1957:175-176) stated that mooneyes have disappeared from some streams formerly occupied in Ohio, owing to increasing turbidity of the water.

The "eye shine" of the mooneye (and the related goldeye) is caused by a reflective layer, the tapetum lucidum, in the retina. Particles composing the tapetum are closely associated with visual cells, and are thought to reinforce the visual stimulus when light is dim (Moore, 1944a).

Trouts
FAMILY SALMONIDAE
Rainbow Trout
Salmo gairdneri Richardson

Salmo irideus, Graham (1885b:78).

Body slightly compressed; mouth large, jaws toothed; adipose fin present; dorsal fin 11- or 12-rayed, originating over pelvic fins; caudal fin slightly forked; anal fin short, with 10 or 11 rays; pelvic fins abdominal, 9- or 10-rayed; pectoral fin-rays 14 or 15; lateral line well-developed, with more than 100 scales (all scales minute).

Olivaceous dorsally, sides dusky or silvery, often with an iridescent pink median streak; dorsum and sides dark-speckled; dorsal, adipose, and caudal fins with dark dots; lower fins dusky.

Although no self-sustaining populations of rainbow trout exist in Kansas, the species has been introduced so often that it probably has occurred at one place or another in the State since the early years of settlement. Places where rainbows have been stocked recently include "strip-pit" lakes in Crawford County, ponds in Barber, Johnson, Kingman, and Scott counties, and a stream (Rose Creek) in Wallace County.

Besides the rainbow, Graham (1885b:78) listed the following salmonids that had been introduced by the State Fish Commission in 1885 or earlier: brook trout, *Salvelinus fontinalis* (reported as *Salmo fontinalis*); Atlantic salmon, *Salmo salar*; and chinook salmon, *Oncorhynchus tshawytscha* (misspelled *tchawytcha*). An account of introductions of Pacific salmon and lake trout (*Salvelinus namaycush*), in 1877-1880, was given by Breukelman (1946:58).

Cope (1865b:85) reported the cutthroat trout, *Salmo clarki,* from Kansas, under the name *Trutta lewisi,* and later (1871:433) described the same species as *Salmo stomias,* "from the Platte River

. . . near Fort Riley, Kansas." Cragin (1885b:109) retained the cutthroat (as *Salmo purpuratus*, var. *stomias*) in his list of Kansas fishes, but the obvious inaccuracies in Cope's locality-designations were soon pointed out by Jordan (1891:12-13) and others. Probably Cope's fish was caught in Wyoming, and dispatched to Philadelphia from Fort Riley in Kansas (see Olund and Cross, 1961:331-332, for itinerary of the collector). Perhaps S. *clarki* and the brown trout, S. *trutta*, have been introduced in Kansas, but I have no definite information to that effect.

I suppose that rainbows and other trout can be grown as an angling novelty wherever suitable supplies of ground-water are available in Kansas. Mr. Floyd T. Amsden of Wichita maintained trout-fishing for a time on his farm in Barber County by use of the following system. In spring or summer, small trout were stocked and fed in a shallow trenchlike pond through which water flowed continuously from an adjacent well. The trout were removed in autumn and released in a large pond for capture by angling in winter and spring. The system works if the volume of water flowing through the rearing-pond or raceway is sufficient to prevent warming above 70° F., and if the ground-water is thoroughly aerated as it is discharged into the pond. Many trout can be raised in the small space provided by such raceways, by regular feeding of pelleted rations that are obtainable from most feed-stores. Raceways for rearing the trout to large size are not essential, because trout of "catchable" size can be purchased from private hatcheries in neighboring states. In the autumn of 1964, Mr. Lawrence Wagner of Overland Park stocked approximately 150 rainbow trout in a small pond in Johnson County. More than half of them were recaptured on hook-and-line the following spring.

Trout will not survive indefinitely in the ponds where they are released, and will not reproduce. Usually, efforts to establish trout in deep ponds and lakes have failed because it was forgotten that Kansas lakes which stratify—thereby retaining cold water in their depths throughout summer—also lose most of their oxygen-reserve in the deeper zones during that season. Therefore, trout that do not succumb on account of excessively high temperature perish by asphyxiation.

None of the reservoirs yet constructed in Kansas has tailwaters that are continuously cool enough, and sufficiently well aerated, to support trout.

Pikes

FAMILY ESOCIDAE

Northern Pike

Esox lucius Linnaeus

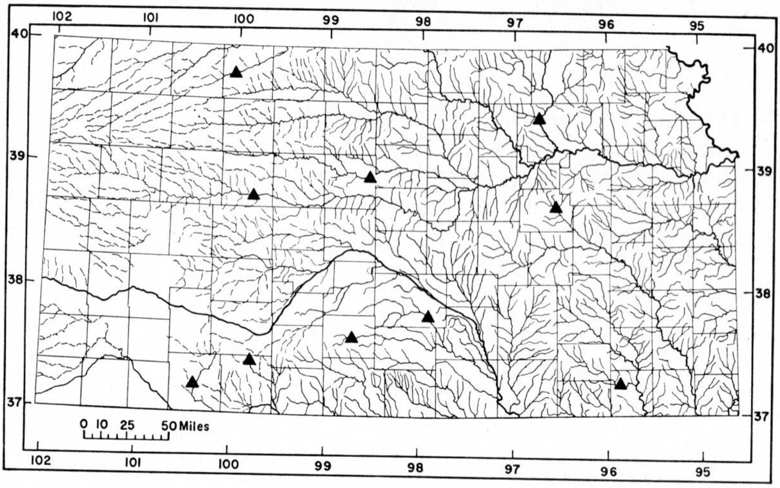

Esox lucius, Cragin (1885b:110); Graham (1885b:78); Metcalf (1966:97).

Body elongate, slightly compressed; jaws long, broad, strongly toothed; dorsal and anal fins short, rounded, with 20 or fewer rays (total count); caudal fin slightly forked; pelvic fins abdominal, with 10 or 11 rays; pectoral fins with 15 or 16 rays; cheeks fully scaled, upper half of opercle scaled (lower half naked); body-scales cycloid, small, more than 100 in lateral line; vertebrae 60-62.

Olivaceous dorsally, variegated laterally; young with irregular light-and-dark vertical bars, sides of adults marked by oval or capsule-shaped pale spots on dark background; dorsal, caudal, and anal fins mottled light and dark, rays of all fins yellowish.

Maximum size approximately 50 pounds (Keleher, 1961:420).

The southwestern limit of the native range of the northern pike is difficult to establish, because of introductions that began almost as early as white settlement of the area that is involved. Cragin and Graham referred to *Esox lucius* as introduced in Kansas, but northern pike may have occurred naturally—albeit rarely—in northeastern Kansas a century ago. Various authors, including Evermann and Cox (1896:415) and Johnson (unpublished doctoral dissertation, University of Michigan, 1942) have recorded northern pike from the Missouri River Drainage of South Dakota, Iowa, and Nebraska. I think *E. lucius* (like the burbot, *Lota lota*) may have occurred as a native fish in or near the Missouri mainstream as far southward as Kansas within relatively recent times. I have seen a specimen (KU 2080), said to have been caught by an angler in the Wakarusa River, Douglas County, in the 1940's, and one caught near the mouth of Fishing River, Ray County, Missouri, in 1952. The latter fish is No. 5763 in collections of William Jewell College, Liberty, Missouri.

Since 1962, introductions of northern pike have been made on a larger scale than any previous attempts to establish this fish in Kansas (Todd, 1962:3; Polson, 1964:3). A total of 5¾ million fry was released in Tuttle Creek Reservoir, on Blue River, in 1962 and 1963; pike have since been stocked in Cedar Bluff, Norton, and Council Grove reservoirs. The results are uncertain at the time of this writing.

Northern pike prefer relatively shallow, weedy, clear water. Although the species is found both in lakes and streams, its abundance in streams diminishes southward, so that it becomes primarily a "lake-fish" near the southern limits of its distribution. *Esox lucius* is a voracious carnivore that grows rapidly to large size; weights of five to ten pounds are attained commonly.

Reproduction occurs in late winter and early spring. Prior to spawning the adults move upstream or inshore into creeks, marshes, or backwaters. Vigorous sparring among rival fish precedes the spawning act, in which one or two males participate with a female, discharging milt and eggs simultaneously. The fertilized eggs adhere to vegetation or debris. They are left to develop unattended by the parental fish, which return when spent to the larger lakes or rivers from which they dispersed for spawning. Scarcity of spawning-grounds, suitable in having stable waterlevels during the developmental stages of eggs and young, may limit the success of pike in reservoirs of the Plains region.

Esox americanus Gmelin.—Crossman (1966:Fig. 1) indicated occurrence of the grass pickerel in the Missouri River at St. Joseph, Missouri. His record was based (pers. comm., 25 April 1966) on four specimens of *E. americanus* in collections at the U. S. National Museum (USNM 6833). The labels associated with these specimens when I examined them in November, 1966, stated only "St. Joseph's Bridger"; the low catalogue number, the appearance of the specimens, and their preservation initially in alcohol all suggest that they are old. I suspect, though, that the "St. Joseph's" intended is elsewhere than in Missouri. Possibly the St. Joseph River in Indiana was meant; that stream is well within the present range of the species. Although grass pickerel occur now in a small part of the Missouri River Basin in Nebraska (Crossman, *loc. cit.*), they are unknown elsewhere in that Basin, and the records from Nebraska may result from introductions.

Minnows

FAMILY CYPRINIDAE

KEY

1. Dorsal fin having more than 15 soft-rays and an anterior spine.... 2
   Dorsal fin having fewer than 10 soft-rays and lacking spine...... 3

2. Two barbels on each side of mouth (Figs. 11, 12), carp, *Cyprinus carpio*, p. 72
   Barbels absent........................goldfish, *Carassius auratus*, p. 75

3. Barbels present (one or two at each corner of mouth, Figs. 11, 12).. 4
   Barbels absent 14

4. A false barbel (in breeding males) consisting of a fleshy outgrowth *on* lips near their juncture; nuptial tubercles or their pits usually present, and confined to snout where they are arranged in transverse rows..........blunt-nosed minnow, *Pimephales notatus*, p. 157
   Barbels genuine, persistent in both sexes, usually projecting from *groove* above or behind lips (Figs. 11, 12); nuptial tubercles, if present, not arranged in definite rows across snout............ 5

5. Two barbels on each side of mouth, speckled chub, *Hybopsis aestivalis*, p. 95
   One barbel on each side of mouth......................... 6

6. Barbel minute and flat, in groove above maxillary; mouth terminal and oblique, upper lip expanded at center; dorsal fin with dark spot anteriorly near base; pharyngeal teeth usually 2,5—4,2 (Fig. 9C) .... creek chub, *Semotilus atromaculatus*, p. 78
   Barbel minute to large, conical, at angle of jaws (Fig. 11); mouth terminal or ventral, upper lip not expanded at center; dorsal fin without dark spot anteriorly; pharyngeal teeth never 2,5—4,2.. 7

7. Most of breast (anterior to pelvic fins) scaled; underside of head not obviously papillose; snout length usually less than least depth of caudal peduncle, except in *Hybopsis x-punctata;* eye diameter more than half distance from hind margin of eye to upper end of gill cleft, except in *Hybopsis gracilis* 8
   Most of breast (anterior to pelvic fins) scaleless; underside of head obviously papillose; snout length greater than least depth of caudal peduncle; eye diameter seldom more than half distance from hind margin of eye to upper end of gill cleft 12

8. Lateral-line scales 44 or more; head at occiput wider than deep; pharyngeal teeth 2,4—4,2 .. flat-headed chub, *Hybopsis gracilis,* p. 84

Lateral-line scales usually fewer than 44; head at occiput deeper than wide; pharyngeal teeth 0 or 1,4—4,1 or 0 9

9. Mouth oblique, terminal or nearly so; eye diameter less than ¼ head length .... hornyhead, *Hybopsis biguttata,* p. 86

Mouth almost horizontal, never terminal; eye diameter at least ¼ head length 10

10. Anal rays usually 7 (Fig. 6B); pharyngeal teeth 0,4—4,0; coloration olivaceous with dark checks or X-markings on sides, gravel chub, *Hybopsis x-punctata,* p. 89

Anal rays usually 8; pharyngeal teeth 1,4—4,1; coloration silvery .. 11

11. Head depth at occiput not more than distance from tip of snout to back of eye; dusky lateral stripe usually present; caudal fin uniformly pigmented .... big-eyed chub, *Hybopsis amblops,* p. 90

Head depth at occiput more than distance from tip of snout to back of eye; no dark lateral stripe; caudal fin white-edged ventrally, darker above .... silver chub, *Hybopsis storeriana,* p. 92

12. Fins falcate; length of first dorsal ray greater than head length; lateral-line scales 45-50 .... sickle-finned chub, *Hybopsis meeki,* p. 94

Fins rounded; length of first dorsal ray less than or about equal to head length; lateral-line scales fewer than 45 13

13. Scales without fleshy ridges or keels; lateral-line scales 35-39; pharyngeal teeth 0,4—4,0; dorsum pallid, with scattered black dots, speckled chub, *Hybopsis aestivalis,* p. 95

Scales with fleshy ridges or keels; lateral-line scales 39-43; pharyngeal teeth 1,4—4,1; dorsum uniformly dusky, without scattered black dots .... sturgeon chub, *Hybopsis gelida,* p. 97

14. Anal rays usually 9 or more (Fig. 6B); pharyngeal arch having one or more teeth in secondary row (Fig. 9C), except in *Notemigonus crysoleucas* 15

Anal rays usually 8 or fewer; pharyngeal arch lacking teeth in secondary row except in *Semotilus atromaculatus, Notropis spilopterus, N. blennius, N. boops,* and *N. dorsalis* 26

15. Anal rays usually more than 9; insertion of pelvic fins distinctly anterior to origin of dorsal fin (Fig. 10A) 16

Anal rays usually 9; insertion of pelvic fins and origin of dorsal fin approximately equidistant from tip of snout (Fig. 10B) 20

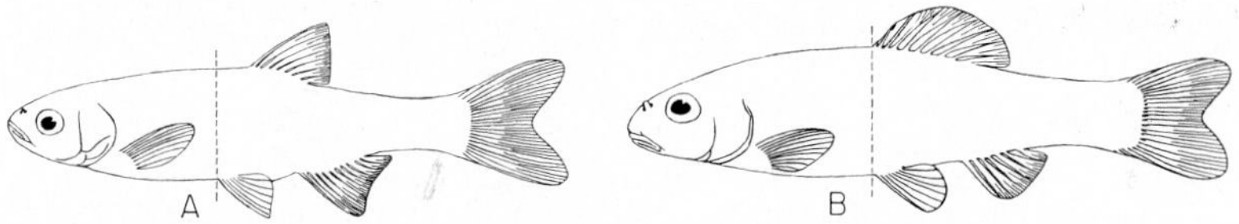

FIG. 10. Differences in position and shape of dorsal fins of minnows.

A. Origin of dorsal fin posterior to insertion of pelvic fins, as indicated by vertical dash-line. Also, the dorsal fin is triangular (pointed at tip), and its anterior rays would extend to or beyond the tips of the posterior rays if the fin were folded downward against the body.

B. Origin of dorsal fin approximately over insertion of pelvic fins. Also, the dorsal fin is rounded, and its anterior rays would not extend to the tips of the posterior rays if the fin were folded downward against the body.

16. Midline of belly (behind base of pelvic fins) having fleshy keel; lateral-line scales more than 45; pharyngeal teeth 5—5,
golden shiner, *Notemigonus crysoleucas*, p. 76

Midline of belly (behind base of pelvic fins) not keeled; lateral-line scales fewer than 45; pharyngeal teeth 4—4 17

17. Body slender, scarcely compressed, greatest width (thickness) equal to distance from crest of back to lateral-line row of scales (at point of greatest decurvature of lateral line); body depth usually contained 4.0 or more times in standard length 18

Body deep, compressed, greatest width (thickness) less than distance from crest of back to lateral-line row of scales (at point of greatest decurvature of lateral line); body depth usually contained less than 4.0 times in standard length 19

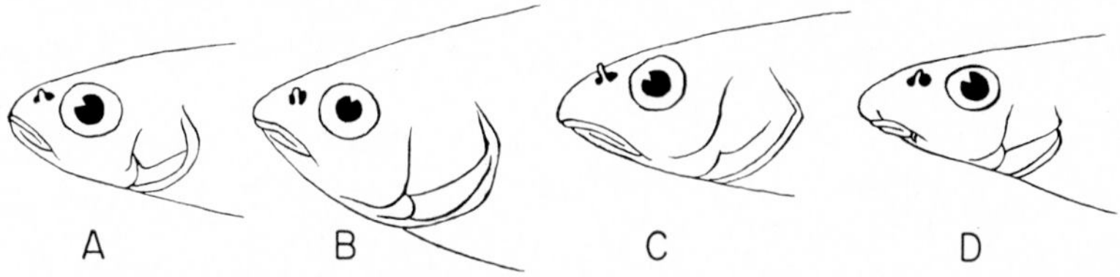

FIG. 11. Characteristics of mouths of minnows (lateral views).

A. Mouth terminal and oblique, upper and lower jaws equal. Big-eyed shiner illustrated.

B. Mouth nearly terminal, oblique, but lower jaw included (shorter than upper jaw, closing within it). Blunt-faced shiner illustrated.

C. Mouth subterminal, scarcely oblique, lower jaw included (shorter than upper jaw, closing within it). Big-mouthed shiner illustrated.

D. Mouth ventral and nearly horizontal. Note also barbel projecting from groove at corner of mouth (barbel absent in A, B, and C). Gravel chub illustrated.

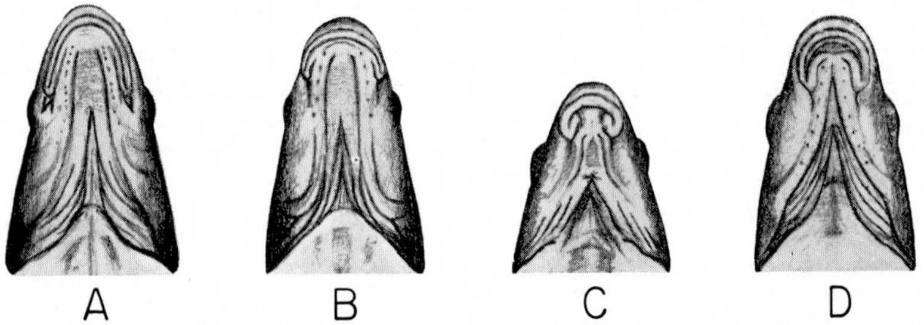

FIG. 12. Characteristics of mouths in four kinds of minnows (ventral views).

A. Flat-headed chub: Deeply U-shaped mouth as in most minnows (note also terminal barbels, projecting from groove behind lips at each corner of mouth).

B. Plains minnow: Shallowly crescentic mouth as in Genus *Hybognathus* (barbels absent).

C. Sucker-mouthed minnow: Note uniquely lobed lips.

D. Stoneroller: Cartilaginous edge exposed along front of lower jaw, not covered by thickened epidermis of lower lip.

18. Snout blunt, its length about equal to eye diameter and contained more than 1.5 times in postorbital length of head (Fig. 4); least depth of caudal peduncle usually exceeding distance from tip of snout to middle of pupil; tip of dorsal fin pointed; rosy pigment lacking, emerald shiner, *Notropis atherinoides,* p. 102

    Snout acute, its length greater than eye diameter and contained less than 1.5 times in postorbital length of head; least depth of caudal peduncle less than distance from tip of snout to middle of pupil; tip of dorsal fin rounded; usually rosy color on head, breast, and base of dorsal fin .... rosy-faced shiner, *Notropis rubellus,* p. 104

19. Predorsal scale-rows 25 or more (scales minute and crowded); lateral-line scales more than 37; slight dark spot at origin of dorsal fin; fins seldom red or orange (in Kansas specimens), red-finned shiner, *Notropis umbratilis,* p. 108

    Predorsal scale-rows fewer than 20 (scales not minute and crowded); lateral-line scales fewer than 37; no dark spot at origin of dorsal fin; fins often red or orange .... red shiner, *Notropis lutrensis,* p. 125

20. Dorsal fin acutely pointed, first principal ray longer than head length; predorsal stripe indistinct or absent; body almost unpigmented, transparent in life; sides having thin, bright silvery longitudinal stripe .... silver-banded shiner, *Notropis shumardi,* p. 106

    Dorsal fin not acutely pointed, first principal ray shorter than head length; predorsal stripe usually prominent; body well pigmented, not transparent in life; sides generally silvery, without longitudinal stripe 21

21. Predorsal length (Fig. 4) less than or equal to distance from dorsal origin to base of caudal fin; lining of body cavity black; lateral-line scales 37 or more 22

    Predorsal length usually greater than distance from dorsal origin to base of caudal fin; lining of body cavity silvery or dusky; lateral line scales 37 or fewer 25

22. Scales on anterior part of sides not notably diamond-shaped, about twice as high as long; lateral-line scales usually 40-44 23

    Scales on anterior part of sides narrowly diamond-shaped, about 3 times as high as long; lateral-line scales usually 37-40 24

23. Cleithrum silvery (no dark crescent behind or beneath edge of operculum); no dark lines between dorsolateral scale rows, dusky-striped shiner, *Notropis pilsbryi,* p. 110

    Cleithrum blackened (dark crescent behind or beneath edge of operculum); dark zigzag lines present between dorsolateral scale rows, converging posteriorly .... bleeding shiner, *Notropis zonatus* *

24. Predorsal scales much smaller than scales on sides, more than 18 scale rows before dorsal fin; no dark lines between dorsolateral scale rows .... northern common shiner, *Notropis cornutus,* p. 113

    Predorsal scales not much smaller than scales on sides, fewer than 18 scale rows before dorsal fin; dark zigzag lines, converging posteriorly atop caudal peduncle, evident between dorsolateral scale rows, central common shiner, *Notropis chrysocephalus,* p. 115

25. Lower jaw shorter than upper jaw, closing into it (Fig. 11B); posterior membranes of dorsal fin blotched, darker than anterior membranes; caudal fin pale (unpigmented) basally, darker distally, blunt-faced shiner, *Notropis camurus,* p. 120

    Upper and lower jaws equal (Figs. 10A, 11A); posterior part of dorsal fin not blotched, not darker than anterior part; caudal fin uniformly pigmented .... red shiner, *Notropis lutrensis,* p. 125

* Hypothetically in Kansas; see account of *Notropis pilsbryi.*

26. Intestine forming single, flattened S-shaped loop longitudinally (Fig. 13A); lining of body cavity silvery, sometimes dusky, black only in *Notropis boops* 27
    Intestine looped transversely across body cavity (Fig. 13B) (only one loop crossing midline, anteriorly, in *Pimephales notatus*); lining of body cavity black 42
27. Anal rays usually 8 28
    Anal rays usually 7 37
28. Lateral-line scales more than 50; dorsal fin with dark spot at origin; pharyngeal teeth 2,5—4,2 . . creek chub, *Semotilus atromaculatus*, p.
    Lateral-line scales fewer than 42; dorsal fin without dark spot at origin; pharyngeal teeth never 2,5—4,2 29
29. Body compressed, lateral line decurved; greatest width of body less than distance from crest of back to lateral line; dorsal fin rounded, anterior rays extending approximately to tips of posterior rays when fin is depressed against body 30
    Body terete, lateral line nearly straight; greatest width of body about equal to distance from crest of back to lateral line; dorsal fin pointed, anterior rays extending beyond tips of posterior rays when fin is depressed against body 31
30. Posterior membranes of dorsal fin more densely pigmented than anterior membranes; lateral-line scales usually more than 35; greatest depth of body 3.6-4.3 in standard length; pharyngeal teeth 1,4—4,1, spot-finned shiner, *Notropis spilopterus*, p. 123
    Posterior membranes of dorsal fin not more densely pigmented than anterior membranes; lateral-line scales usually 35 or fewer; greatest depth of body 3.0-3.6 in standard length; pharyngeal teeth usually 0,4—4,0 . . . . . red shiner, *Notropis lutrensis*, p. 125
31. Mouth strongly oblique, upper and lower jaws equal or the lower jaw protruding (Fig. 11A); lower lip pigmented 32
    Mouth scarcely oblique, lower jaw shorter than upper jaw, closing within it (Fig. 11C); lower lip unpigmented 33
32. Dorsal rays 9; lateral-line scales 36-40; pharyngeal teeth 0,5—5,0; lining of body cavity silvery, pug-nosed minnow, *Opsopoeodus emiliae*, p. 83
    Dorsal rays 8; lateral-line scales 34-36; pharyngeal teeth, 1,4—4,1; lining of body cavity black . . . . big-eyed shiner, *Notropis boops*, p. 119

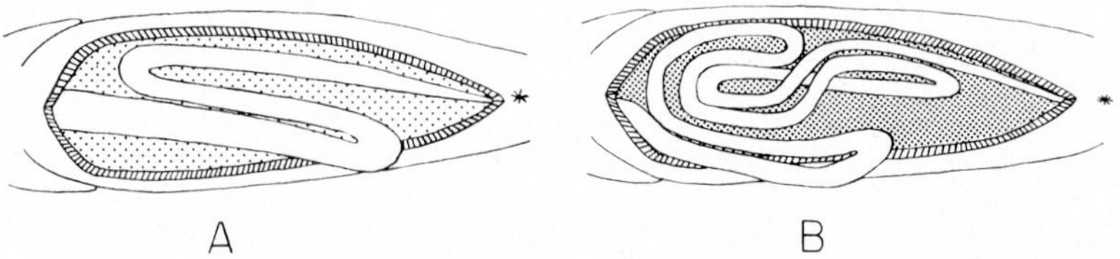

FIG. 13. Ventral views (diagrammatic) of body cavities in minnows, as they would appear if lower body-wall were cut away.

A. Intestine short, forming a single S-shaped loop; peritoneum silvery.
B. Intestine long, looped transversely across body cavity; peritoneum dark (usually black).

33. Eye diameter less than length of upper jaw; anterior lateral-line scales not higher than scales in rows above and below lateral line; circumferential scales 26 or more 34

Eye diameter greater than length of upper jaw; anterior lateral-line scales higher than scales in rows above and below lateral line; circumferential scales fewer than 26 35

34. Origin of dorsal fin nearer base of caudal fin than tip of snout; eye diameter greater than ¼ head length; predorsal dark stripe well developed, caudal spot absent; pharyngeal teeth 1,4—4,1,
big-mouthed shiner, *Notropis dorsalis*, p. 130

Origin of dorsal fin nearer tip of snout than base of caudal fin; eye diameter less than ¼ head length; predorsal stripe faint or absent, small caudal spot present; pharyngeal teeth 0,4—4,0,
Arkansas River shiner, *Notropis girardi*, p. 135

35. Dark lateral stripe intense, continuous around snout; anterior lateral-line scales having chevronlike markings with apices directed forward; snout length not less than eye diameter,
black-nosed shiner, *Notropis heterolepis*, p. 141

Dark lateral stripe faint or absent; anterior lateral-line scales lacking chevronlike markings; snout length less than eye diameter 36

36. Dorsolateral scales outlined by dark pigment, upper sides about as well pigmented as dorsal surface; longest ray in dorsal fin usually shorter than head length; infraorbital canal complete (Fig. 4),
mimic shiner, *Notropis volucellus*, p. 137

Dorsolateral scales not outlined by dark pigment, upper sides with an unpigmented space; longest ray in dorsal fin longer than head length; infraorbital canal incomplete (Fig. 4)
ghost shiner, *Notropis buchanani*, p. 139

37. Lower lip thick, with prominent lobes at corners of mouth (Fig. 12C),
sucker-mouthed minnow, *Phenacobius mirabilis*, p. 99

Lower lip uniformly thin, without lobes at corners of mouth 38

38. Dorsal fin pointed at tip, unspotted; anterior rays of dorsal extending to or beyond tips of posterior rays when fin is depressed against body (Fig. 10A); lateral-line scales 32-37 39

Dorsal fin rounded, with anterior dark spot; anterior rays of dorsal not extending to tips of posterior rays when fin is depressed against body (Fig. 10B); lateral-line scales 37-41 41

39. Dark lateral band present, terminating in discrete triangular caudal spot; length of caudal peduncle equal to head length; mouth small, distance from front of mandible to end of maxilla about ½ distance from end of maxilla to lower end of gill cleft (union of gill membrane to isthmus) . . . . Topeka shiner, *Notropis topeka*, p. 128

Dark lateral band absent, caudal spot usually absent (diffuse if present); length of caudal peduncle less than head length; mouth large, distance from front of mandible to end of maxilla at least ⅔ distance from end of maxilla to lower end of gill cleft (union of gill membrane to isthmus) 40

40. Mid-dorsal stripe divided around base of dorsal fin, not intensified within base (no black dash in base of dorsal); lateral line not accented by melanophores; pharyngeal teeth 1 or 2,4—4,2 or 1,
river shiner, *Notropis blennius*, p. 117

Mid-dorsal stripe not divided around base of dorsal fin, intensified within base (black dash present in base of dorsal); lateral line usually accented by melanophores; pharyngeal teeth 0,4—4,0,
sand shiner, *Notropis stramineus*, p. 133

41. Dorsum not cross-hatched (pigment dispersed on scales); spot at base of caudal fin wedge-shaped; dark lateral stripe indistinct or absent; least depth of caudal peduncle usually greater than ½ its length (body stout); nuptial tubercles usually 9, in 2 rows,
bull-headed minnow, *Pimephales vigilax*, p. 153

Dorsum cross-hatched (pigment concentrated along margins of scales); spot at base of caudal fin vertically elongate; dark lateral stripe well-defined; least depth of caudal peduncle usually less than ½ its length (body slender); nuptial tubercles usually 11-13, in 3 rows,
slim minnow, *Pimephales tenellus*, p. 155

42. Intestine wound spirally around air bladder; lower jaw with hardened cartilaginous cutting-edge (often concealed—pry mouth open) and submarginal fold of thick skin (Fig. 12D),
stoneroller, *Campostoma anomalum*, p. 159

Intestine having all its loops ventral to air bladder, never completely encircling it; lower jaw not as above, its edge exposed, sometimes thin and hard, but without submarginal fold of skin 43

43. Lateral line incomplete; scales minute, 65-90 in lateral-line row; origin of dorsal fin behind insertion of pelvics; body having two dark lateral stripes; pharyngeal teeth 0,5—5,0,
red-bellied dace, *Chrosomus erythrogaster*, p. 81

Lateral line usually complete; scales large, fewer than 50 in lateral-line row; origin of dorsal fin not behind insertion of pelvics; body not having two dark lateral stripes; pharyngeal teeth 0,4—4,0 . . 44

44. Dorsal fin rounded, anterior rays not extending to tips of posterior rays when fin is depressed against body (Fig. 10B); lateral-line scales usually more than 40; anal rays usually 7; breast naked (below pectoral fins) 45

Dorsal fin triangular, anterior rays extending to tips of posterior rays when fin is depressed against body (Fig. 10A); lateral-line scales usually fewer than 40; anal rays usually 8; breast scaled (below pectoral fins) 46

45. Scale rows around body 38 or more; caudal fin usually lacking basal spot; intestine with several loops across body cavity,
fat-headed minnow, *Pimephales promelas*, p. 149

Scale rows around body 32 or fewer; caudal fin having distinct black basal spot; loops of intestine few and mostly longitudinal,
blunt-nosed minnow, *Pimephales notatus*, p. 157

46. Mouth ∩-shaped (Fig. 12A); eye diameter more than ¼ head length, equal to snout length; pharyngeal teeth hooked; lateral line outlined by dark dots . . . . ozark minnow, *Dionda nubila*, p. 143

Mouth ⌒-shaped (Fig. 12B); eye diameter usually less than ¼ head length, less than snout length; pharyngeal teeth not hooked; lateral line not outlined by dark dots 47

47. Dorsal fin rounded at tip; caudal fin uniformly pigmented (lower rudimentary rays pigmented); sides with a brassy sheen in life, dusky lateral band usually evident,
brassy minnow, *Hybognathus hankinsoni*, p. 144

Dorsal fin pointed at tip; caudal fin pale-edged ventrally (lower rudimentary rays unpigmented); sides silvery in life, no dusky lateral band 48

48. Ventral scale-rows (below lateral-line series, crossing in front of pelvic fins) usually 15-18; posterior process of basioccipital bone rodlike (Fig. 14A) . . . . plains minnow, *Hybognathus placitus*, p. 146

Ventral scale-rows (below lateral-line series, crossing in front of pelvic fins) usually 12-14; posterior process of basioccipital bone thin and broad (Fig. 14B) . . . . silvery minnow, *Hybognathus nuchalis*, p. 148

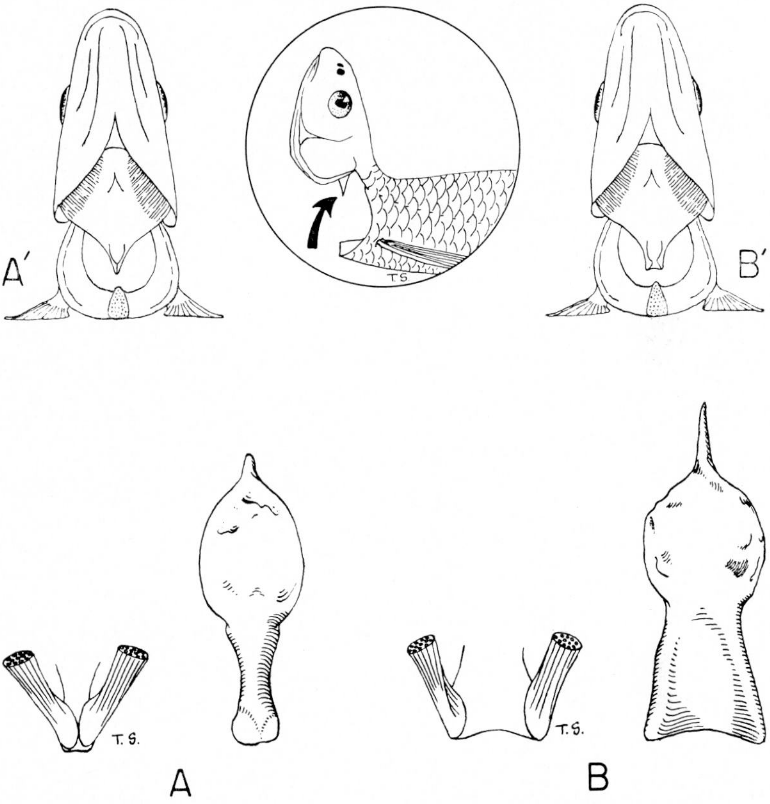

FIG. 14. Basioccipital bones in two species of *Hybognathus*. Upper three figures indicate a method of revealing the structure, by cutting across the isthmus and bending the head backward. Lower four figures (redrawn from Bailey and Allum, 1962:Pl. 1) show details of undersurface of basioccipital.

A′ and A. Plains minnow: posterior process of basioccipital rodlike, with contiguous muscle-attachments at tip.

B′ and B. Silvery minnow: posterior process of basioccipital expanded, with widely separated muscle-attachments at tip.

Carp

Cyprinus carpio Linnaeus

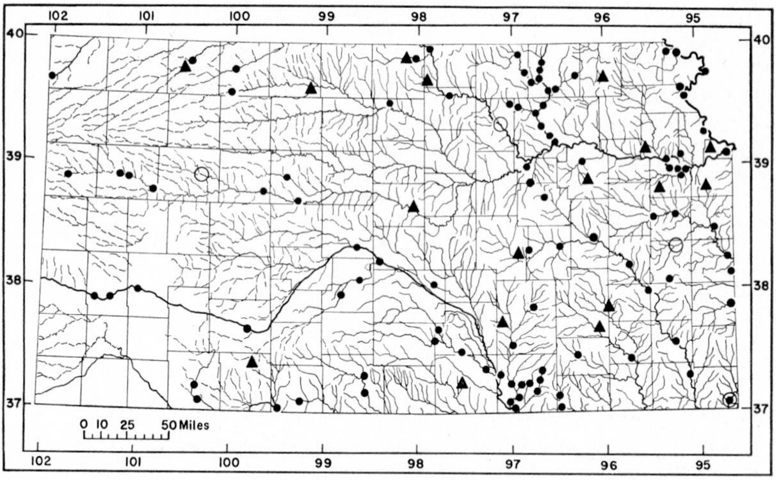

Cyprinus carpio, Cragin (1885b:109); Graham (1885b:78); Dyche (1914: 124-129); Hall (1934:230); Breukelman (1940a:369, 1940b:380, 1960: 34); Jennings (1942:364); Cross (1954:308); Cross and Hastings (1956:86); Greer and Cross (1956:360); Schelske (1957:39); Clarke, Breukelman, and Andrews (1958:167); Cross, Deacon, and Ward (1959: 163); Metcalf (1959:365, 1966:97); Minckley (1959:418); Deacon (1961:378-379); Deacon and Metcalf (1961:316); Fisher (1962:427).
Carp—Schoonover and Thompson (1954:176).

Body compressed, back arched, ventral line nearly straight; dorsal fin with 19-22 rays, first ray bony (spinous) and saw-edged posteriorly; anal fin with 6 rays, first ray spinous; mouth terminal, slightly oblique, thin-lipped, with two pairs of barbels; pharyngeal arch broad, its teeth molarlike, in three rows; vertebrae 35-40.

Color gray to brassy, fins yellowish to orange.

Weight of largest specimen from Kansas 24 pounds, 9 ounces.

Information about the earliest introductions of carp into the United States has been summarized by Forbes and Richardson (1920:105-106); in Kansas, Breukelman (1946:58) and Call (1961: 32-33) have discussed the arrival of the carp in 1880 and 1881, and its propagation in ponds during the next few years. The excited optimism with which the first fish were received is, in retrospect, highly interesting: "There are few farmers in Kansas who could not furnish a quarter or half an acre of ground, which might be devoted to the raising of these valuable fishes; . . . and as fish ponds, be made the most pleasant and profitable parts of the farm" (Call, 1961:32, as quoted from a report in 1881 by Professor E. M. Shelton of Kansas State College).

Although Cragin (1885b:109) wrote that carp were being "raised for food in artificial ponds in all parts of the State" by 1885, it is noteworthy that none of the following mentioned carp from streams in Kansas: Cragin (1885b) and Graham (1885b), state-wide lists of fishes; Jordan and Meek (1885), Missouri River opposite St. Joseph; Gilbert (1886, 1889) and Hay (1887), various streams, mostly in western Kansas; Jordan (1891), Arkansas River at Wichita. Thus it seems unlikely that carp became abundant in natural waters until the 1890's or early 1900's. In 1910-1912, personnel of the State Biological Survey found carp in the following rivers or tributaries thereto: Smoky Hill, Republican, Kansas, Marais des Cygnes, and Spring. By 1914, carp occurred "in nearly all Kansas streams" according to Dyche (1914:125). He spoke of carp as "perhaps the greatest pond fish in the world" and (*loc. cit.*: 124-129) published observations on the habits of the species under culture at the State Fish Hatchery near Pratt. The carp is now (1966) statewide in distribution, and is the predominant large fish in the lower Kansas River. In the Missouri River, the commercial catch of carp greatly exceeds that of any other species.

The early enthusiasm for carp waned gradually, and the species now has few advocates, even among commercial fishermen. Over the years, the catches of other fishes declined as carp increased. Carp have the lowest value, per pound, of any fish now taken commercially in the Missouri River, and many of the carp caught are not salable because the supply exceeds the demand for them. In many parts of the United States, the commercial income derived from carp is partly offset by large sums that are expended annually in efforts to control or eradicate carp.

Eradication of carp now seems impossible, except in small lakes that are wholly isolated from other surface-waters. "Control" short of eradication requires carefully-planned and costly efforts, every year *ad infinitum,* if sustained benefits are to result. Thus, the prevalence of carp is to be accepted as the result of a lamentable mistake, and should be remembered when introductions of other non-native fishes are proposed.

Since they are here to stay, carp should be utilized as fully as possible. They are not bad sport fish in terms of their fighting ability, being stronger and more tenacious than bass and most other game-fish of similar weight. Carp grow larger than any species classed as game fish in Kansas other than the flathead, channel catfish, and blue catfish. The current "state-record" carp, caught by Harvey W. Haas in Clarks Creek near Skiddy, Morris County, weighed 24 pounds, 9 ounces. That record is not likely to stand. The largest carp that I have heard about weighed 74 pounds (when caught in Rankin County Lake, Mississippi). Mississippi Fish and Game Magazine (Vol. 24, No. 18, p. 9, 1964) states that this particular carp "broke water, like a depth charge of dynamite" when hooked, and that the angler as well as the fish ultimately collapsed in exhaustion.

Carp are remarkably adaptable animals, a fact that accounts for the general success attending their introduction over much of the world. They feed on plant-material as well as many kinds of aquatic animals. Carp congregate near points of discharge from sewage treatment plants and other sources of organic effluent in streams, consuming the refuse or the microorganisms found there. I have watched carp as they neatly stripped the grain from each fallen head of wheat in flooded fields, where water was less deep than the bodies of the fish. Under such flood-conditions, many a Kansas farm-boy has enjoyed carp-catching bonanzas in which the fish were taken by hand, pitchfork, shotgun, bow-and-arrow, and such other means as personal ingenuity engendered.

Seldom are carp predaceous on other fishes, but carp undoubtedly compete for food with many kinds of native fish and alter habitats in ways detrimental to other species.

Carp reproduce intermittently over a lengthy period each year. Spawning sometimes begins as early as March, and extends to July or later; peaks of reproductive activity usually follow rises in waterlevel in late April, May, and June. The eggs are scattered over vegetation or debris in shallow water, without prior preparation of nest-sites or subsequent protection by the parental fish. The fecundity of carp is high. One 17-pound carp that I examined, from the Kansas River in Kansas City, contained approximately 2,300,000 eggs.

Limited information on growth-rates of carp in Kansas has been recorded by Schoonover and Thompson (1954:176) and by Minckley (1959:418).

Goldfish

Carassius auratus (Linnaeus)

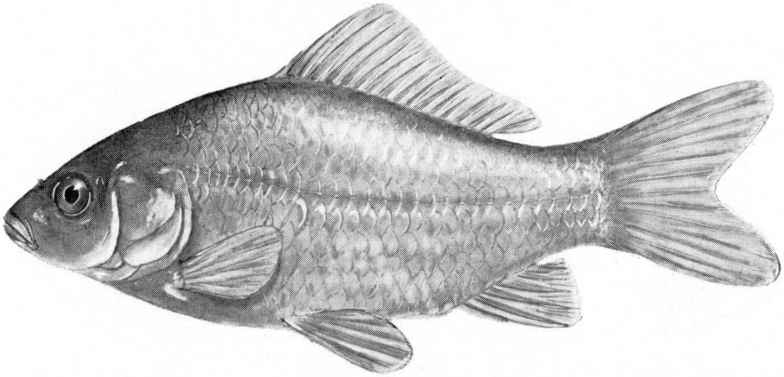

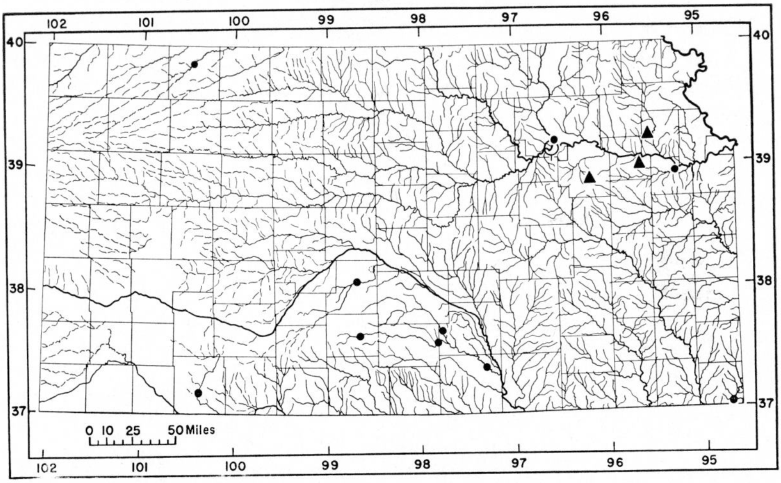

Carassius auratus, Jennings (1942:364); Clarke, Breukelman, and Andrews (1958:167); Minckley (1959:419); Breukelman (1960:34); Metcalf (1966:98).

Goldfish—Dyche (1914:129-132, 151-153).

Body moderately compressed; dorsal fin with 18 or 19 rays, first ray bony (spinous) and saw-edged posteriorly; anal fin with 6 or 7 rays, first spinous; mouth oblique, thin-lipped, without barbels; pharyngeal teeth 0,4—4,0, arch strong; vertebrae 30-31.

Color variable, commonly orange but dull gray or bronze in "wild-type." Maximum size approximately three pounds.

The first reference to goldfish in Kansas seems to be that of Dyche (1914), concerning production of this species in ponds at the State Fish Hatchery near Pratt. Dyche (1914:130) stated, "We hatch them in great numbers and raise them to different ages and sizes as food for other fishes," and (*op. cit.*:131), "Full-grown specimens at from three to five years of age will attain a weight of from two to three pounds."

Subsequent records of goldfish are few, and several are from impoundments where the occurrence may reflect release of goldfish used as bait. Not indicated on the map is a report by Clarke, Breukelman, and Andrews (1958:167) that the species is "Sometimes abundant locally" in Lyon County. The only stream from which I have taken goldfish repeatedly is the Ninnescah River, below the State Fish Hatchery, although that hatchery ceased production of goldfish many years ago. Elsewhere the species seems scarce in natural waters, but the scattered distribution of recent records suggests that goldfish might be found almost anywhere in Kansas.

Thoughtless release of goldfish endangers native fishes through competition. The goldfish has no advantage as a bait-minnow over various native species. Therefore, the production and use of goldfish as bait involves unnecessary risk that anglers ought not be willing to accept.

Golden shiner
Notemigonus crysoleucas (Mitchill)

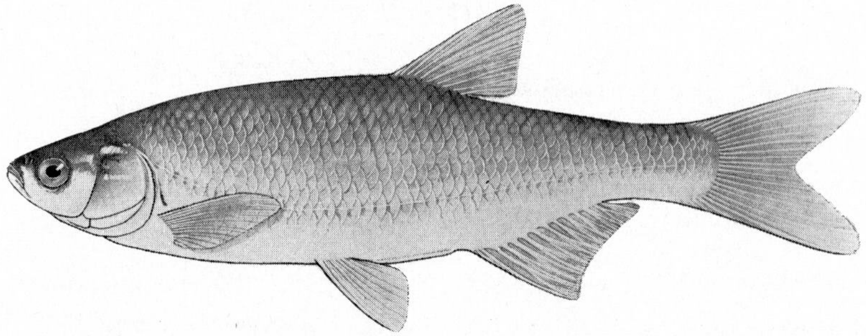

Notemigonus chrysoleucus, Graham (1885b:74); Evermann and Fordice (1886:185).

Notemigonus crysoleucas, Hall (1934:230); Moore and Buck (1955:22); Greer and Cross (1956:360); Schelske (1957:39, 45); Clarke, Breukelman, and Andrews (1958:167); Cross, Deacon, and Ward (1959:163); Metcalf (1959:372, 1966:98); Breukelman (1960:34); Deacon (1961:379); Deacon and Metcalf (1961:316).

Notemigonus crysoleucas auratus, Breukelman (1940a:370); Jennings (1942:365).

Notemigonus chrysoleucas auratus, Breukelman (1940b:380).

Golden shiner—Breukelman (1946:63).

Body deeply compressed; head small, mouth small and highly oblique; ventrum keeled from pelvic fins to anus; lateral line deeply decurved, with 47-54 scales; scale rows around body 20-25—2—11-14; dorsal fin high, acutely pointed, originating posterior to insertion of pelvics; dorsal fin-rays 8; anal fin-rays 11-15; pelvic rays usually 9; pectoral rays 15; pharyngeal teeth 0,5—5,0; intestine short, peritoneum dusky; vertebrae usually 37-38.

Olivaceous dorsally, silvery to brassy laterally and ventrally; fins usually colorless, without dark spots near their bases.

Length 12 inches or less.

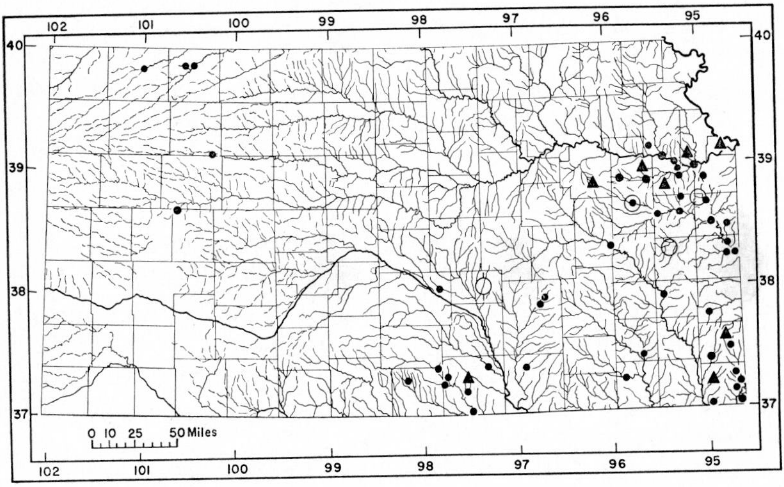

The golden shiner is more common in eastern than in western Kansas, but may now be nearly statewide in occurrence. The scarcity of records prior to 1900 suggests than *N. crysoleucas* has increased its abundance in recent years. For several reasons, I think the species now occurs more generally than is indicated by the map above. First, the fish has a decided preference for deep, quiet pools and lakes, especially where aquatic vegetation grows rankly and seining is difficult; furthermore, the golden shiner is an unusually fast, elusive minnow, not easily captured by seining. Second, impoundments throughout the State have provided much new habitat suitable for golden shiners, and frequent use of this species as bait may have facilitated its establishment where the species had been rare or absent. All the records (see map) in northwestern Kansas were obtained from pools below dams. Several lakes in eastern Kansas (Leavenworth and Crawford county state lakes, Wyandotte County Lake, Lone Star Lake, Lake Wabaunsee, Gardner City Lake) have limited populations of golden shiners that attain lengths of 10 inches or more. Some of the golden shiners netted from those lakes weigh more than most crappie, bluegill, and other panfishes in the same lakes.

Apart from impoundments, the usual habitat of *Notemigonus* is in oxbows and in pools of small creeks that have reasonably clear water. The species seldom is found in streams that are highly-intermittent, or in the mainstreams of our larger rivers.

Notemigonus spawns in late spring and summer. The eggs are scattered, often in weed-beds, where they adhere during their development to stems and finely-divided leaves. The spawning fish prepare no nests nor do they protect the eggs and young.

Creek chub

Semotilus atromaculatus (Mitchill)

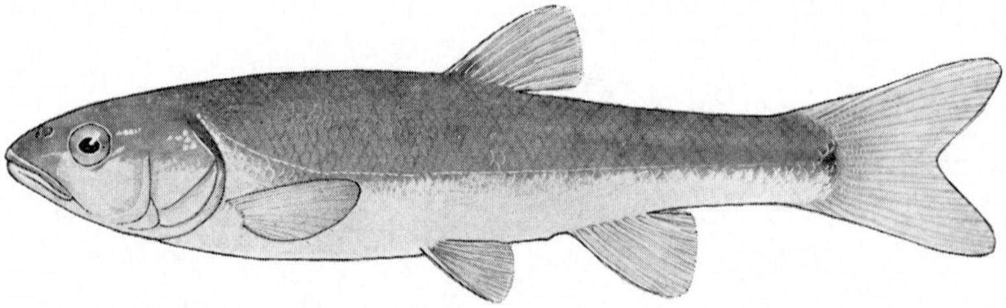

Semotilus Hammondii Abbott (1860a:474 [orig. descr., based on a tuberculate male, locality given only as "Kansas"]).

Semotilus corporalis, Cope (1865b:85); Gilbert (1884:15).

Semotilis atromaculatus, Graham (1885a:4).

Semotilus atromaculatus, Gilbert (1885b:99, 1889:39, 40, 42); Cragin 1885b:109); Graham (1885b:74); Hay (1887:243, 247, 249, 250, 252); Crevecoeur (1908:155); Fowler (1925:396); Breukelman (1940a:370, 1940b:380, 1960:34); Jennings (1942:364); Cross (1954:308); Minckley (1956:354, 1959:419); Clarke, Breukelman, and Andrews (1958:168); Minckley and Cross (1959:212); Minckley and Deacon (1959:348); Cross and Minckley (1960:7); Deacon (1961:379); Deacon and Metcalf (1961:316); Olund and Cross (1961:341); Metcalf (1966:98).

Semotilus atromaculus, Hall (1934:230).

Squalius elongatus, Hay (1887:249 [misidentification, a single abnormal specimen reidentified as S. *atromaculatus* by Hubbs, 1951b:191-192]).

Body nearly terete; head large, its length 3.2-3.6 in standard length; mouth large, terminal, oblique; upper lip expanded medially and dark-pigmented; small, flaplike barbel (sometimes obsolescent) recessed in groove above upper lip, anterior to corner of mouth; fins small and rounded; dorsal fin 8-rayed, originating posterior to insertion of pelvic fins; anal and pelvic fin-rays 8, pectoral rays 15-17; lateral line complete, slightly decurved, with (usually) 55-65 scales; predorsal scales small, crowded; scale rows around body 23-26—2—23-29, around caudal peduncle 11-12—2—10-12; pharyngeal arch large, teeth 2,5—4,2; intestine short, peritoneum silvery; vertebrae 42-45.

Blue-gray or olivaceous dorsally, white ventrally; sides with narrow, dusky

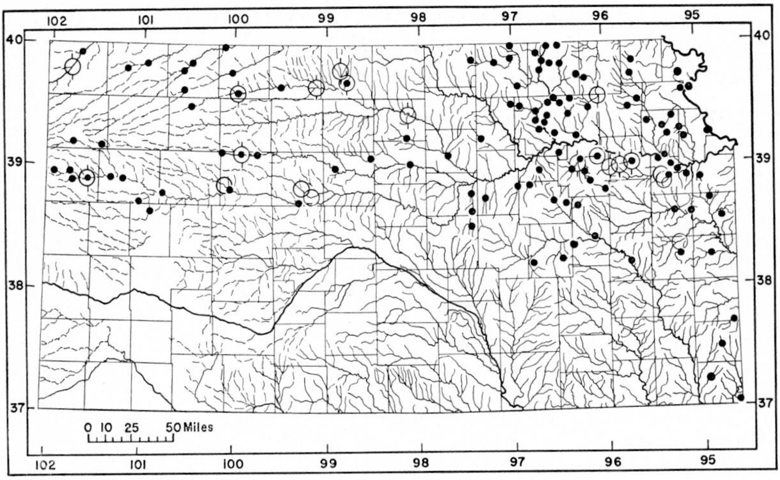

longitudinal streak, terminating in small wedge-shaped spot at base of caudal fin; dorsal fin with dark basal blotch anteriorly; mid-dorsal stripe well developed; sides of breeding males rosy with purple iridescence; lower fins yellowish; cleithrum blackened.

Breeding males with few large tubercles, aligned in two rows on head—usually four above each eye and a pair before each narial pit; pectoral rays 2-9 with one file of tubercles basally, double file on branched (distal) part of each ray; marginal row of small tubercles on some scales of caudal peduncle; upper rudimentary rays of caudal fin tuberculate.

Length 12 inches or less.

The creek chub occurs throughout the Kansas River Basin but only at a few localities in the Arkansas River System. The species characteristically occupies small tributaries rather than rivers, as its name implies and as nearly all authors have verified in their accounts of *Semotilus*. Nevertheless, I have often caught "strays" in the mainstream of the Kansas River near Lawrence. Creek chubs may have unusual vagility under the variable environmental conditions in Plains streams; wandering individuals may account for rapid redispersal of *Semotilus* into tributaries that are ill-suited for creek chubs during droughts.

Many streams where *Semotilus* occurs in the Kansas River System are intermittent and muddy. In contrast, only the clearest, permanently-flowing streams in the Arkansas River System harbor *Semotilus*. I fail to understand why it is absent from many small streams in southeastern Kansas that appear to provide habitats better than those where creek chubs persist in the Kansas River Basin. Starrett (1950:122) considered *Semotilus* to be an exceptionally hardy, pioneering fish in Iowa; that description seems applicable to populations of creek chubs in the Kansas River Basin but not to those in the Arkansas River Basin. The species certainly is native to the Arkansas System, judging from Pleistocene evidence and Recent occurrences southwestward across that river basin to the headwaters of the Rio Grande.

Creek chubs reproduce early in the year. Most males captured in late March are tuberculate, although not actually spawning. The peak of spawning activity probably occurs in April in most years. Males construct and guard nests that have the form of gravel ridges. The nest is elongated downstream as successive batches of eggs are deposited, fertilized, and covered by addition of stones at the lower end of the nest.

The brief spawning period of *Semotilus* usually occurs at the time when streams are clearest and their waterlevels are most nearly stable. Spring-flow in tributaries is strong because vegetation still is dormant, minimizing loss of ground-water through transpiration; and, rains seldom cause high, muddy waters until late spring and summer, after completion of the creek chub's reproductive cycle.

Semotilus is an opportunistic carnivore. In Iowa, Dinsmore (1962) reported that fish, annelids, crayfish, mollusks, an assortment of insects, and some aquatic vegetation are eaten by creek chubs. After noting the temporary occurrence of large numbers of ground-beetles in diets of creek chubs during floods, Dinsmore suggested, "This adaptability, along with the wide variety of food accepted, perhaps partly explains why the chub is such a wide-ranging fish."

Large creek chubs are easily caught by hook-and-line, on live bait or small artificial lures. On light tackle this fish is surprisingly sporty, making fast runs and jumping occasionally, but it lacks endurance.

S. *atromaculatus* sometimes hybridizes in Kansas with *Chrosomus erythrogaster, Notropis cornutus,* and *Campostoma anomalum* (Cross and Minckley, 1960).

Southern red-bellied dace

Chrosomus erythrogaster (Rafinesque)

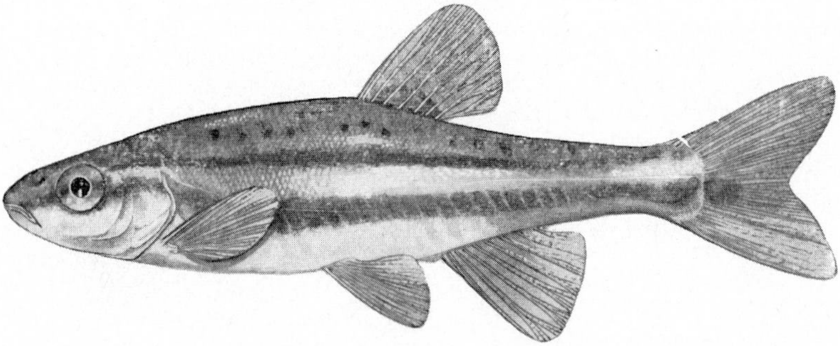

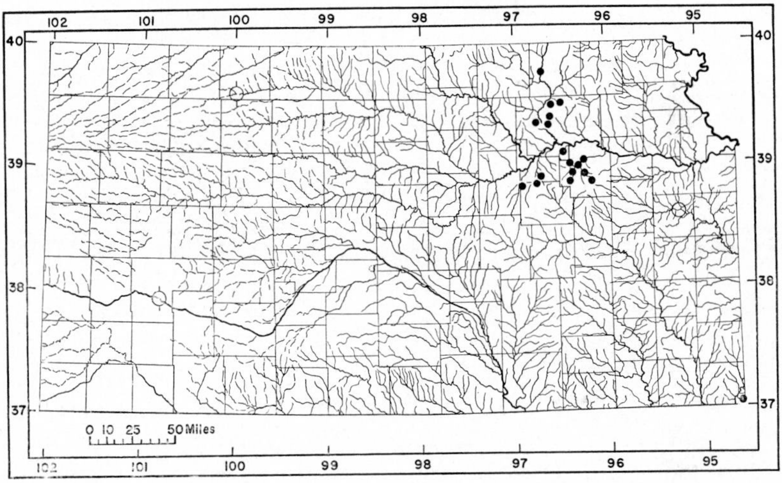

Chrosomus erythrogaster, Gilbert (1885b:98; 1889:40); Cragin (1885b: 108); Graham (1885b:72); Hay (1887:249); Breukelman (1940a:370); Jennings (1942:365); Clarke, Breukelman, and Andrews (1958:167); Minckley and Cross (1959:212); Minckley (1959:419); Cross and Minckley (1960:4, 7); Metcalf (1966:102).

Body terete; head small, conical, its length 3.8-4.2 in standard length; mouth small, nearly terminal, slightly oblique; fins small, rounded; dorsal fin 8-rayed, originating behind insertion of pelvic fins; anal fin-rays 7 or 8; pelvic rays 8; pectoral rays 14 or 15; scales minute, more than 65 in lateral-line row (lateral line incomplete); peritoneum black; intestine long, with several loops crossing midventral line; pharyngeal teeth 0,5—5,0; vertebrae 37-39.

Olivaceous dorsally, with mid-dorsal dark streak and usually with scattered dark flecks; two dark bands laterally: one originating near parietal spot and terminating in several narrowly-interrupted dark spots on upper part of caudal peduncle, another (below and wider than the first) extending from front of lips across snout, through eye and across opercle, continuously on sides to base of caudal fin; silvery horizontal band between dark bands; head silvery below eyes and on lower part of operculum; lower sides and venter white; fins colorless except for dark pigment on dorsal and caudal fins near bases. Pattern (as described above) intensified in breeding males by heightened contrast of light and dark areas; silvery lateral band yellowish; venter mostly brilliant red; lips red at corners of mouth; chin having red patch extending backward onto gill-membranes; isthmus with triangular yellow spot, surrounded by red pigment; base of pectoral fin silvery, encircled by red pigment; lower sides and breast wholly red, or having ventrolateral red patches separated by midventral white line; ventrolateral red patches extending backward above pelvic and anal fins, attenuated posteriorly; belly, base of anal fin, and midventral line of caudal peduncle bright yellow; pectoral, pelvic, and anal fins yellow; dorsal fin yellow, less brilliant than lower fins, without a basal red spot in Kansas specimens; caudal fin clear or faintly tinged with yellow, with bright yellow pigment on lower procurrent rays. See Plate 1.

Breeding males finely but densely tuberculate; head with numerous tubercles dorsally and dorsolaterally, few tubercles on snout and below eye, none on undersurface; most scales, except in abdominal region, with coalescent tubercles marginally; anterodorsal scales mostly with single tubercles (one point), tubercles on posterodorsal scales with 1-3 points; scales above base of anal fin and on lower part of caudal peduncle having 2-5 points; discrete, callouslike patch of tuberculate scales, peculiar to genus *Chrosomus*, before base of each pectoral fin (8 or 9 diagonal rows of scales bearing 1-3 tubercles per scale); pectoral fins with large tubercles on rays 2-5; pelvic rays 1-3 tuberculate; dorsal and anal fins with single file of tubercles on anterior ray, other rays sparsely tuberculate; caudal fin not tuberculate.

Length 2¾ inches or less.

The red-bellied dace now occurs in Cherokee County (Spring River Drainage) and in streams draining the Flint Hills in the Kansas River Basin. Formerly the species was more widespread, if the records of Gilbert (1885b:98, Finney County), Hay (1887: 249, Norton County), and Graham ("Marais des Cygnes River") are valid. Gilbert's record may result from mixing of fishes from "Garden City" with specimens from Snokomo Creek in Wabaunsee County (see account of *Etheostoma cragini*). The record from Lyon County (Clarke, Breukelman, and Andrews, 1958:167) is indefinite as to locality of capture.

Chrosomus is confined to small, clear, permanent streams and is common only near sources of springs. Although the streams occupied are mainly rocky, upland brooks, the red-bellied dace usually occurs over bottoms of soft muck where seepage-water emerges from the bases of high stream-banks. Thus a scarcity of permanent springs, rather than gradient or bottom-type, probably limits the distribution of this species in Kansas. The number of springs has diminished since settlement by European man. Unless the remaining springs are preserved in their natural state, undisturbed by livestock or by cultivation of adjacent lands, this handsome fish may disappear from Kansas.

Red-bellied dace spawn from late March until May, most often in April, when water-temperatures are 50° to 60° F. *C. erythrogaster* sometimes hybridizes with *Semotilus atromaculatus, Notropis cornutus,* and *Campostoma anomalum* in Kansas; the frequency of this hybridization probably indicates a scarcity of suitable habitat (or deterioration of habitat) for *Chrosomus* in Kansas.

Pug-nosed minnow
Opsopoeodus emiliae Hay

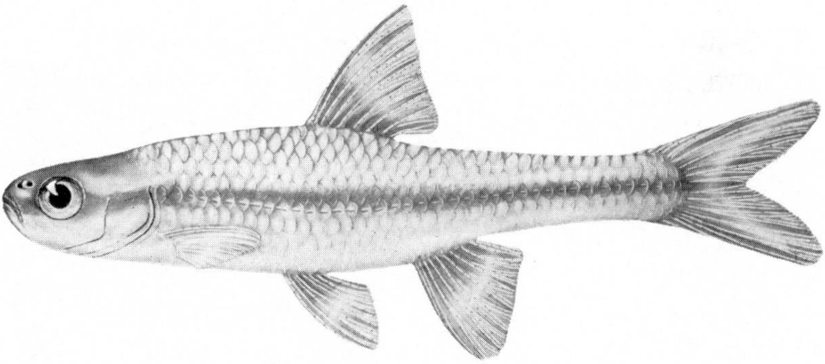

Body stout anteriorly, caudal peduncle slender; head small, its length usually less than ¼ standard length; snout blunt, usually shorter than eye-diameter; mouth small, strongly oblique, nearly vertical (posterior extremity anterior to nares); dorsal fin acutely pointed and high, anterior rays equal to or longer than head length; origin of dorsal fin approximately over insertion of pelvics; dorsal rays 9; anal and pelvic rays 8; pectoral rays 15; lateral line slightly decurved, with 36-40 scales; scale-rows around body usually 13—2—11, around caudal peduncle 5—2—5; pharyngeal teeth 0,5—5,0; intestine short, peritoneum silvery; vertebrae 37-38.

Greenish dorsally, transparent or silvery laterally and ventrally; dorsal and lateral scales well outlined by melanophores; mid-dorsal stripe obscure or absent; lateral dark band narrow and dusky, often absent; fins unspotted.

Length 2½ inches or less.

The pug-nosed minnow has not been reported from Kansas previously, but one series of four specimens from Woodson County is deposited in the University of Michigan Museum of Zoology (UMMZ 97750). The locality of capture is given as Big Sandy Creek, tributary to Verdigris River, 5½ mi. NE Coyville; the date of capture was 6 July 1931. I have collected fishes at the same locality but found no *Opsopoeodus.* The pug-nosed minnow is mainly southern in its distribution, occurring most commonly in low-gradient streams or swamps on the coastal plain. The existence of this species in southeastern Kansas is not surprising, because records of it have been obtained from southwestern Missouri and eastern Oklahoma (Arkansas River System).

Flat-headed chub

Hybopsis gracilis (Richardson)

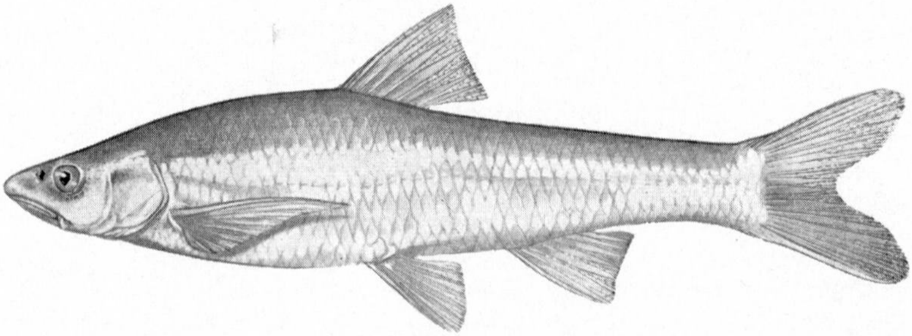

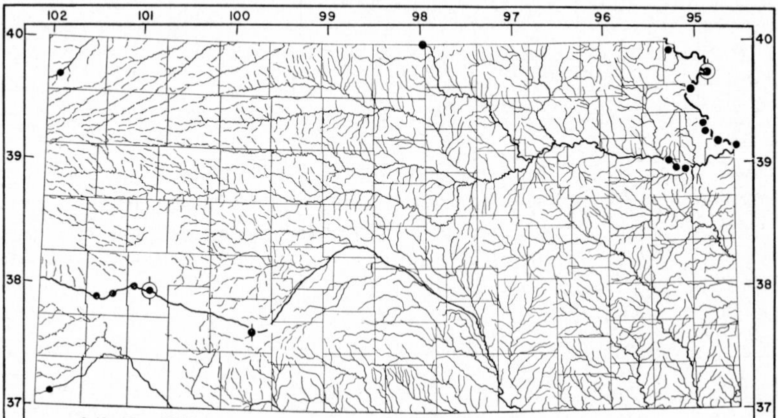

Platygobio gulonellus, Cope (1865b:85 [locality erroneously given as "Platte River, near Fort Riley"; specimens probably from North Platte River in Wyoming]).

Platygobio gracilis, Jordan and Meek (1885:13); Gilbert (1885b:98); Cragin (1885b:109); Graham (1885a:4; 1885b:74); Breukelman (1946:57).

Hybopsis gracilis, Fisher (1962:427); Metcalf (1966:103).

Hybopsis gracilis gracilis, Olund and Cross (1961:329).

Hybopsis gracilis gulonella, Olund and Cross (1961:332).

Body terete; head broad, flattened dorsally, its length about ¼ of standard length; snout conical, never turgid, scarcely protruding beyond mouth (Fig. 12A); mouth large, subterminal, slightly oblique; barbels conspicuous; eye small, diameter less than ⅙ of head length in adults; lateral line scales 42-56; scale rows around body 30-42, most often 15—2—17; fins rather high, falcate; origin of dorsal fin over or slightly anterior to insertion of pelvics; dorsal, anal, and pelvic rays 8; pectoral rays usually 16-18; pharyngeal teeth 2,4—4,2; intestine short, peritoneum silvery; vertebrae 40-46.

Plain brownish dorsally, silvery laterally, without obvious markings; lower lobe of caudal fin darker than upper lobe, fins otherwise colorless.

In breeding males, minute tubercles densely distributed on top of head and snout; peripheral rows of tubercles on scales of nape, and rarely on scales of caudal peduncle; rays 2-8 of pectoral fin tuberculate; minute tubercles usually present on dorsal, pelvic, and anal fins.

Maximum length about 9 inches.

Subspecific characters.—H. g. gracilis: size large; body slender, fins strongly falcate; vertebrae 40-42; lateral line scales usually 50 or more; pectoral fin-rays usually 17 or more. *H. g. gulonella* (Cope): size smaller; body stout, fins less falcate; vertebrae 36-38; lateral line scales usually fewer than 50; pectoral fin-rays usually fewer than 17.

Two subspecies of the flat-headed chub have been recognized in Kansas (Olund and Cross, 1961). *H. g. gracilis* occurs in the Missouri River, where it lives in strong currents of the mainstream. *H. g. gulonella* inhabits the western part of the Arkansas River System, where it is found mainly in pools. Specimens from the Kansas River Basin seem to be intergrades that resemble *H. g. gracilis* more than *gulonella.*

Bailey and Allum (1962:44) questioned the taxonomic significance of variation in this species; they suspected that morphological differences result from direct environmental influences, such as differential temperatures during embryonic development. My opinion is that northern and southern stocks of the species differentiated genetically prior to formation of the present Missouri Basin in early Pleistocene. Subsequently, northern streams (inhabited by *gracilis*) were diverted southward by glacial fronts and acquired as tributaries several streams that were inhabited by *gulonella; gracilis* spread southward in the Missouri mainstream, accounting for the disjunct distribution of present stocks of *gulonella.* That hypothesis was expressed by Metcalf (1966:104), who reviewed evidence of Pliocene drainage systems on the Great Plains and discussed Pleistocene changes in the drainage patterns, in relation to the present distribution of this species and several other kinds of fishes in the Kansas River Basin.

The reproductive habits of *H. gracilis* are unknown. Both subspecies probably spawn in July and August, because most specimens caught in those months are tuberculate (or gravid) whereas specimens caught in other months usually lack these evidences of reproductive activity. Tuberculate males have been taken in the Arkansas River in Colorado in early September, but females caught with them were spent. At that time, water temperatures in different streams inhabited by *H. g. gulonella* varied from 65° F. (in the mainstream of Arkansas River) to 92° F. (in the Purgatoire River); diurnal change in temperature is great in most streams of that area. The late spawning period in this species seemingly coincides with low waterlevels and relatively warm temperatures, following passage of meltwaters and spring runoff from the mountainous headwaters of most Plains streams.

The food of this chub consists of insects, a large proportion of which are terrestrial kinds that fall accidentally into the water.

Hornyhead

Hybopsis biguttata (Kirtland)

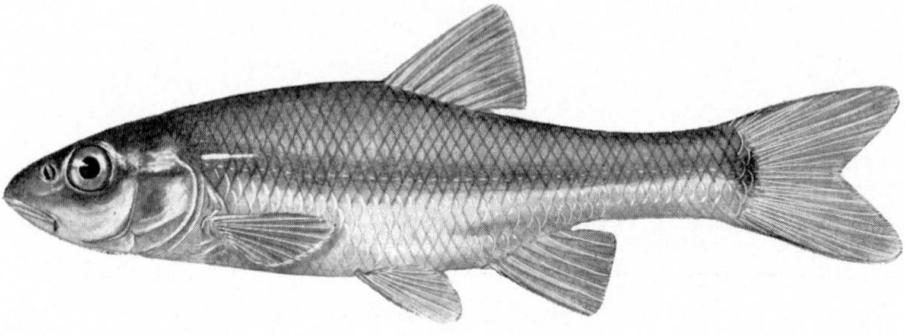

Ceratichthys cyclotis, Cope (1865b:85).

Hybopsis biguttatus, Gilbert (1885b:98; 1886:210; 1889:40, 42); Cragin (1885b:109); Graham (1885a:4; 1885b:74); Hay (1887:250, 252).

Hybopsis kentuckiensis, Fowler (1925:411-412).

Nocomis biguttatus, Breukelman (1940a:370; 1940b:380; 1946:65); Jennings (1942:365).

Hybopsis biguttata, Cross (1954:308); Clarke, Breukelman, and Andrews (1958:167); Metcalf (1959:393); Cross and Minckley (1960:11), Breukelman (1960:34); Deacon and Metcalf (1961:316); Metcalf (1966:105).

Body robust; head large, compressed, its length 3.4-3.8 in standard length; mouth large, oblique, terminal; barbels inconspicuous; eye moderate in size, its diameter 4.0 to 5.0 in head length; lateral-line scales 40-43; scale rows around body 15-16—2—16-18; fins low and rounded, never falcate; dorsal and pelvic rays 8; anal rays 7; pectoral rays usually 16; pharyngeal teeth usually 1,4—4,1; intestine short, peritoneum silvery; vertebrae 35-37.

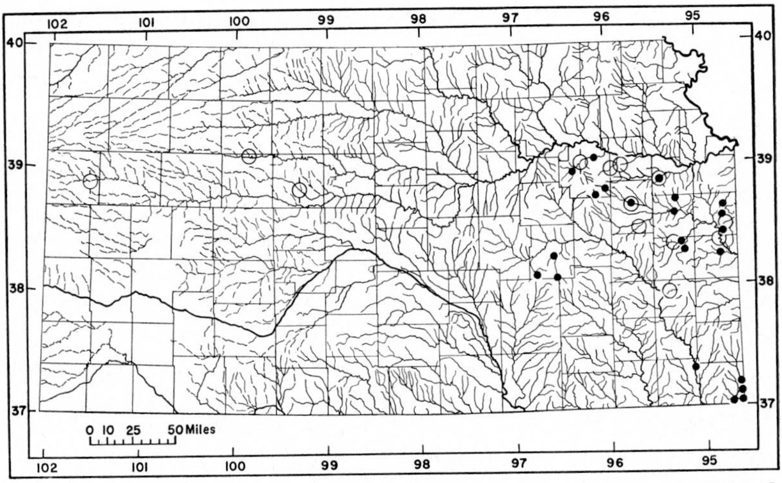

Olivaceous, white ventrally, sides not silvery; young with dark lateral band, prominent caudal spot, and orange fins (these markings and mid-dorsal dark stripe obsolescent in adults, except when spawning); dorsolateral scales not dark-outlined. Breeding males with distinctive red spot behind eye; tubercles large and numerous atop head, but absent from snout, sides of head, and body; pectoral fins bearing tubercles on rays 2-5, sometimes on ray 1; other fins devoid of tubercles.

Maximum length approximately 10 inches.

The hornyhead is confined to clear, permanent, rocky creeks in Kansas. The species now occurs widely in the Marais des Cygnes System; elsewhere, isolated populations persist in upland streams of the Kansas, Cottonwood, and Spring River drainages. The record from the mainstream of the Neosho River (see map) rests on a single specimen obtained in severe drought.

The range and abundance of *H. biguttata* have decreased in the past century. Graham (1885b:74) listed the hornyhead as "very common" in Kansas. Metcalf (1966:105) reported several specimens collected in Big Creek at Fort Hays, Ellis County, in 1871. Hay (1887:250) reported "numerous large specimens" from the Saline River near WaKeeney, Trego County, and obtained others in the Smoky Hill River in Wallace County. Breukelman (1940a: 370) found none at Hay's localities in 1938, despite special efforts to get hornyheads there. My students and I have found none in any western stream in the course of our work—1952 to 1966. In the Wakarusa Basin of northeastern Kansas, many specimens were taken from 1898 to 1912, but none since 1924 despite frequent collecting in that stream.

The hornyhead spawns in spring, from late May through June according to some reports, and from late April to early June according to others. The time of spawning varies locally, depending on water-temperatures, but probably is of short duration at any one locality. One series of tuberculate males in the KU collections is labeled as having been caught in Rock Creek, Douglas County, on July 14, 1898. That date seems late for reproduction by the species, especially at this latitude in the southern part of its range. Unless the date is erroneous, its lateness may indicate disruption of the normal breeding cycle by unfavorable environmental conditions.

The male hornyhead builds and guards a nest that consists of a mound of gravel. One or more females deposit eggs in the nest in an interval of several days. The attendant male enlarges the nest by addition of gravel after successive batches of eggs are laid and fertilized. Old nests may be as large as three feet in diameter and six inches high. Current flowing through the loose gravel provides oxygen necessary for egg-development.

I suspect that two factors associated with the reproductive requirements of the hornyhead account for its disappearance from many streams in Kansas. First, siltation in stream-channels may have covered suitable gravelly nest-sites, reducing the amount of habitat available for spawning. Second, frequent intermittency (cessation of flow) and increased turbidity of streams may have caused reproductive failure in places where this species formerly occurred.

Gravel chub

Hybopsis x-punctata Hubbs and Crowe

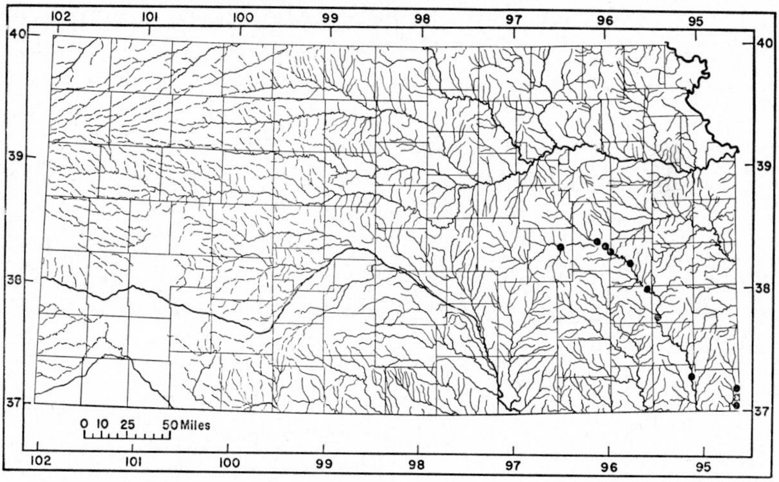

Hybopsis species, Cross (1954:308).
Hybopsis x-punctata x-punctata, Hubbs and Crowe (1956:4, 7 [orig. descr.]).
Hybopsis x-punctata, Clarke, Breukelman, and Andrews (1958:167); Metcalf (1959:393); Deacon (1961:380).

Body slender, terete, somewhat sinuous in shape; head depressed, its length 3.6-4.0 in standard length; snout protruding slightly beyond mouth; barbels short but conspicuous; eye large, its diameter 3.3-3.8 in head length; lateral line straight, with (usually) 40-43 scales; scale rows around body usually 13—2—17 (11-13—2—15-18); dorsal fin slightly falcate, originating slightly anterior to insertion of pelvic fins; dorsal and pelvic fin-rays 8, anal rays 7, pectoral rays 15 or 16; pharyngeal teeth 0,4—4,0; intestine short, peritoneum dark; vertebrae 38-39.

Olivaceous dorsally, silvery laterally and ventrally; dark spots or "X-markings" usually present dorsolaterally (outlining adjacent scales); mid-dorsal stripe present but not prominent; no dark lateral band or caudal spot; fins colorless or dusky (lower lobe of caudal not darker than upper lobe).

Breeding males with minute tubercles densely distributed on top and sides of head; most scales with tubercles, variably situated on much of the exposed surface (not confined to margin of scale pocket); pectoral fins bearing conical tubercles, larger than those on body, in single file on basal part and distal branches of rays 2-9; other fins lacking tubercles.

Length 3½ inches or less.

The gravel chub occupies deep riffles over gravel bottom in the larger streams of the Neosho System. The species is not abundant. The largest numbers that I have collected came from the mainstream of the Neosho River in 1952-1955, when the water was relatively low and clear, and flow was continuous throughout the length of that stream. Subsequently, the Neosho dried, except for isolated pools, and the gravel chub almost disappeared from collections. *H. x-punctata* was one of the last species to re-establish a substantial population after the Neosho regained its normal flow in 1957. Many gravel chubs were again found in the Neosho River in the summer of 1959; the species seemingly became more common there, and in the Cottonwood River, during wet years that followed.

Gravel chubs that seemed to be spawning were taken in the Neosho River on April 9, 1953, when the water temperature was 60° F. Adults that freely extruded eggs or milt were concentrated in water two to three feet deep, adjacent to a gravel bar, where the current was swiftest. Presumably, spawning is limited to a brief period in early spring.

Big-eyed chub
Hybopsis amblops (Rafinesque)

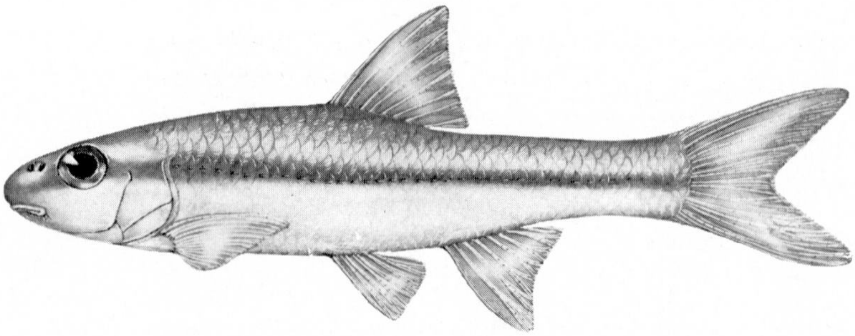

Hybopsis amblops, Graham (1885b:74); Metcalf (1959:393).

Body slender; head long, depressed; snout turgid, protruding slightly beyond mouth; mouth ventral, terminating below anterior margin or orbit; barbels minute; eye large, its diameter 3.0-3.5 in head length; lateral line straight, with 35 or 36 scales; scale rows around body usually 9—2—11 (breast well scaled); dorsal fin high, its tip acute (anterior rays extending beyond tips of posterior rays when fin is depressed against body); dorsal fin originating slightly behind insertion of pelvic fins; dorsal, anal, and pelvic rays 8; pectoral rays usually 15; pharyngeal teeth usually 1,4—4,1; intestine short, peritoneum silvery; vertebrae 36-37.

Olivaceous dorsally, silvery laterally and ventrally; dorsolateral scales large, weakly outlined by melanin, mid-dorsal stripe obsolescent; lateral line marked by dark dots anteriorly, or sides having dusky band from base of tail forward across opercle and onto snout; fins unpigmented (except at edges of dorsal and caudal rays); no spot at base of caudal fin.

In breeding males, minute tubercles present on crest of head and anterior scales of nape; rays 1-8 of pectoral fin tuberculate, in single or double file; fins and body otherwise devoid of tubercles.

Length 3½ inches or less.

I know of only one definite record of the big-eyed chub in Kansas. That record is based on one juvenile (KU 4215, 36.5 mm. in standard length), obtained from the South Fork of the Cottonwood River at Matfield Green, Chase County, by a biology class from Kansas State Teachers College, Emporia. The date of its capture is unknown, but preceded the survey of the South Fork by Cross (1954), when collections from the same locality failed to include *H. amblops.* Relic populations in the Flint Hills (including the one designated by Graham as "Neosho River") may have been extirpated.

Trautman (1957:303) and Zahuranek (1962:843) have called attention to the dwindling abundance of this species in Ohio. The decline seems attributable to recent accumulations of silt over stream bottoms that were formerly composed of clean sand or gravel. Most often, *H. amblops* occupies clear water where currents are not swift, but where sediments are coarse and firm rather than flocculent.

Although I have not found the big-eyed chub in the Spring River-Shoal Creek drainage of Cherokee county, future records there seem likely because numerous records exist from the upper parts of the same drainage in Missouri. The species is abundant in many Ozarkian streams.

The big-eyed chub spawns between late April and early June.

Silver chub

Hybopsis storeriana (Kirtland)

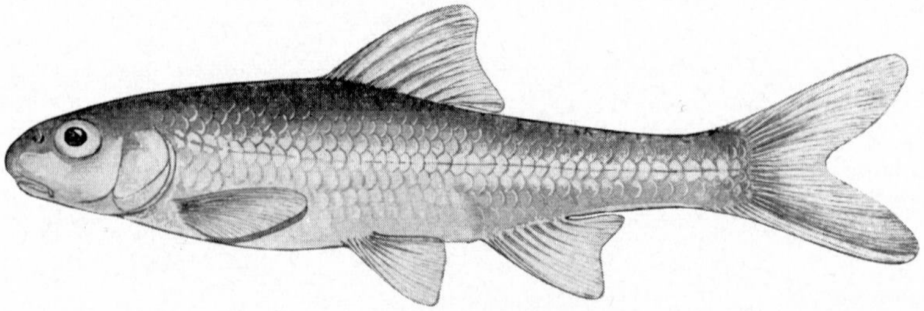

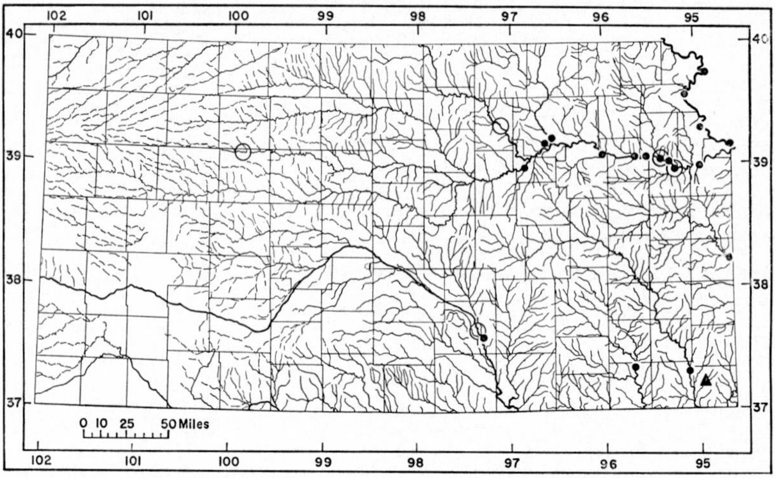

Hybopsis storerianus, Graham (1885b:74); Hay (1887:250); Jordan (1891: 17); Hall (1934:230); Breukelman (1940a:370, 1940b:380).

Hybopsis storeriana, Minckley (1959:419); Deacon (1961:379); Deacon and Metcalf (1961:316); Fisher (1962:427); Metcalf (1966:106).

Body slightly compressed, stout; head short, rounded, its length 4.0-4.5 in standard length; snout blunt, protruding slightly beyond mouth; barbels short; eye large, its diameter 4.0-4.5 in head length; scales large, 38-40 in lateral line; usually 13—2—13 scale rows around body; breast fully scaled; fins slightly falcate; dorsal, pelvic, and anal fin-rays 8; pectoral rays 15-19, usually 16 or 17; pharyngeal teeth usually 1,4—4,1; intestine short, peritoneum silvery; vertebrae 39-40.

Coloration pallid, translucent in life except for white abdomen and narrow silvery lateral stripe; mid-dorsal dark streak obscure, dorsolateral scales faintly dark-outlined; lower lobe of caudal fin dark, but with white lower edge; fins otherwise colorless.

Breeding males with tubercles confined to pectoral fin, on rays 2-8 (head bears numerous minute sensory buds but not breeding-tubercles).

Largest Kansas specimen approximately six inches in total length.

The silver chub inhabits large, sandy rivers; it seems common only in the Kansas and Missouri rivers. In the Kansas River, the number obtained in different collections varies greatly, suggesting that *H. storeriana* is vagile and perhaps seasonally migratory. The largest series of adults in collections at the University of Kansas were captured in fall or early spring; probably, the species occupies strong currents in the deeper parts of the mainstream during summer, where it is less accessible to capture by seining. The only specimens in our collections from the Blue, Neosho, and Smoky Hill rivers are breeding adults caught in April and early May.

I think that the silver chub occurs more widely in the Arkansas River mainstream than records (see map) now indicate, and that this species could be obtained farther west in the Kansas River System than the localities mapped. Metcalf (1966:106) reported *H. storeriana* from the Republican River in western Nebraska (Dundy County). He verified also that specimens tentatively identified as *H. storeriana* by Hay (1887:250) are indeed this species, but these specimens (USNM 37938) are labeled as having been taken at Wallace, rather than in the Saline River north of WaKeeney, where Hay reported their capture.

The silver chub spawns in April or May, judging from dates on which tuberculate males were taken in the Missouri, Kansas, and other rivers in Kansas.

With limited confidence, I associate Kansas records of *Notropis hudsonius* (Clinton) with the silver chub. All reports of *N. hudsonius* are attributable to I. D. Graham, who reported it (1885a:4) from "Wildcat Creek" (Riley County) and later (1885b:73) from "Kansas river branches"; Cragin (1885b:108) repeated Graham's record from Wildcat Creek. Although *H. storeriana* and *N. hudsonius* differ markedly, their nomenclature was confused prior to the time of Graham's publications (see Jordan and Gilbert, 1882:171 and Jordan and Meek, 1885:24). In his second report, Graham (1885b:74) listed *H. storeriana* as well as *N. hudsonius,* but only from the Osage River; the silver chub must then, as now, have been more abundant in the Kansas River than in the Osage System. One specimen of *N. hudsonius* (KSU 2835) is extant in collections of Kansas State University, bearing only the data "I. D. Graham, 1886" (Metcalf, 1966:163). The date indicates that this is not a specimen on which the published records were based; it may have come from Indiana, where Graham obtained other fishes in his collections. The localities nearest to Kansas from which verifiable records exist for *N. hudsonius* are in northern Iowa, and in the Mississippi River in Missouri.

Sickle-finned chub

Hybopsis meeki Jordan and Evermann

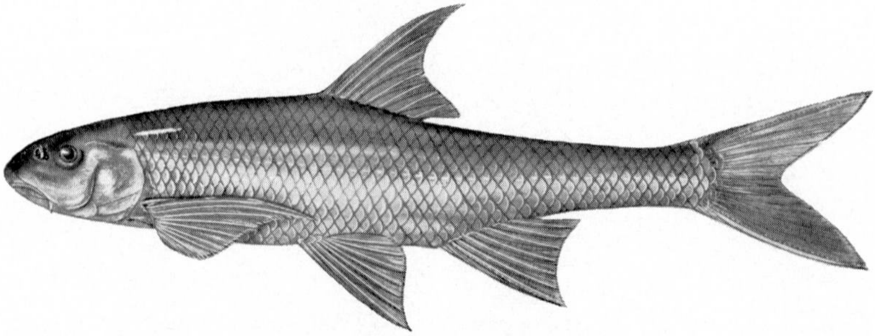

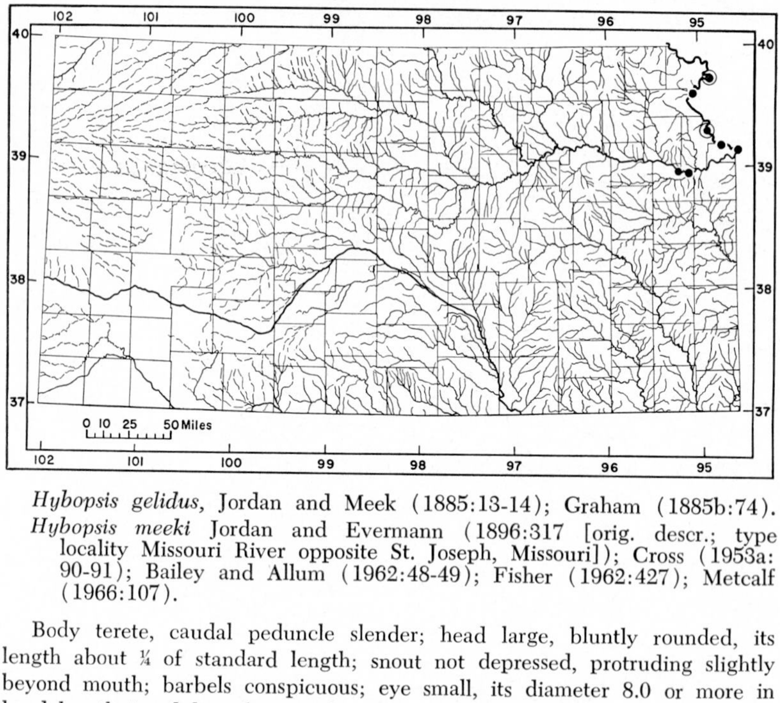

Hybopsis gelidus, Jordan and Meek (1885:13-14); Graham (1885b:74).
Hybopsis meeki Jordan and Evermann (1896:317 [orig. descr.; type locality Missouri River opposite St. Joseph, Missouri]); Cross (1953a: 90-91); Bailey and Allum (1962:48-49); Fisher (1962:427); Metcalf (1966:107).

Body terete, caudal peduncle slender; head large, bluntly rounded, its length about ¼ of standard length; snout not depressed, protruding slightly beyond mouth; barbels conspicuous; eye small, its diameter 8.0 or more in head length in adults, often partly overgrown by skin; scale pockets studded with taste buds but without fleshy ridges; lateral-line scales 46-50 (given as 44 by Jordan and Evermann, *loc. cit.*); scale rows around body 17—2—21, breast mostly scaleless; fins large and strongly falcate; pectoral fins longer than head, and extending beyond insertion of pelvics; dorsal, anal, and pelvic fin-rays 8, pectoral rays 15 or 16; pharyngeal teeth 0,4—4,0; intestine short, peritoneum silvery; vertebrae usually 43.

Coloration pallid, silvery; lower lobe of caudal fin dark-pigmented, with narrow white ventral edge; fins otherwise unpigmented.

Longest Kansas specimen 4 inches.

The sickle-finned chub inhabits the mainstream of the Missouri River and the Mississippi mainstream below the mouth of the Missouri (Bailey and Allum, 1963:48-49). The only records in any tributary of either of those rivers are from the Kansas River at Lawrence and Eudora, Douglas County. *H. meeki* lives on smooth, sand-or-gravel bottom in deep water where currents are strong. The species seems so specialized for life in the large, silt-laden Missouri-Mississippi River that its survival may be threatened by impoundments and other modifications of habitat throughout its limited range.

Information is lacking on the life history of this peculiar fish.

Speckled chub
Hybopsis aestivalis (Girard)

Hybopsis tetranemus Gilbert (1886:208-209 [orig. descr.]); Jordan (1891: 17); Hubbs and Ortenburger (1929a:25).

Extrarius aestivalis, Breukelman (1940b:377).

Extrarius aestivalis: sesquialis × tetranemus, Breukelman (1940b:380).

Hybopsis aestivalis, Minckley (1959:419-420); Deacon and Metcalf (1961: 316); Branson (1963).

Hybopsis aestivalis tetranemus, Metcalf (1959:365); Kilgore and Rising (1965:139).

Hybopsis aestivalis hyostoma, Metcalf (1966:108).

Body terete, head depressed; snout fleshy, protruding far forward of horizontal mouth; barbels long; eye small; scales smooth, without fleshy ridges; breast mostly scaleless (in front of pelvic fins); scale rows over back, above lateral line, 11-13; 4-7 rows of scales on each side below lateral line; fins large, pointed but not strongly falcate; dorsal, anal, and pelvic fins usually 8-rayed; pectoral fin-rays 12-15, usually 14; pharyngeal teeth 0,4—4,0; gut short, peritoneum silvery; vertebrae 36-38.

Coloration pallid, translucent in life; sides with silvery longitudinal stripe; venter white; body with scattered dark speckles; dark spot before each narial pit; diffuse dark blotch near base of each lobe of caudal fin; fins otherwise unpigmented; no chromatic breeding colors.

Breeding males having tubercles confined to rays 2-9 of pectoral fins, in single file on basal part and each branch of each ray.

The speckled chub is represented by two subspecies in Kansas. One, tentatively identified as *H. a. hyostoma* by Metcalf (1966:

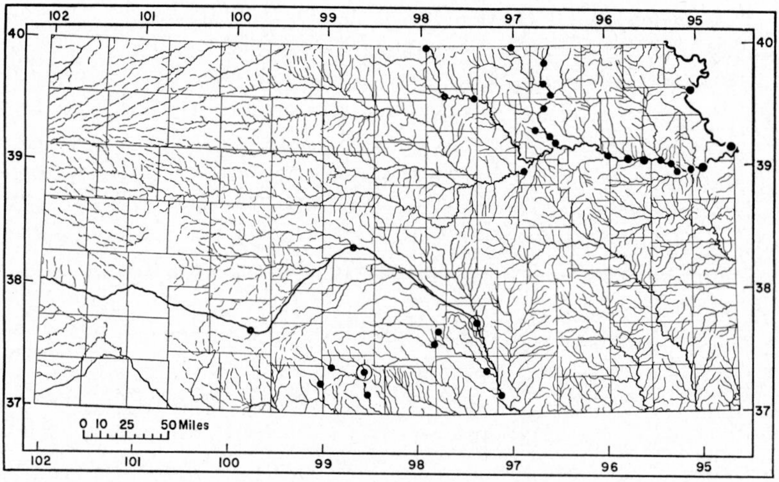

108), inhabits the Missouri River and the eastern part of the Kansas River Basin. Moore (1950: 82, 85) referred to the same fish as *Extrarius aestivalis*, Plains subspecies, and Breukelman (1940b:380) called it *Extrarius aestivalis: sesquialis* × *tetranemus* (but *sesquialis* is a *nomen nudum*). The second subspecies, *H. a. tetranemus*, occurs in the Arkansas River and its western tributaries, westward to about 100° longitude. The type locality of *Hybopsis tetranemus* was given by Gilbert (1886:209) as "Elm and Spring Creeks, near Medicine Lodge." Elm Creek, a tributary of the Medicine River in Barber County, flows along the east and south sides of the present town of Medicine Lodge. *H. a. tetranemus* remains common there; the "Spring" creek cited by Gilbert is unknown to me.

The two subspecies can be distinguished as follows: *H. a. hyostoma* has one barbel at each corner of the mouth, whereas *tetranemus* has two; the eye diameter usually is more than ⅕ the head length in *hyostoma*, less than ⅕ the head length in *tetranemus*; *hyostoma* has fewer lateral line scales (35-39) than *tetranemus* (36-43); and many specimens of *hyostoma* have a narrow bridge of scales across the breast, in front of the pelvic fins, whereas the breast is entirely naked in *tetranemus*. *H. a. tetranemus* commonly attains larger size than *hyostoma* in Kansas, although neither exceeds a length of three inches.

The habitat of both subspecies is limited to the shallow channels of large, permanently flowing, sandy streams. Speckled chubs usually occupy currents over a substrate of clean, fine sand, avoiding areas of calm water and silted stream bottoms.

The reproductive period of *H. aestivalis* seems long, inasmuch as tuberculate males and egg-laden females have been taken from late May through August, always when water temperatures exceeded 70° F. The reproductive habits have been described by Starrett (1951:18).

Sturgeon chub

Hybopsis gelida (Girard)

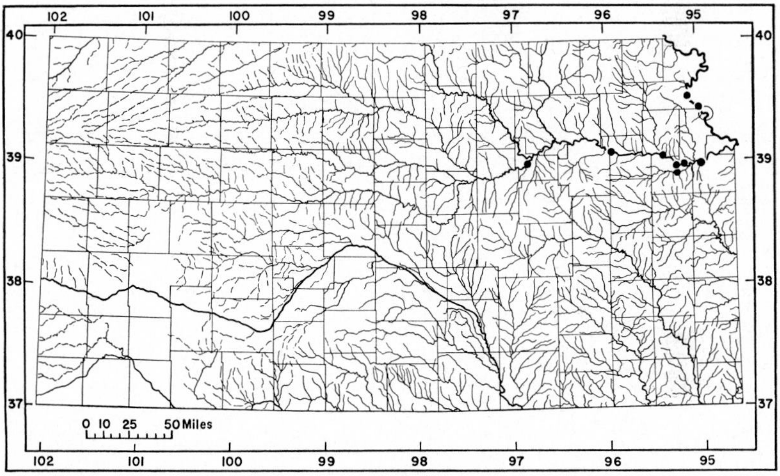

Hybopsis gelidus, Gilbert (1886:209); Cross (1953a).
Hybopsis gelida, Bailey and Allum (1962:46-47); Branson (1963); Metcalf (1966:110).

Body slender, with fleshy longitudinal ridges on scale pockets; head depressed, with minute sensory buds dorsally and large sensory papillae ventrally; snout long, depressed, and fleshy, extending far forward of horizontal mouth; single barbel at each corner of mouth; eye small, diameter 1/5 to 1/6 of head length; lateral line scales 39-43; scale rows over back, above lateral line 13 or 14; 4-7 rows below lateral line, venter naked in front of pelvic fins; fins low, not strongly falcate; dorsal, pelvic, and anal rays usually 8; pectoral rays 13-15; pharyngeal teeth 1,4—4,1; intestine short, peritoneum silvery; vertebrae 39-40.

Coloration pallid, brown dorsally, silvery on lower sides and venter; less transparent in life than, and lacking discrete dark speckles characteristic of *H. aestivalis;* caudal fin with lower lobe dark-pigmented except along its milky-white ventral margin; fins otherwise unpigmented.

Breeding males seemingly lack tubercles except on rays 2-9 of pectoral fins; tubercles small, in single file on basal stem and branches of each ray, best developed distally.

Longest Kansas specimen 3½ inches.

In Kansas, the sturgeon chub is known only from the Kansas River, the lower Smoky Hill River, and the Missouri River. The record of *H. gelida* by Jordan and Meek (1885:13-14) and probably the record by Graham (1885b:74) are erroneous, having been based on specimens of *H. meeki* (Jordan and Evermann, 1896:317; Cross, 1953a). The record by Gilbert (1886:209), from the Missouri River at Leavenworth, is valid if the "nuptial tubercles" described by Gilbert are a misrepresentation of the fleshy epidermal outgrowths peculiar to *H. gelida;* in other respects Gilbert's account fits *gelida* and *meeki* equally well.

The sturgeon chub may occur more widely in the Kansas River Basin than the mapped records indicate, because this species has been found in the Republican River in Nebraska (Bailey and Allum, *loc. cit.;* Metcalf, 1966:108). The habitat of *H. gelida,* as described by Bailey and Allum, is "in the larger streams of the northern Plains" where it "lives in a strong current, usually over a gravel bottom. Thus, though widely distributed . . . it is spotty in occurrence since sand constitutes the predominant bottom material of the region." In the Kansas River I have found sturgeon chubs most often where shallow flow across sandbars causes turbulence, in contrast to the streaming flow in most parts of the channel. Favorable sites occur where the channel divides at the upstream ends of small sand islands; in these places, extensive areas have depths of only two to four inches, and turbulent action of the current prevents accumulation of fine sands on the substrate. Presumably the sturgeon chub evolved at a time when the prevalent bottom materials in major tributaries of the Missouri River were more coarsely divided than at present.

Few fish seem so strikingly adapted as the sturgeon chub for life in turbid rivers on the plains. Currents in shallow water have a considerable downward (as well as horizontal) component of force. The depressed head of the sturgeon chub and its slender body, somewhat wedge-shaped in cross-section and tapering tailward, provide minimal resistance to the horizontal flow and make use of the downward force to hold the fish on the bottom. The small eyes, which have limited utility in turbid rivers, are partly shielded against abrasion by sand grains that are borne by the current. Sturgeon chubs have highly developed olfactory structures (Branson, 1963); these, and a profusion of taste buds on the head and body (presumably including the fleshy keels, although the histologic nature of that tissue remains to be demonstrated) may replace vision as the primary means of locating food.

The unique dermal keels may serve another purpose, functionally equivalent to the multiple narrow keels that are incorporated into the design of some small, fast boats. The latter keels aid in stabilizing and "planing" the boat as it speeds over the water surface; perhaps the chub's keels aid in "planing" the swiftly flowing water over the body of the fish as it rests on the floor of the river.

The reproductive habits of the sturgeon chub are unknown. Breeding may be confined to a brief period in late spring or early summer. Males in the University of Kansas collections that have well-developed tubercles were taken from the Smoky Hill River in May (water temperature 73° F.), and the Powder River in Wyoming in late June. Some weakly tuberculate specimens have been obtained from the Kansas River in early June, but those caught in July and August lack tubercles.

Sucker-mouthed minnow
Phenacobius mirabilis (Girard)

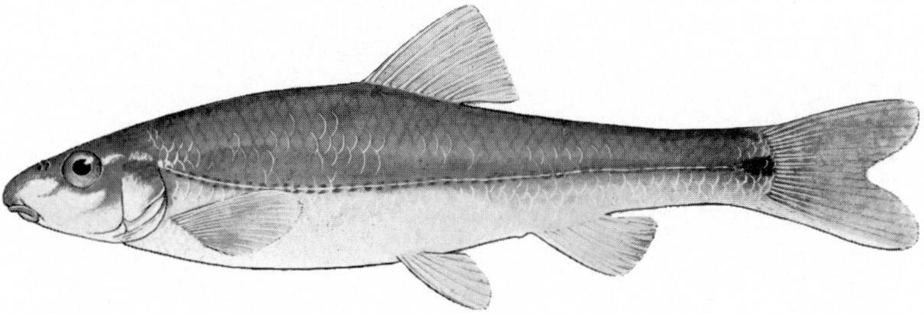

Sarcidium scopiferum Cope (1871:440 [orig. descr.]).
Phenacobius mirabilis, Gilbert (1884:14, 1885b:98, 1886:210, 1889:39, 40); Cragin (1885b:109); Graham (1885a:4, 1885b:74); Hay (1887:243, 249, 250, 252); Jordan (1891:17); Breukelman (1940a:371, 1940b:380); Fowler (1925:405); Hubbs and Ortenburger (1929b:87-88); Jennings (1942:365); Cross (1954:308); Moore and Buck (1955:22); Schelske (1957:45); Clarke, Breukelman, and Andrews (1958:168); Metcalf (1959:372, 1966:111); Minckley (1960:420); Deacon (1961:380); Kilgore and Rising (1965:139).

Body slender, fusiform, contours slightly sinuous; head decurved dorsally, straight ventrally, length about ¼ standard length; eye small, 4.2-5.0 in head length; snout long, nearly twice eye diameter, projecting forward of ventral,

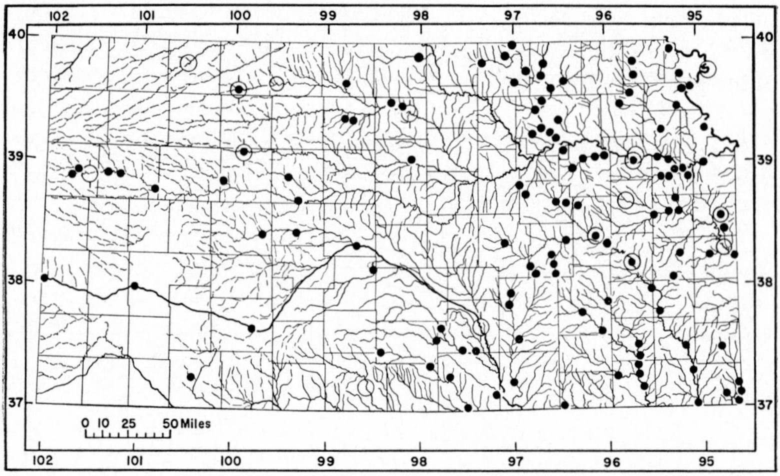

horizontal mouth; lips thick, with characteristic lateral lobes (see Fig. 12C); barbels absent; fins small, mostly rounded at tips; dorsal fin originating anterior to pelvic insertion; dorsal and pelvic rays 8; anal rays usually 7 (rarely 6); pectoral rays 13-16, usually 14; lateral line nearly straight, with 42-50 scales; scale rows around body 13-16 (usually 15)—2—19-21, scales on venter embedded; scale rows around caudal peduncle usually 7—2—7; pharyngeal teeth 0,4—4,0; intestine short, peritoneum silvery; vertebrae usually 38-40.

Yellowish to dark olivaceous dorsally, silvery to creamy ventrally; silver lateral stripe underlain by dusky band of variable intensity, terminating in prominent, elongate black spot at base of caudal fin; mid-dorsal dark streak narrow, indistinct; dorsolateral scales outlined by melanophores but not boldly cross-hatched; no pronounced difference between coloration of breeding and nonbreeding individuals, nor between sexes.

In breeding males, minute tubercles densely distributed over top of head and opercles; tubercles lacking on lower part of head, below eyes and nares; dorsolateral scales rimmed by minute tubercles, diminishing posteriorly. Pectoral rays 2-8 (or 9) having well-developed tubercles in single file basally, dividing into double, then multiple files (4 or 5 rows) on branched parts of anterior rays. Pelvic, dorsal, and anal fins with few small tubercles.

Maximum length approximately 3¾ inches.

The sucker-mouthed minnow is almost statewide in occurrence. It has been taken in the smallest of upland creeks and the largest of rivers in Kansas, but is most abundant in tributaries that have permanent flow, moderate gradient, and bottoms of mixed sand and small gravel. *Phenacobius* is adapted for a riffle-existence, but seems more tolerant of fluctuating waterlevels and high turbidity than are other species that inhabit riffles; no other riffle-dwelling minnow except the stoneroller, *Campostoma anomalum,* is so widespread in Kansas as is *P. mirabilis.*

Judging from the number of specimens in collections, the sucker-mouthed minnow comprises only a minor part of the total fish-population at most localities. But, *Phenacobius* is abundant in several small, direct tributaries of the Missouri River in extreme northeastern Kansas, and in some tributaries of the Kansas River System. Few other riffle-fishes are found in those streams. Where several species of riffle-dwelling minnows and darters occur, the sucker-mouthed minnow seems scarce.

In the Neosho and Marais des Cygnes rivers, Deacon (1961:380) found that the population of sucker-mouthed minnows increased rapidly in the first two years of normal flow, after drought had reduced those streams to intermittency. He also reported (*op. cit.*: 414, 416, 418) that *P. mirabilis* is mainly sedentary in habit, although some individuals that he marked were recaptured on riffles upstream from the point of their initial capture and release.

Phenacobius mirabilis has a longer reproductive period than does any other riffle-fish in Kansas. Specimens bearing tubercles and having enlarged gonads have been taken in all months from April through August. I think that males remain reproductively active, and females spawn two or more times, in that five-month interval. Most minnows that are widespread in Kansas have long breeding periods—probably as an adaptation to the erratic flow in rivers of the Plains region. The dispersal of reproductive effort over a lengthy interval may, in contrast, be disadvantageous in streams that maintain stable waterlevels. In those streams, the most abundant kinds of fish generally have short reproductive intervals. Local differences in the relative abundance of *P. mirabilis* probably are associated with differences in the reproductive habits of this species and its riffle-dwelling competitors.

Trautman (1957:323-325) and Zahuranek (1962:842-843) have documented eastward expansion of the range of *P. mirabilis* in the Ohio River System, correlated with 1) increased stream siltation in recent decades, and 2) a decline of several species that seem to require continuously clear water and firm, rocky bottoms.

Emerald shiner

Notropis atherinoides Rafinesque

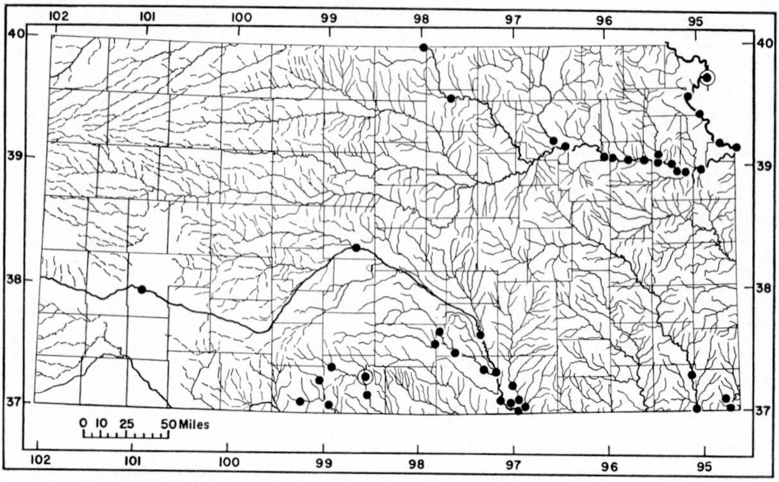

Alburnus oligaspis Cope (1864:282 [orig. descr.]; 1865b:85).

Alburnellus percobromus Cope (1871:440 [orig. descr.]).

Notropis dilectus, Cragin (1885b:109); Graham (1885b:74); Gilbert (1886:208); Fowler (1910:290).

Notropis percobromus, Cragin (1885b:109); Hubbs (1945:16-17); Hubbs and Bonham (1951:94); Greer and Cross (1956:362); Clarke, Breukelman, and Andrews (1958:167); Metcalf (1959:369-370); Minckley (1959:420); Deacon and Metcalf (1961:316).

Notropis atherinoides dilectus, Breukelman (1940b:380); Jennings (1942: 365, erroneously).

Notropis atherinoides, Bailey and Allum (1962:56-60); Kilgore and Rising (1965:139); Metcalf (1966:112).

Body slender but compressed, greatest depth usually more than 4.0 in standard length; snout rounded, its length about equal to eye diameter and contained more than 1.5 times in postorbital length of head; mouth terminal, oblique; dorsal fin pointed at tip, its origin obviously posterior to insertion of pelvic fins; dorsal fin-rays 8, anterior rays usually extending beyond tips of posterior rays when fin is depressed; anal fin-rays 10 or 11; pelvic rays 8; pectoral rays usually 14 or 15; lateral-line scales 35-38; scale rows around body 13-15—2—9-11, around caudal peduncle 7—2—5; pharyngeal teeth 2,4—4,2; intestine short, peritoneum silvery; vertebrae 36-40.

Coloration pallid, body translucent with a shining silvery lateral stripe; mid-dorsal dark stripe narrow but complete from occiput to base of caudal fin; dorsolateral scales weakly outlined by melanin (scarcely evident in life); fins colorless; breeding males devoid of chromatic pigment (never having rosy pigment, a trait useful in distinguishing this species from *N. rubellus*).

Breeding males having minute tubercles on pectoral fin-rays 2-10; other fins (and body) devoid of tubercles.

Length 3¼ inches or less.

I follow Bailey and Allum (1962:56-60) in using the binomial *N. atherinoides* for this fish, although Kansas specimens have characters ascribed to *N. percobromus* by Hubbs (1945:16-17) and Hubbs and Bonham (1951: 93-95). Nomenclatural and taxonomic problems remain in this section of the subgenus *Notropis;* but, *Alburnus oligaspis* Cope 1864 has priority over *Alburnellus percobromus* Cope 1871, and seems applicable to the fish long known by the latter name, which Bailey and Allum (*loc. cit.*) treat as conspecific with (and subspecifically inseparable from) *N. atherinoides* Rafinesque 1818.

The emerald shiner is a characteristic, abundant inhabitant of the larger sandy rivers of Kansas. Probably *N. atherinoides* occurs throughout the mainstreams of the Missouri, Kansas-Republican, and Arkansas rivers. It is common in some western tributaries of the Arkansas River, such as the Ninnescah and Salt Fork rivers. East of the Arkansas mainstream, emerald shiners are found sporadically, only in the lower parts of major tributaries (Walnut, Neosho, and Spring rivers). The species rarely enters tributaries of the Kansas River, although I suspect that additional collecting may reveal its presence in the Smoky Hill System. Minckley (1959:420) found emerald shiners only in the lowermost part of the Blue River. The species is pelagic in habit, occupying the upper zones of the water both in shallows alongshore and in the deeper parts of the channel, where the current is moderate.

Emerald shiners seem to have a protracted reproductive period in Kansas, where spawning occurs mainly in late spring and early summer. Tuberculate males have been taken as early as April (in Cherokee County in 1953, an exceptionally warm, dry year). Most males captured in June and July are tuberculate.

Rosy-faced shiner
Notropis rubellus (Agassiz)

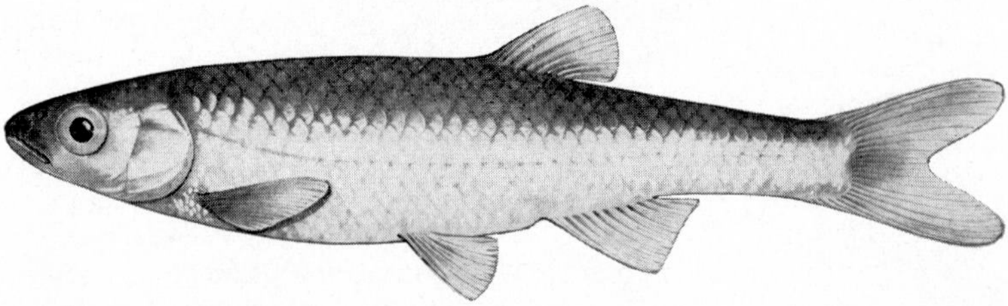

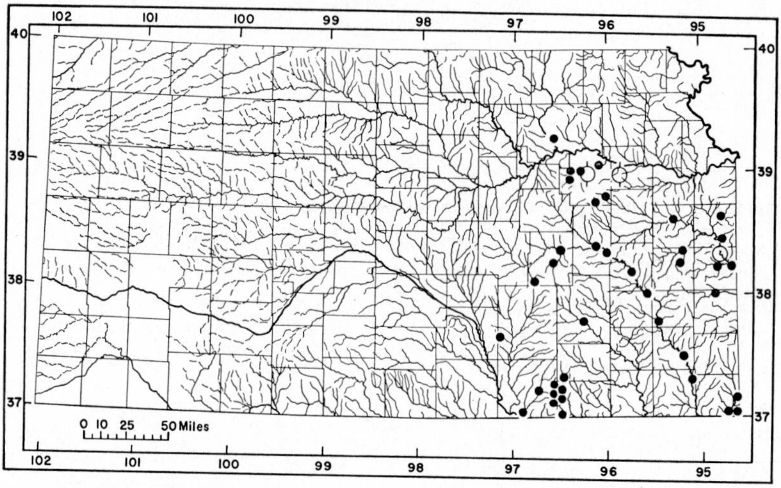

Notropis rubrifrons, Graham (1885b:73, perhaps erroneously); Gilbert (1886:208; 1889:40).

Notropis rubella, Cross (1954:308); Clarke, Breukelman, and Andrews (1958:168).

Notropis rubellus, Minckley and Cross (1959:212); Metcalf (1959:370-371); Minckley (1959:420); Deacon (1961:380-381); Metcalf (1966:114).

Notropis atherinoides dilectus, Jennings (1942:365, misidentification).

Body slender, greatest depth usually more than 4.0 in standard length; snout acute, length greater than eye diameter and contained less than 1.5 times in postorbital length of head; mouth terminal, oblique; dorsal fin rounded, originating posterior to insertion of pelvic fins; dorsal fin-rays 8; anal rays 10, sometimes 9; pelvic rays 8; pectoral rays 12-14; lateral line scales 36-38; scale rows around body 11-15—2—10-12, usually 13—2—11; scale rows around caudal peduncle 7—2—5; pharyngeal teeth 2,4—4,2; intestine short, peritoneum silvery; vertebrae 38-41.

Olivaceous dorsally, silvery white laterally and ventrally, with silvery lateral stripe; body almost opaque (in contrast with translucence of *N. atherinoides*); dark dorsal stripe narrow but well developed, especially posteriorly, dorsolateral scales outlined by melanophores; lateral line marked by dark dots anteriorly; fins transparent, unspotted, but base of dorsal fin (viewed vertically) always rosy in life. Breeding males suffused with pink or orange pigment, most intensely on fin bases, lateral line scales, lips, top of head, and snout; bright orange pigment in axil of pectoral fin extending upward narrowly along cleithrum to conjoin with similar pigment atop head; cheeks, opercles, and narrow strip (1 to 2½ scale rows wide) above lateral line mainly silvery; lower sides pink or orange, brighter posteriorly than anteriorly; all fins bright pink or orange proximally, fading to colorless distally. Ripe females with traces of orange pigment in bases of fins, atop head, and ventrally on body.

Breeding males having minute tubercles densely distributed over head and body, except scales of venter; crest of head and snout uniformly tuberculate, underside of head with multiple files of tubercles extending along mandibles, anterior rami of preopercle, and onto interopercle and subopercle; sides of head, behind eye, scarcely tuberculate; pectoral fins with large tubercles in single file (branching distally) on rays 2-5, obsolescent tubercles on 6th ray; dorsal, caudal, anal, and pelvic fins with minute tubercles.

Length 2¾ inches or less.

The rosy-faced shiner is found in upland streams of the Kansas, Osage, and Arkansas river systems, especially where stream beds are composed of limestone and gradients are steep. *N. rubellus* is absent from streams west of the Walnut River in the Arkansas Drainage, and from streams in the glaciated area north of the mainstream of the Kansas River. A single specimen from McIntire Creek of the Blue River System (Pottawatomie County) is an exceptional record. In wet years, McIntire Creek and other small tributaries in the Flint-hills segment of the Blue River Basin appear to provide habitat as suitable for rosy-faced shiners as is the habitat in Mill Creek, on the south side of Kansas River opposite McIntire Creek, where *N. rubellus* abounds. In drought, however, the rocky mainstream of Mill Creek serves as a refugium for *N. rubellus* whereas the more turbid, sandy Blue River may not provide a satisfactory refugium. The sand-filled channels of the Kansas and Arkansas rivers are effective barriers to dispersal of the species. This evidence casts doubt on the validity of Graham's (1885b:73) report of *N. rubrifrons* from "Kansas and Missouri rivers"; Minckley (1959: 420) assumed that Graham's record applies to *N. percobromus* (= *atherinoides*), which was often confused with *N. rubellus* in Graham's time. On the other hand, specimens reported by Jennings (1942:365) as *N. atherinoides dilectus* from the Osage River, Osage County (KSU 4940), are instead *N. rubellus* (13 specimens) and *N. lutrensis* (1 specimen).

In the Arkansas River System, *N. rubellus* occurs commonly in the Spring River Drainage (Cherokee County) and in parts of the Caney and Neosho basins. Collections from the Neosho River proper indicate that rosy-faced shiners are rare in the lower mainstream except in drought.

The rosy-faced shiner usually spawns between late April and early June in Kansas; rarely, tuberculate males and females that retain some eggs are found as late as July. Pfeiffer (1955) has described the breeding behavior and other aspects of the natural history of *N. rubellus* in New York State, and cited other literature pertaining to this species. The following observations, made in Shoal Creek, Cherokee County, on April 25, 1959, are indicative of the site and manner of reproduction by *N. rubellus* in Kansas: Schools of rosy-faced shiners congregated for spawning in eddies adjacent to a deep gravel bar that extended across the channel and sloped abruptly into a large pool. Spawning activity was confined to the shoreward edges of the bar, where flow slackened and eddied back against a swift riffle that coursed over the center of the gravel bed. The substrate where eggs were being deposited consisted of coarse gravel, loosely deposited and free of silt. Throughout the afternoon, intermittent bursts of breeding activity were indicated by sudden agitation of the water surface and by numerous leaping shiners.

Silver-banded shiner

Notropis shumardi (Girard)

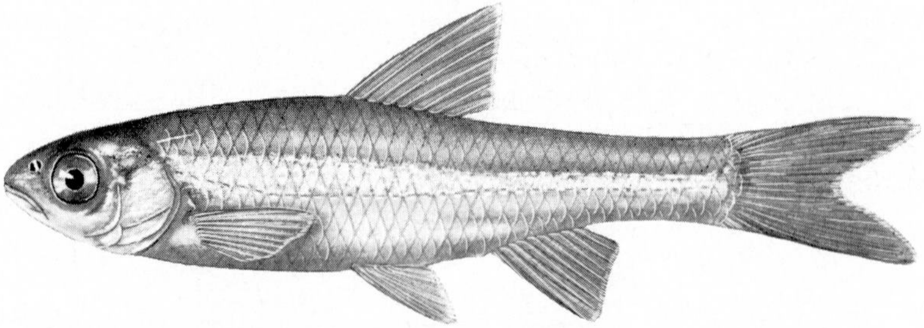

Notropis illecebrosus, Cross and Minckley (1958:104-105).
Notropis shumardi, Gilbert and Bailey (1962); Metcalf (1966:118).

Body moderately compressed, its depth about equal to head length, 4.0 in standard length; snout rounded, shorter than eye diameter; mouth terminal, oblique; eye large, diameter about 3.5 in head length; dorsal fin originating over insertion of pelvic fins; dorsal exceptionally high and acutely pointed, its anterior rays about equal to head length; dorsal fin-rays 8; anal and pelvic rays usually 9, pectoral rays usually 14; lateral-line scales 34-37; predorsal

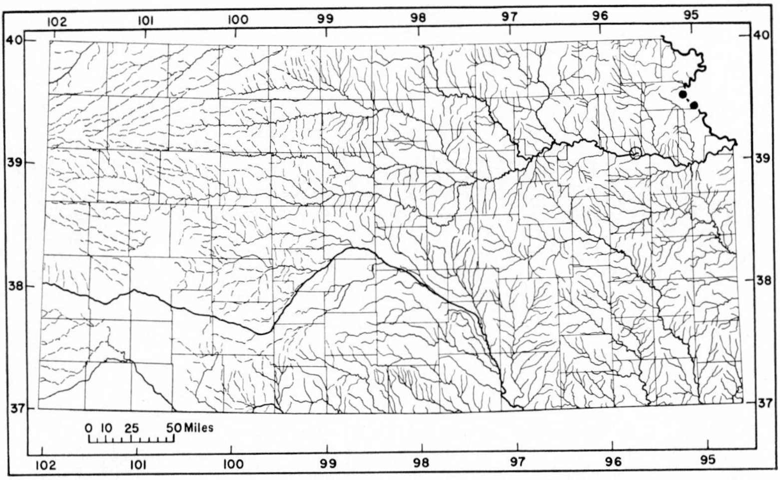

scale rows about 15; scale rows around body 11-14—2—9-12, total 23-26; rows around caudal peduncle 5—2—5; pharyngeal teeth, 2,4—4,2; intestine short, peritoneum silvery; vertebrae 37-39.

Coloration pallid, translucent, with narrow bright-silvery lateral band; mid-dorsal stripe dusky, divided around base of dorsal fin, continuous to base of caudal fin; dorsolateral scales weakly dark-outlined; venter white; fins unpigmented, dorsal and caudal without basal spots; no chromatic breeding colors.

Nuptial tubercles of males minute, on upper and lower surfaces of head, concentrated on tip of snout; pectoral rays 1-6 tuberculate.

Length 2¾ inches or less.

Except for one specimen from "Topeka" reported by Metcalf (1966:118), the silver-banded shiner has been found in Kansas only in the mainstream of the Missouri River, where it is rare. Little is known of the ecology of this species, apart from its restriction to large rivers. Recently, Gilbert and Bailey (1962) comprehensively characterized the silver-banded shiner, mapped its known distribution, and reviewed its nomenclatural history. They substituted the name *shumardi* for *illecebrosus,* on the basis of line-priority in Girard's (1856:194) descriptive accounts, and usage of *shumardi* by Jordan and Gilbert (1882:192-193) (interpreted as first revisers). Previously, most authors had used the name *illecebrosus,* because no type specimen of *shumardi* is extant, and because Girard's description of *shumardi* is not so complete as to be clearly identifiable with the silver-banded shiner.

Red-finned shiner

Notropis umbratilis (Girard)

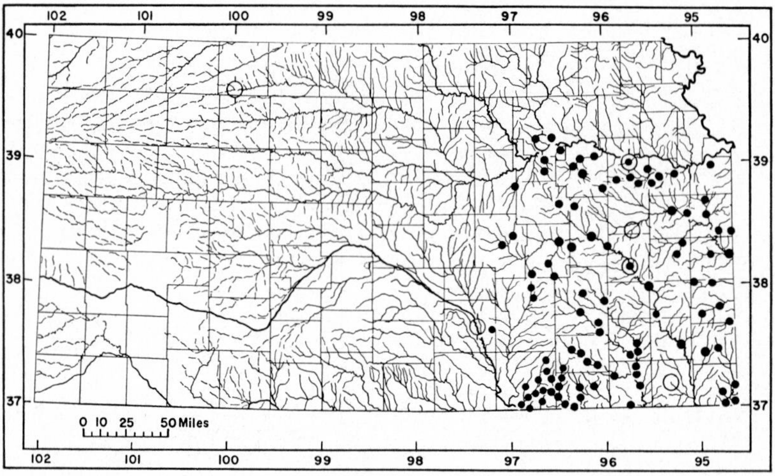

Minnilus nigripinnis Gilbert (1884:14 [orig. descr.], 1885a:513-514).

Notropis nigripinnis, Gilbert (1885b:98); Cragin (1885b:109); Graham (1885b:73); Hay (1887:249); Jordan (1891:17); Clarke, Breukelman, and Andrews (1958:168); Minckley and Cross (1959:212); Metcalf (1959:371-372, 1966:116); Deacon (1961:381); Deacon and Metcalf (1961:316).

Notropis umbratilis umbratilis, Breukelman (1940a:370, 1940b:380); Jennings (1942:365); Cross (1954:309); Schelske (1957:45).

Body moderately deep, strongly compressed, its greatest depth 4.0 or less in standard length of adults; head short, snout rounded; mouth terminal, strongly oblique; eye large, diameter equal to or slightly less than snout length and 3.4-4.0 in head length of adults; dorsal fin acute at tip, originating posterior to insertion of pelvic fins; dorsal fin-rays 8; anal rays 9-11 (most often 10); pelvic rays 8; pectoral rays 12-14; lateral line abruptly decurved anteriorly, with 37-44 (usually 39-42) scales; predorsal scales small; scale rows around body 18-21—2—12-15, around caudal peduncle usually 7—2—7, sometimes 7—2—5; pharyngeal teeth 2,4—4,2; intestine short, peritoneum silvery; vertebrae 35-38.

Bluish-gray dorsally, silver ventrolaterally; upper sides often with fine chevronlike markings anteriorly; scales not prominently dark-outlined; mid-dorsal stripe narrow anteriorly, obsolescent posteriorly, intensified at origin of dorsal fin and forming diffuse dark spot on and anterior to rudimentary dorsal fin-rays; in young, distinctive row of melanophores on each side of dorsal midline (on nape); mid-sides with scattered large melanophores forming diffuse, dusky lateral streak, mostly dorsal to lateral line; fins dusky or colorless. Breeding males dark, with bluish iridescence; fins dark, especially medially, due to saturation of melanin in crotches of branched rays; dorsal, caudal, and anal fins lightly suffused with rosy pigment (appearance of fins reddish-black or purplish-black, never brilliantly red or orange); pelvic fins black, without rosy pigment; leading edge of pectoral fin dark, remainder of that fin colorless.

Head of breeding males clothed by tubercles of uniformly small size (on operculum, branchiostegals, gill membranes, gular area, and mandibles as well as top and sides of head, excluding only lips); most scales of body with minute tubercles, largest and most numerous on nape; tubercles usually absent on ventral scales, often absent on caudal peduncle; pectoral fin tuberculate on rays 1-9, ray 1 with weak single file, other rays with multiple files; leading edges of dorsal, anal, and pelvic fins tuberculate.

Length 3 inches or less.

The vernacular "redfin" is a misnomer for the Kansas subspecies (*N. u. umbratilis*) because its fins never are truly red, whereas the fins of some other shiners of this region usually are red.

All known occurrences of *N. umbratilis* in Kansas are in the eastern part of the State, except for a single record from Norton County by Hay (1887:249) that was recently verified by Metcalf (1966:116). The species is rare or absent in streams that drain glaciated terrain north of the Kansas River, but substantial populations of *N. umbratilis* occur in most southern tributaries of Kansas River. In the Arkansas and Marais des Cygnes drainages, *N. umbratilis* is an abundant inhabitant of creeks that drain limestone-uplands. Schools of red-finned shiners, cruising near the surface in the faintly blue-gray waters of deep pools, represent one of the most characteristic faunistic features of the Flint Hills area. Although red-finned shiners rarely occupy rapidly flowing water, the species is abundant only in streams that have high gradients and rocky riffles. The westward distribution of this fish may be limited by siltation of stream-channels, especially by sand, coupled with the high turbidity and fluctuation in volume of flow that characterize most western streams.

Spawning occurs mainly in June, at water-temperatures of 70° F. or higher, but extends from May through July.

Dusky-striped shiner
Notropis pilsbryi Fowler

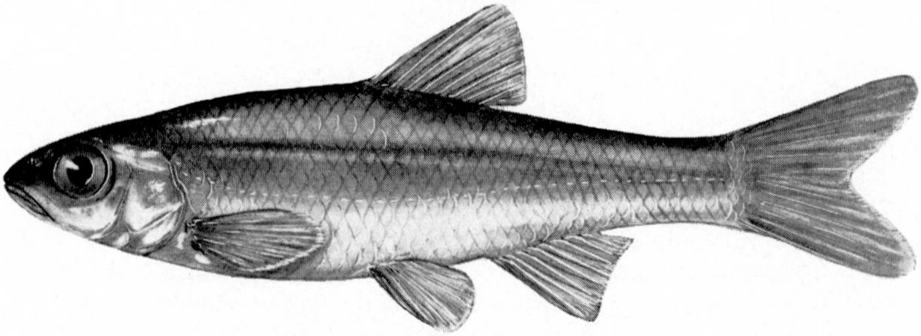

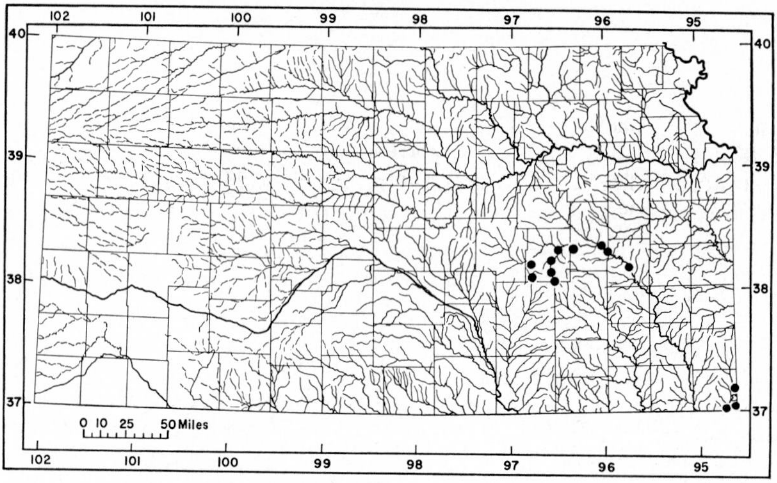

Notropis megalops, Graham (1885a:4).

Notropis zonatus, Cragin (1185b:108); Graham (1885b:74); Minckley and Cross (1959:212).

Notropis zonatus pilsbryi, Hubbs and Moore (1940:94); Breukelman (1946: 57); Metcalf (1959:393).

Notropis zonata pilsbryi, Cross (1954:309); Clarke, Breukelman, and Andrews (1958:168).

Notropis cornutus frontalis (misidentifications), Breukelman (1940b:380) (part of specimens from Neosho River System); Jennings (1942:365).

Notropis pilsbryi, Gilbert (1964:133-136).

Body slightly compressed, nearly fusiform; head length 3.6-4.2 in standard length; snout rather sharp, equal to or slightly longer than diameter of eye; eye large, 3.4-4.0 in head length of adults; mouth oblique, jaws equal or lower jaw closing inside upper jaw; dorsal fin triangular, anterior rays extending to or beyond tips of posterior rays in depressed fin; dorsal fin originating nearly over insertion of pelvic fins, both these fins 8-rayed; anal rays usually 9; pectoral rays 15 or 16; scales not notably diamond-shaped, nor smaller dorsally than laterally; lateral line slightly decurved, with 40-44 scales; scale rows around body 11-14—2—12-14, around caudal peduncle usually 7—2—7; pharyngeal teeth 2,4—4,2; intestine short but peritoneum black or dusky; vertebrae 39-41.

Olivaceous dorsally, with prominent, broad mid-dorsal stripe from occiput to caudal fin, surrounding dorsal fin-base; lower sides silvery, opaque; broad, dusky lateral stripe usually evident, from darkened lips through eye, across upper part of operculum, along mid-sides to base of caudal fin; median caudal rays often darkened, but no discrete basicaudal spot; above dusky lateral band, a fine, dark, longitudinal line usually evident on third or fourth scale row below mid-dorsal row of scales; fins mostly colorless except in breeding season. Breeding males with rich, deep red (not orange) pigment on head, lower sides, and all fins excepting their distal margins; lateral band broad and intensely black in nuptial males. See Plate 1.

Breeding males with tubercles of moderate size atop head, scattered or tending toward longitudinal alignment, best developed along dorsal rim of orbit and across front of snout; mandibles with few weak tubercles or none (in Arkansas River System); minute tubercles occurring in vertical lines on anterior scales, including scales of breast, but best developed dorsolaterally; margins of most scale pockets thickened, sometimes with tubercles in single peripheral row; pectoral fins with single file of tubercles on basal parts of rays 2 through 8 (or 10), dividing into double files on branched extremities of rays; other fins not tuberculate, or having few minute tubercles on anterior rays.

Length 4¼ inches or less.

The dusky-striped shiner abounds in Shoal Creek and Spring River, Cherokee County, and occurs as a relic in the upper Neosho River (Chase, Lyon, and Coffey counties). The species seems to require clear, flowing water where the substrate is limestone rubble and gravel, devoid of silt. At night I have seen *N. pilsbryi* drift into shallow, quiet water alongshore, where it settled to the bottom at rest.

N. pilsbryi spawns in spring, usually in April and May. I suspect that the precise timing is temperature-dependent, hence variable from year to year in response to prevailing weather each spring. Breeding takes place diurnally, in or immediately below swift, shallow riffles.

The earliest records of this fish in Kansas suggest that the bleeding shiner, *N. zonatus* (Agassiz), as well as *N. pilsbryi,* occurred here in the late 1800's; the latter species was not recognized and described by Fowler until 1904. These two fishes closely resemble each other, and were generally regarded as subspecies until Gilbert (1964) recommended that they be treated as distinct species, on the basis of allopatry.

Both Cragin (1885b:108) and Graham (1885b:74) reported "*N. zonatus*" from the Missouri River System, where only the bleeding shiner is now known to occur. That species is abundant in Ozarkian tributaries of the Osage River not far to the east of Kansas, and may formerly have existed farther upstream in the Marais des Cygnes, Little Osage, or Marmaton river. However, the manner in which Cragin and Graham reported *N. zonatus* suggests that their records were presumptive, based on the fact that the type locality is in the Osage River, Missouri, rather than being based on specimens actually captured in the Missouri River Drainage of Kansas. Graham's report (*loc. cit.*) of *N. zonatus* from the Neosho River is an acceptable record for *N. pilsbryi,* because six specimens collected by him in Rock Creek, Chase County (Neosho System) in 1885 are that species. The same specimens (KSU 2755) were erroneously listed by Jennings (1942:365) as *N. cornutus frontalis.*

N. zonatus differs from *N. pilsbryi* in having the cleithrum blackened; the dorsolateral scales better outlined by melanophores, forming striking zigzag lines, converging posteriorly, between adjacent scale rows; the snout blunter, shorter, and more decurved; the interorbital area arched rather than flattened; and the lips flexed abruptly downward posteriorly, rather than nearly straight. Additionally, breeding males of *zonatus* are less extensively red than males of *pilsbryi,* red pigment being concentrated on the lips, crest of head, margin of preopercle, axil of pectoral fin, and central part of all fin membranes in *zonatus.* Males of *zonatus* have a single file of 8-10 well developed tubercles along the full length of the mandibles, whereas mandibular tubercles are absent or poorly developed in *pilsbryi.* Tubercles are larger and more numerous on the snout in *zonatus* than in *pilsbryi.*

Northern common shiner

Notropis cornutus (Mitchill)

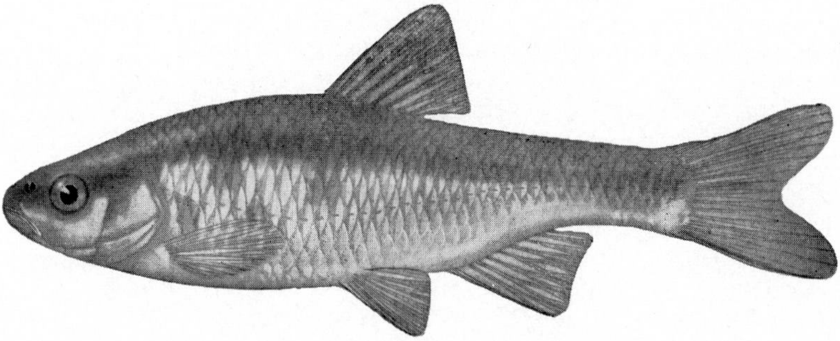

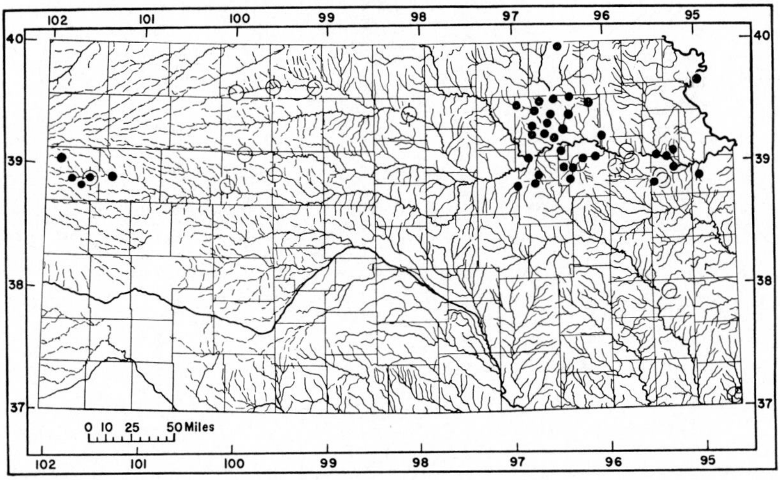

Minnilus cornutus, Gilbert (1884:14).

Notropis megalops, Gilbert (1885b:98; 1886:210; 1889:40); Cragin (1885b:108-109); Graham (1885b:73); Hay (1887:243, 247, 249, 250, 252).

Notropis cornutus, Fowler (1910:283-284); Minckley (1956:353, 355); Minckley and Cross (1959:212); Gilbert (1961:189, 1964:146); Metcalf (1966:117).

Notropis cornuta, Clarke, Breukelman, and Andrews (1958:167).

Notropis cornutus frontalis, Breukelman (1940a:370, 1940b:380 in part); Jennings (1942:365 in part); Minckley (1959:421); Minckley and Cross (1960:4-7); Deacon and Metcalf (1961:316).

Notropis cornuta frontalis, Cross (1954:309).

Body compressed; head length about 3.5 in standard length; snout blunt, length about equal to eye diameter (longer than eye in largest adults); eye large, its diameter 4.0 or more in head length of adults, much less than 4.0 in juveniles; mouth terminal, oblique, jaws equal; dorsal fin originating approximately over insertion of pelvics, both these fins 8-rayed; anal fin-rays usually 9; pectoral rays 14-16; scales on sides high and diamond-shaped, those on nape small, crowded, in 18 or more rows anterior to dorsal fin; lateral line decurved, with 38-41 scales; scale rows around body commonly 16-18—2—15-16, around caudal peduncle usually 9—2—7; pharyngeal teeth 2,4—4,2; intestine short, peritoneum black; vertebrae 38-41.

Olivaceous dorsally, with broad stripe on mid-line, surrounding base of dorsal fin; sides silvery, sometimes brassy, often with scattered dark crescents; fins colorless or dusky, without basal spots; no fine, dark stripes between dorsolateral scale-rows (single broad, dusky streak present dorsolaterally in nuptial males). Breeding males blue-gray, with rosy (pink) pigment and purplish iridescence on sides of head and body; gill membranes rosy; fins with rosy pigment near distal margins; transitory golden stripe dorsolaterally, and mid-dorsal stripe golden.

Breeding males with tubercles densely crowded on snout, becoming more scattered posteriorly on crest of head; anterior half of cheek densely tuberculate (operculum not tuberculate); mandible with one prominent row of tubercles and few scattered tubercles; scales of nape and leading edge of dorsal fin with small tubercles; rays 2-8 of pectoral fins with single file of well-developed tubercles.

Maximum length about 7 inches.

Eighty years ago the common shiner inhabited most of the Kansas River Basin. Its disappearance from many western streams is persuasive evidence of their deterioration in one or more of the following ways: more frequent intermittency; increasing deposits of fine sediments; and higher temperatures. Although *N. cornutus* is a widespread, relatively tolerant species, it "prefers small to medium-sized streams with clear, cool, weedless water, a moderate to swift current, and alternating pools and riffles, the latter with a gravel or rubble bottom" (Gilbert, 1964:149-150). Common shiners persist today in some Plains streams as far south as the Smoky Hill River in Wallace County, but only where flow is permanent. In eastern Kansas *N. cornutus* remains abundant in streams of the Flint Hills, but the species is rare in areas where the terrain is flatter, soils are deeper, cultivation is more extensive, and springs are not constant. The few records of *N. cornutus* from the Arkansas River in Kansas (Breukelman, 1940b:380; Jennings, 1942:365) probably are erroneous; those that I have been able to check have been based on misidentifications of other shiners (especially *N. pilsbryi*) or on incorrect citations of localities of capture. Probably the common shiner dispersed westward into the Kansas River Basin in late Pleistocene, after disruption of the Ancestral Plains Stream (Metcalf, 1966), and too late to gain access to the Arkansas River System.

Several accounts of the reproductive habits of *N. cornutus* (Raney, 1940; Gilbert, 1964) indicate that spawning usually occurs from late May through early July, at water-temperatures higher than 64° F. but lower than 80° F. In Kansas, males near the peak of their reproductive development have been caught as early as 18 April (water-temperature 51° F.) and as late as 14 July. The specimens on which this time-span is based were collected from different streams, and in the period 1898 to 1958. At a single locality in a given year, the reproductive period is much less extensive than the April to July dates might indicate; Raney (1940: 4) stated that spawning usually is completed in a 10-day interval at any one place. Sites where eggs are deposited are always in the current over rubble or gravel bottom, but the common shiner otherwise selects its nest-sites fortuitously. Sometimes it utilizes naturally-occurring patches of clean gravel at the base of strong riffles; on other occasions *N. cornutus* spawns in crude nests of its own making, or over gravel-nests of other fishes (*Hybopsis biguttata, Semotilus atromaculatus*). Hybrids of *N. cornutus* with *Semotilus* and with *N. rubellus* have been taken in Kansas as well as in other parts of the range of the common shiner. Miller (1964) analyzed hybridization of *N. cornutus* and *N. rubellus,* in a detailed study of the reproductive behavior of the common shiner and several other minnows that spawn concurrently in streams of New York State.

N. cornutus feeds mainly on aquatic insects.

Central common shiner

Notropis chrysocephalus (Rafinesque)

Body compressed; head length 3.5 (juveniles) to 4.0 (adults) in standard length; snout blunt, length about equal to eye diameter in juveniles, longer than eye in adults; eye large, 3.5 (juveniles) to 4.3 (adults) in head length; mouth terminal, oblique; jaws equal or lower jaw protruding slightly; dorsal fin originating over insertion of pelvics, both fins 8-rayed; anal fin-rays usually 9; occasionally 8, rarely 10; pectoral rays 14-16; scales on sides high, narrowly diamond-shaped; dorsolateral scales not especially small, predorsal scale rows 16 or fewer; lateral line decurved, with 37-40 scales; scale rows around body 12-14—2—12-13, around caudal peduncle 7—2—7; pharyngeal teeth 2,4—4,2; intestine short, peritoneum dark; vertebrae usually 39-40.

Color like that of *N. cornutus,* except upper sides usually marked by 3 or more parallel dark lines extending lengthwise on body, between scale rows; dark pigment usually present on chin and gular area; cleithrum intensely blackened in nuptial males.

Tubercles situated as in *N. cornutus.*

Length 8 inches or less.

Although no Kansas records of the central common shiner have been published, Dr. Branley Branson has obtained this species from Spring River (personal communication, May 27, 1963, and duplicated list of fishes from southeastern Kansas). Gilbert (1964, Map 5) indicated six localities of occurrence in the Spring River System in southwestern Missouri, and stated that this species "should occur in the extreme southeast corner" of Kansas. I have never found *N. chrysocephalus* in lower Shoal Creek nor Spring River in Cherokee County.

The central common shiner inhabits the Osage (Missouri System) as well as the Arkansas River Basin in Missouri, but is restricted to streams that drain the Ozark Plateau in this (westernmost) part of the range. The habitats occupied are described by Gilbert (1964: 165) as small to medium sized streams having clear, weedless water and moderate to swift current. Central common shiners are most common near the margins of riffles, over gravel- or rubble-bottom. The species seldom enters the swiftest currents on riffles except when spawning, and seemingly avoids the calm water of large pools. The reproductive habits of *N. chrysocephalus* are generally like those of the common shiner, *N. cornutus.* These two species closely resemble each other and were long considered to be conspecific.

River shiner

Notropis blennius (Girard)

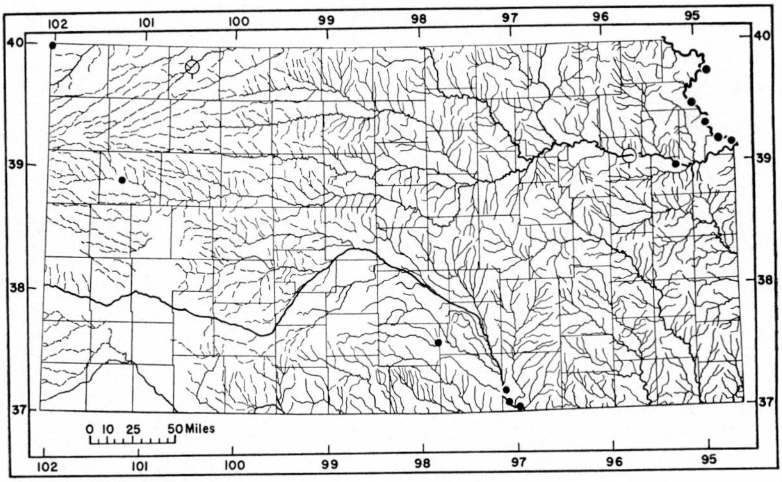

N. jejunus, Gilbert (1889:39).
Notropis blennius, Metcalf (1959:365, 394; 1966:119).
Notropis blennius blennius, Hubbs and Bonham (1951:103).

Body stout; head large, its length 3.6-4.0 in standard length; eye large, 4.0-4.5 in head length; mouth large, moderately oblique; fins low, dorsal fin originating approximately over insertion of pelvic fins; dorsal and pelvic fin-rays 8, anal rays 7, pectoral rays 14 or 15; lateral-line scales 34-36; scale rows around body 11-13—2—11-13; pharyngeal teeth 1 or 2,4—4,2 or 1; intestine short, peritoneum silvery; vertebrae 34-37.

Coloration pallid, light brown dorsally with silvery lateral stripe; no basi-caudal spot; fins plain; mid-dorsal stripe prominent, surrounding dorsal fin base, lateral line not marked by melanophores; dorsolateral scales not well outlined by melanophores. No chromatic breeding colors.

Breeding males having few minute tubercles on front of snout; tubercles otherwise confined to pectoral fins (rays 2-7), where minute, in multiple files on each ray.

Length 3¼ inches or less.

The river shiner is common only in the Missouri River, but has been taken in both the western and eastern sectors of the Kansas River Basin and in the lower Arkansas River. The species seems to require flowing water over sand bottom; it is found most often in large streams having broad, exposed channels. Specimens in spawning condition have been taken from mid-June to mid-July in Kansas.

The earliest known record of the species in Kansas is that of Gilbert (1889:39) from Decatur County. The record from Logan County (Smoky Hill River) was obtained in 1958, and several recent records exist from the Republican River in Nebraska (Metcalf, 1966). Seemingly, these western populations are isolated from populations in the mainstream of the Missouri River by an extensive zone in the central part of the Kansas River Basin unoccupied by river shiners. The two records from the Kansas River (at Topeka and Lawrence) consist of one and two specimens, indicative of rarity in view of the numerous collections that have been made in the stream.

Records of *N. blennius* by Evermann and Cox (1896:406) are not applicable to the river shiner, pertaining instead to the sand shiner, *N. stramineus;* Evermann and Cox called the river shiner *N. jejunus.* Hubbs and Bonham (1951:103) treat *jejunus* as a weakly differentiated subspecies of *N. blennius.* They refer material "in the Arkansas and Missouri rivers in Kansas" to *N. b. blennius.* The other subspecies (*N. b. jejunus*) is mainly northern in distribution, but extends down the central Mississippi System to Missouri and Arkansas, and westward to the Illinois and Neosho drainages in Oklahoma. Thus, specimens referable to *jejunus* may sometime be found in southeastern Kansas.

Big-eyed shiner

Notropis boops Gilbert

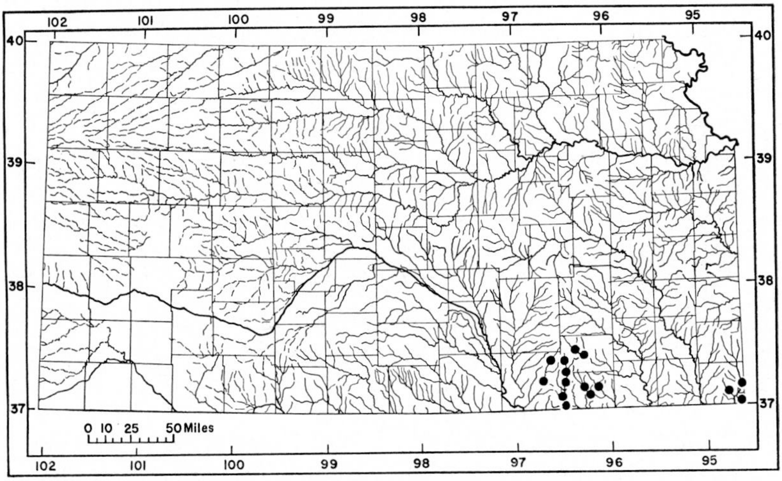

Notropis nux, Hall (1934:230) [presumptive allocation].
Notropis boops, Cross (1955:474); Metcalf (1959:365-366, 393-394).

Body fusiform; mouth large, terminal, strongly oblique; eye large, diameter 3.0 or less in head length; dorsal fin originating almost over insertion of pelvic fins; dorsal fin high, acutely pointed, anterior rays extending beyond tips of posterior rays when fin is depressed; dorsal, anal, and pelvic fin-rays 8; pectoral rays 15; predorsal scales large; lateral line nearly straight, with 34-36 scales; scale rows around body 11-12—2—10-11; pharyngeal teeth 1,4—4,1; intestine short but peritoneum black; vertebrae usually 35-37.

Greenish dorsally, silvery laterally; sides with dark longitudinal stripe, extending forward through center of eye to tip of snout, or with lateral line prominently outlined by melanophores; lips dark-pigmented anteriorly; mid-dorsal stripe thin or obsolescent; dorsolateral scales dark-outlined, except for row above lateral-line row of scales, causing illusion of light stripe above dark lateral band; fins usually colorless, leading edge of pectoral sometimes dark. No chromatic breeding colors.

Breeding males with dense band of tubercles on front of snout (below and anterior to nares); top of head with minute tubercles, densely distributed; lower surface of head strongly tuberculate, mandibular tubercles numerous and large, those on branchiostegals and gill membranes sparse; opercles with few, scattered tubercles; dorsolateral scales weakly tuberculate; tubercles diminishing posteriorly, none on caudal peduncle; pectoral fins with multiple files of tubercles on rays 1-7; dorsal and anal fins tuberculate on leading edges near body; fins otherwise lacking tubercles.

Length 2¾ inches or less.

The big-eyed shiner is common locally in the Spring River System (Cherokee County) and in tributaries of the Verdigris, Caney, and Arkansas rivers in the southern Flint Hills. The absence of authenticated records from the intervening Neosho Drainage is perplexing. Interestingly, the distribution of this species complements that of the sand shiner, *Notropis stramineus.* Although both *N. boops* and *N. stramineus* occur in the Walnut River Drainage, the two have not been taken in the same streams; elsewhere, the big-eyed shiner is restricted to the few river-systems in Kansas where sand shiners are unknown.

N. boops seems to require clear water. In much of its range, the species inhabits small upland tributaries that have high gradients and rocky bottoms. But *N. boops* inhabits not only brooks; it is abundant also in large, clear rivers of the Ozarks, where it occupies varied habitats.

The big-eyed shiner spawns in summer in Kansas, at temperatures of 80° F. or higher. Tuberculate males have been taken from mid-June through August, most often in the latter month.

Blunt-faced shiner

Notropis camurus (Jordan and Meek)

Notropis camurus, Cragin (1885b:108); Graham (1885a:4, 1885b:73); Gilbert (1886:208, 1889:40-42); Jordan (1891:18); Moore and Buck (1955:22); Metcalf (1959:367-368, 393); Deacon (1961:381); Gibbs (1961).

Notropis camura, Cross (1954:309, 1955:475); Schelske (1957:45); Clarke, Breukelman, and Andrews (1958:167).

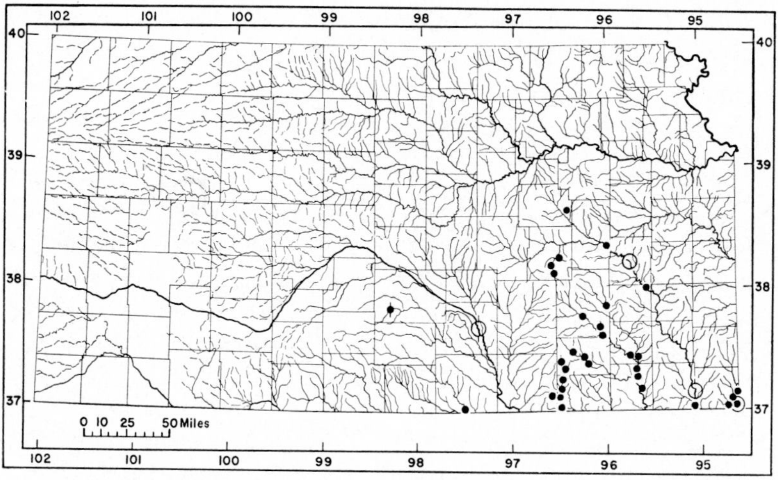

Body compressed, greatest depth approximately 4.0 in standard length, nearly equal to head length; snout blunt; mouth oblique, not quite terminal; lips decurved, lower jaw closing inside upper jaw; eye of moderate size, diameter usually less than snout length; dorsal fin rounded, originating over or slightly behind pelvic insertion; dorsal and pelvic fin-rays 8, anal fin-rays 9, pectoral rays 15 or 16; lateral line decurved, with 34-38 scales; scale rows around body 13-15—2—11, around caudal peduncle 7—2—5; pharyngeal teeth 1,4—4,1; intestine short, peritoneum silvery; vertebrae usually 37-38.

Olivaceous dorsally, silvery laterally; mid-dorsal stripe broad and prominent; no dark lateral band; lateral scales well outlined by melanophores, appearing diamond-shaped; caudal fin unpigmented near base, darker posteriorly; dorsal fin with black blotches on posterior membranes. In breeding males, all lateral scales with blue submarginal crescents; dark blue or purplish shoulder-bar (immediately behind operculum), followed posteriorly by broad light area, and diffuse dark bluish vertical band located about midway between pectoral and pelvic fin-bases; tip of snout rosy; top of head blue-gray; lower sides of head yellowish; all lower fins pinkish-orange centrally, light basally and distally; caudal fin milky white basally, dark blue-gray distally and suffused with rosy pigment; dorsal fin enlarged, dark blue-gray, with posterior rays light pink, contrasting sharply with black interradial membranes.

Nuptial tubercles in males rather large, distributed almost uniformly over top of head (most dense across front of snout, from eye to eye below nares); two rows of tubercles on each chin-ramus, sometimes with additional tubercles between those rows and on lower lip; sides of head, below and behind eyes, devoid of tubercles; minute tubercles on most scales, but no distinct patch of well-developed tubercles on lower part of caudal peduncle; rays of all fins with minute tubercles.

Length 5 inches or less.

The blunt-faced shiner is common in small and medium-sized streams of the Flint Hills, and in the Spring River Drainage of Cherokee County. The species prefers moderately fast, clear water, and displaces the related red shiner (*N. lutrensis*) from that habitat in streams that harbor both species. *N. camurus* is rarely found in creeks that have low gradients and bottoms of mud or sand. Most specimens from the mainstream of the Verdigris and Neosho rivers were obtained in droughts. Records from the Arkansas mainstream are few, but their existence lends credence to Jordan's (1891:18) report of *camurus* as "very abundant" in the Arkansas River at Wichita. Many of the species listed by Jordan (but not collected by him) are improbable inhabitants of the Arkansas mainstream, leading me to think that the collection "at Wichita" was a composite one, including fishes from upland streams in that vicinity as well as from the Arkansas River itself.

The type locality of *N. camurus* was given by Jordan and Meek (1884:474) as Fort Lyon, Colorado, far to the west of every other record. Gibbs (1961:350) suggests that "the range of the species is contracting at present, and . . . the southwestern Ozark region is its stronghold." Interestingly, however, *camurus* was not among species reported from Garden City by Gilbert and Cragin in several publications in 1885-1889, although the collections from Garden City contained other clear-water fishes. Neither was *camurus* reported by Jordan (1891) in any of his collections from the Arkansas System in Colorado. Statements by Gilbert (1889:42) regarding occurrences of *camurus* are in general conformity with the distribution and abundance of the blunt-faced shiner as known at present in the Arkansas Basin. I doubt that the type specimen of *camurus* was captured at Fort Lyon. I doubt also that isolated records of the blunt-faced shiner in the upper Osage and White river drainages represent relic populations, as Gibbs (1961:350) suggested. Erroneous designations of localities of capture and/or bait-introductions probably account for those records. Likewise, Branson's (1964:746) record of the white-tailed shiner, *Notropis galacturus* (Cope), from Kansas seems best interpreted as a bait-introduction. The single specimen (KU 7448) reportedly was taken in 1962 from Spring River at Baxter Springs, Cherokee County; no other records of *galacturus* exist from the Arkansas River Basin exclusive of the White River. *Notropis camurus* and *N. galacturus* probably represent a species-pair, closely related, ecologically equivalent, but mutually exclusive (allopatric) in their natural distributions.

N. camurus spawns in late spring and summer, when temperatures are in the 80's (° F). Specimens in breeding condition have been taken from early June to mid-July in the same year, from localities in the same stream-systems in Kansas. Tuberculate males have been found as early as April 6, and as late as August 14; in those two sets of specimens, taken in different streams and different years, the tubercles were incipient on the former date, and mostly deciduous on the latter date. In the unusually warm, dry spring of 1963, a male in breeding condition was obtained in Shoal Creek (Cherokee County) on May 12, when the water-temperature was 77° F.

Spot-finned shiner

Notropis spilopterus (Cope)

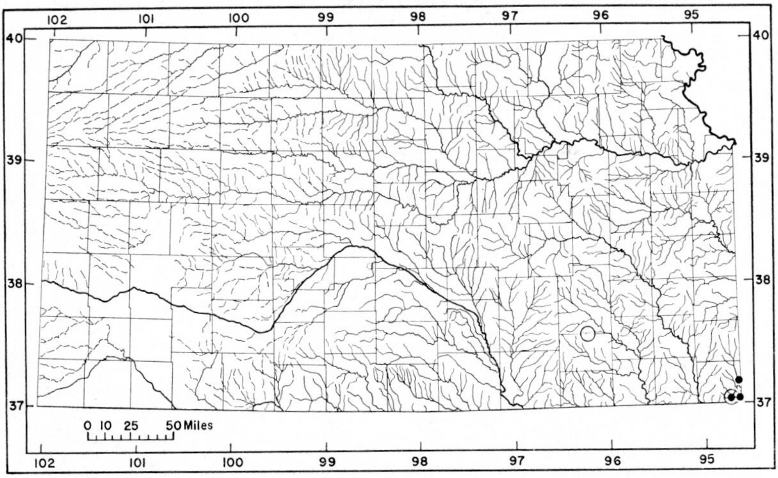

Notropis spilopterus, Cross (1955:475); Clarke, Breukelman, and Andrews (1958:168).

Notropis spilopterus hypsisomatus Gibbs (1957 [orig. descr.]).

Notropis cornutus frontalis, Breukelman (1940b:380, misidentifications in part).

Body moderately compressed, greatest depth 3.6-4.3 in standard length, greater than head length; snout acute; mouth oblique, terminal, cleft straight in lateral aspect; eye of moderate size, diameter less than snout length, 4.5 or less in head length; jaws equal or nearly so; dorsal fin originating slightly behind pelvic insertion; dorsal, anal, and pelvic rays 8; pectoral rays 13-15; lateral line decurved, with 35-38 scales; scale rows around body 13-15—2—11, around caudal peduncle 7—2—5; pharyngeal teeth 1,4—4,1; intestine short, peritoneum silvery; vertebrae 35-38.

Olivaceous dorsally, mid-dorsal stripe prominent; dorsolateral and most lateral scales dark-outlined, diamond-shaped; lower sides silvery or white; dorsal fin with dark blotches on posterior membranes in adults; caudal fin uniformly pigmented, without light basal area. Breeding males steely blue, with darker blue vertical crescent behind head and broad dusky band on sides posteriorly; fins milky white distally, lower fins yellowish basally; snout yellowish, never red; membranes of dorsal fin intensely blackened, but that fin not enlarged in breeding males.

Nuptial tubercles in dense patch across snout; tubercles on crest of head numerous, large, tips directed forward, and distinctly separated from tubercles on snout by naked space before nares; chin having single file of 3 or 4 tubercles on each mandible, plus additional small organs on symphysis; large tubercles on scales of nape; most lateral scales with minute tubercles, enlarged on lower part of caudal peduncle; all fins tuberculate—pectoral rays 1-7, pelvic rays 1-6, anal rays 1-7 and second anterior rudiment, dorsal rays 1-6 and second anterior rudiment; caudal fin with few minute tubercles on principal rays except uppermost and lowermost.

Length 3 inches or less.

I have found spot-finned shiners only in the Spring River Drainage in Cherokee County. Probably the species is, or once was, more widespread in southeastern Kansas. Clarke, Breukelman, and Andrews reported *N. spilopterus* as "scarce" in Lyon County. They did not record dates or precise localities of capture. Collections at the University of Kansas contain one series of *N. spilopterus* labeled as captured in Salt Creek (probably Greenwood County) in 1912, by personnel of the State Biological Survey. These specimens and an additional series from Spring River, Cherokee County, dated July 7, 1911, were reported as *N. cornutus frontalis* by Breukelman (1940b:380).

Hankinson (1930:73) stated that the spot-finned shiner strongly preferred clear, clean waters with sandy bottoms and scant vegetation, in shallows of rivers and lakes. Gibbs (1957) recorded *N. spilopterus,* at the southwestern edge of its range, only from Ozarkian streams (Spring and Illinois rivers) of the Arkansas River System. I have taken numerous specimens in the lower (Kansas) part of Shoal Creek in years of drought, but in years of heavy rainfall *spilopterus* has been scarce in collections from lower Shoal Creek. The species was taken most often in moderate current adjacent to gently sloping, clean gravel bars, at depths of one to four feet. The spot-finned shiner and *N. camurus* occurred in the same seine hauls, together with lesser numbers of *N. lutrensis.*

I have no information on reproduction by *N. spilopterus* in Kansas. Males obtained in April and May of several years have only incipient tubercles or none. Males taken in July of 1911 and 1912, by the State Biological Survey, have partly deciduous tubercles. Pflieger (1965) published a detailed account of the reproductive habits of *N. spilopterus* in streams of Ohio. There, spawning occurs from early June until early August, on submerged logs near riffles where at least a slight current exists. Pflieger (1965:3) indicated that the spot-finned shiner "seemed to be quite exacting with regard to the spawning substrate and spawned only on logs having loose bark or crevices for egg deposition."

Red shiner

Notropis lutrensis (Baird and Girard)

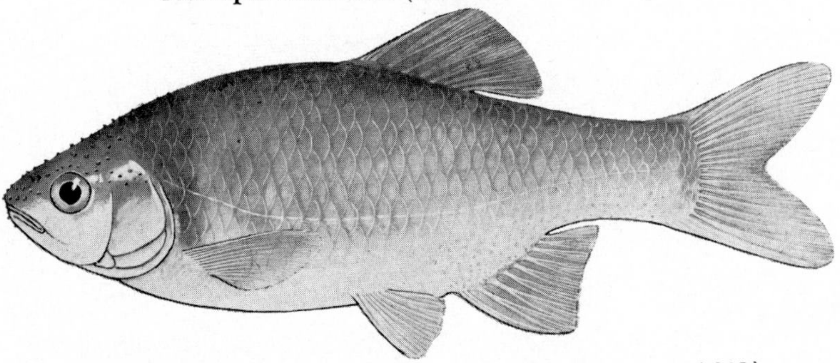

Cyprinella beckwithi Girard (1856:33 [orig. descr.]; 1858:267-268).
Cyprinella billingsiana Cope (1871:439 [orig. descr.]).
Moniana jugalis Cope (1871:439 [orig. descr.]).
Cliola gibbosa, Gilbert (1884:13).
Notropis lutrensis, Gilbert (1885b:98; 1886:210; 1889:39, 40); Cragin 1885b:108); Graham (1885a:4, 1885b:73); Evermann and Fordice (1886:185); Hay (1887:242, 248, 249, 250, 252, 253); Jordan (1891: 18); Evermann and Cox (1896:404); Fowler (1910:279-280); Hall (1934:230); Cross (1955:475); Minckley (1956:354); Greer and Cross (1956:362); Schelske (1957:45); Clarke, Breukelman, and Andrews (1958:167); Minckley and Cross (1959:212); Metcalf (1959: 369, 1966:118); Minckley (1959:421-422); Minckley and Deacon (1960:348); Breukelman (1960:34); Deacon (1961:381-382); Deacon and Metcalf (1961:316); Fisher (1962:427); Kilgore and Rising (1965:140).
Notropis Billingsiana, Cragin (1885b:108).
Notropis billingsiana, Graham (1885b:73).
Notropis bubalina, Graham (1885b:73).
Notropis lutrenis, Hay (1887:243).
Notropis macrostoma, Hay (1887:244).
Notropis bubalinus, Jordan (1891:18); Fowler (1910:280).
Notropis lutrensis lutrensis, Breukelman (1940a:370; 1940b:380); Jennings (1942:365); Cross (1954:309-310); Moore and Buck (1955:22).
Notropis atherinoides dilectus, Jennings (1942:365, misidentifications in part).

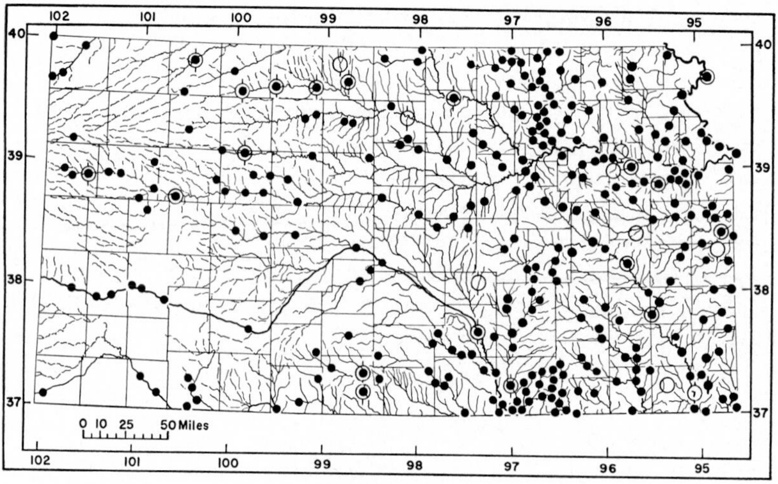

Body highly compressed, greatest depth in adults 3.0-3.6 in standard length and more than head length; snout blunt; mouth terminal and oblique, jaws equal or nearly so; eye diameter less than snout length, 4.0 or more in head length of adult; dorsal fin rounded, originating over or slightly behind insertion of pelvics; dorsal and pelvic rays 8; anal rays 8-10, most often 9; pectoral rays usually 14; lateral line decurved, with 33-36 scales, most often 35; scale rows around body usually 13—2—11, around caudal peduncle 7—2—5; pharyngeal teeth usually 0,4—4,0; intestine short, peritoneum silvery; vertebrae usually 34-36.

Tan to olivaceous dorsally, silvery laterally and white ventrally; mid-dorsal stripe present, not intensified in base of dorsal fin; dorsolateral scales moderately outlined by melanophores; dorsal and caudal fins uniformly pigmented (anterior membranes as dark as posterior membranes). Males in spring and summer with caudal and all lower fins red or orange; sides of breeding males bright pale-blue, with prominent purplish crescent behind head; top of head red, its sides rosy; dorsal fin entirely dark, scarcely reddish. See Plate 1.

In breeding males, dense patch of contiguous tubercles on snout; top of head with scattered, moderately large tubercles having tips directed forward; chin commonly without tubercles or with 1 to 4 tubercles at mandibular symphysis, sometimes with file of 3 or 4 tubercles extending backward along mandibles; large tubercles on scales of nape; discrete patch of large tubercles on scales of caudal region below lateral line; other scales with marginal row of minute tubercles; all fins bearing tubercles—on pectoral rays 1-8, in single file basally, dividing onto branches; on pelvic rays 1-4; on anal rays 1-8; on all caudal rays, from base to mid-point of length; on dorsal rays 1-6, sparsely on basal part of rays.

Length 3 inches or less.

The red shiner is one of the most abundant fishes in Kansas, and is almost ubiquitous in its distribution. The species is least common in the largest rivers and in the clearest, most stable streams of southeastern Kansas. *N. lutrensis* seems to thrive under conditions of intermittent flow, frequent high turbidity, and other environmental variations that characterize many Plains streams. In general, red shiners are most numerous where few other kinds of fish occur. In clear streams having relatively constant flow, *N. lutrensis* gives way to several other kinds of fish, each of which has more restrictive, specialized habitat-requirements than those of the red shiner.

The abundance of *N. lutrensis* and of a group of other species of minnows fluctuates in eastern Kansas, depending on weather-cycles. During droughts, *lutrensis* predominates and many other species decline in abundance in streams having steep gradients. In the first year or two of a wet cycle, *lutrensis* continues to abound, occupying nearly all available habitats from swift riffles to quiet pools, regardless of the depth and the nature of the stream bottom. If the wet cycle continues, *lutrensis* declines, disappearing first from riffles (as obligate riffle-fishes regain abundance), then diminishing on gravel shoals, and finally being reduced to residual populations that occupy shallow pools having silted bottoms.

The reproductive interval in *N. lutrensis* extends from May to October in Kansas, at water-temperatures of 60° to 85° F. Although "high" males and females have been taken at different times and places throughout the interval mentioned above, most spawning probably takes place in June and July if local environmental conditions are favorable in those months. Spawning occurs both in lakes and streams.

Reproduction usually occurs in calm water, less often in shallow riffles over bottoms of fine gravel. The sites selected for spawning vary in other respects. I have observed spawning-activity adjacent to large logs, submerged roots of trees, aquatic plants, and brush or other debris (such as a tumbleweed) that has washed into the streams; the substrate varied from gravel to sand to mud. Minckley (1959:421-422) reported spawning-activity by red shiners above nests of sunfishes. Hubbs and Strawn (1956:344) reported that *N. lutrensis* spawned in aquaria in gravel at the bottom of the tank and in vegetation floating on the surface.

I have taken males that seemed to be patrolling individual "territories" adjacent to small patches of vegetation and in other places fine roots of trees; but I have also observed groups of more than 50 nuptial males surrounding the end of a large stump that was polished by the cleaning-activity of these fish.

When females enter the area occupied by males, a rapid chase ensues, culminating in the discharge and fertilization of eggs that then adhere to the first objects contacted, and develop without parental attention.

Adaptability with reference to the site and timing of its reproduction may account for the great success of *N. lutrensis* in the erratically variable environments afforded by Plains streams. Where stream-environments are relatively stable, this plasticity seems to place the red shiner at a competitive disadvantage in the presence of species that concentrate their reproductive effort in brief intervals at precise locations.

Topeka shiner

Notropis topeka (Gilbert)

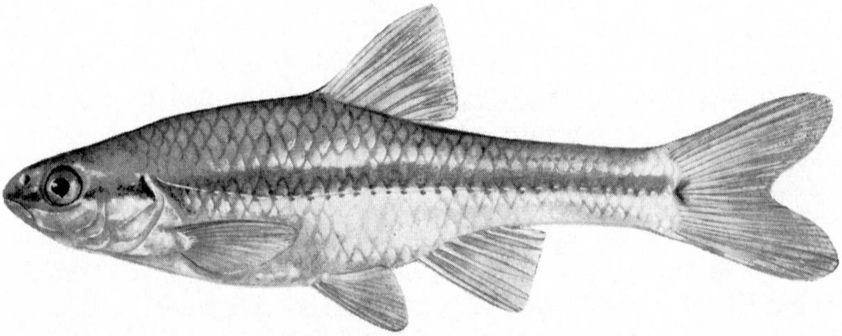

Cliola topeka Gilbert (1884:12 [orig. descr.], 1885a:513).

Notropis topeka, Gilbert (1885b:98, 1886:210, 1889:39); Cragin (1885b: 108); Graham (1885b:73); Evermann and Fordice (1886:185); Hay (1887:246); Jordan (1891:18); Breukelman (1940a:371, 1940b:380); Jennings (1942:365); Cross (1954:310); Minckley (1956:353-354, 1959: 423); Minckley and Cross (1959); Metcalf (1959:371); Deacon and Metcalf (1961:317); Bailey and Allum (1962:68-70); Metcalf (1966: 132).

Notropis aeneolus Hay (1887:245 [orig. descr.], 248, 251, 252).

Body stout, little compressed; head short, length 3.6-4.0 in standard length; snout rounded, shorter than or about equal to eye diameter, eye 3.6-4.3 in head length; mouth small, moderately oblique, jaws equal or the lower included; mouth terminating anterior to orbit; dorsal fin large, height more than ½ predorsal length of fish; dorsal originating approximately over insertion of pelvic fins; dorsal and pelvic rays 8, anal rays 7, pectoral rays usually 13; lateral line nearly straight, with 35-37 scales; scale rows around body 11-13—2—13-15, around caudal peduncle 7—2—7; pharyngeal teeth 0,4—4,0; intestine short, peritoneum silvery; vertebrae usually 36 or 37.

Dark olivaceous dorsally; predorsal stripe prominent; dorsolateral scales strongly outlined by melanophores (cross-hatched); mid-sides with dusky longitudinal stripe or dark punctulations along full length of lateral line; body lacking dark pigment (silvery white) below lateral line; discrete chevronlike dark spot at base of caudal fin. Breeding males suffused with orange, espe-

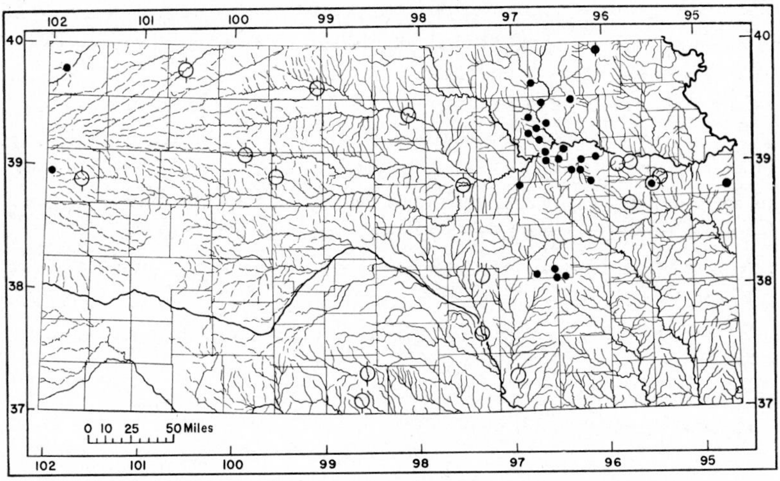

cially ventrally; cheeks and opercles orange; all fins red-orange medially, colorless basally and on distal margins. See Plate 1.

In breeding males, top of head and snout densely tuberculate; several tubercles on mandibular symphysis and single file on each lower jaw; few or no tubercles on operculum, nor on cheek below eye; nape and dorsolateral scales with tubercles, number and size diminishing posteriorly to caudal peduncle; pectoral fin-rays 1 through 8 tuberculate—in single or double file on ray 1, multiple files (3 or 4 rows) on rays 2-6, double file on ray 7, weak single file (sometimes absent) on ray 8; dorsal and anal fins with prominent tubercles on leading edges (rudimentary rays only), obsolescent tubercles on other rays in some specimens; caudal fin with few small tubercles on dorsal procurrent rays; pelvics usually not tuberculate, sometimes with few minute organs. Ripe females with minute tubercles atop head.

Length 2¼ inches or less.

The Topeka shiner formerly occurred in all major drainages of Kansas. The species now seems rare except in tributaries of the Kansas River that drain limestone uplands of the Flint Hills. Prior to 1900, *N. topeka* was reported from many western streams, but recent records west of the Flint Hills are few. Breukelman (1940a) failed to find this species in his studies of streams in northwestern Kansas in the late 1930's, and I know of but two records from that area in subsequent years: one specimen from Cherry Creek, Cheyenne County, in 1947; and nine specimens from headwaters of the Smoky Hill River, 5 miles north of Weskan, in 1965. To my knowledge, no other specimens have been obtained since 1900 west of 97° longitude in Kansas.

The Topeka shiner is most common in large, open pools of small streams. The streams occupied approach intermittency in summer, but their pools are maintained at relatively stable waterlevels by weak springs or percolation through intervening gravelly riffles. Water in the pools is usually clear, except that plankton blooms develop in most pools in summer. Probably many western streams provided this kind of habitat prior to plowing of the prairie sod.

The normal life span of *N. topeka* is two to three years. Young-of-the-year attain lengths of 20 to 40 mm. (average 30 mm.), yearlings 35 to 55 mm. (average about 43 mm.), and 2-year-olds 47-64 mm. (average 55 mm.). These sizes are based mainly on data given me by W. L. Minckley, who ascertained sizes and ages of 772 Topeka shiners captured in Deep Creek, Riley County, in October, 1956.

Topeka shiners mature as yearlings; reproduction occurs in summer (late June through August).

Big-mouthed shiner

Notropis dorsalis (Agassiz)

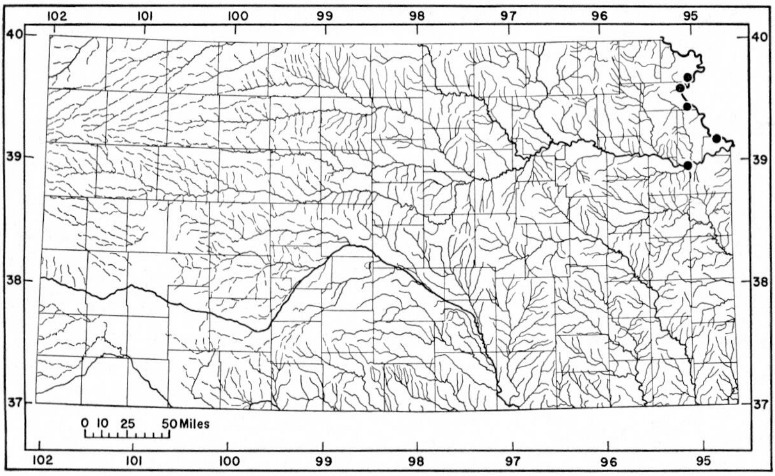

Notropis dorsalis, Cross and Minckley (1958:105-106); Metcalf (1966:122).

Body slender, back arched; head long, flattened dorsally, eyes high on head; snout long, projecting slightly beyond large ventral mouth; snout length contained less than 1.5 times in postorbital length of head; origin of dorsal fin usually nearer base of caudal than tip of snout; dorsal fin high, 8-rayed, anterior rays extending beyond tips of posterior rays in depressed fin; anal rays usually 8; pelvic rays 8; pectoral rays 13 or 14; lateral-line scales 33-37, usually 34 or 35; predorsal scale-rows 15-20, usually 17 or 18; scale rows around body 11-15—2—13-16, total circumference scales 26-33, usually 27-30; pharyngeal teeth 1,4—4,1; intestine short, peritoneum silvery; vertebrae 34-36.

Coloration pallid, brownish dorsally and silver or white laterally and ventrally; dorsolateral scales weakly outlined; mid-dorsal stripe conspicuous although narrow, divided at dorsal fin-base; lateral line marked by fine, dark punctulations; fins plain, breeding males without bright colors.

Breeding males having top and sides of head weakly tuberculate; tubercles granular, best-developed below eye, sparse on opercle, obsolescent on front of snout; scales of nape with few scattered tubercles; rays 2-10 of pectoral fins tuberculate, tubercles small, in multiple files (6 or more rows on most rays).

Length 2¾ inches or less.

The southwestern limit of the range of the big-mouthed shiner is in extreme northeastern Kansas, where this species inhabits several small, sandy creeks tributary to the Missouri River. *N. dorsalis* is found also in the mainstream of the Missouri River, but that is not its usual habitat. Tributaries of the Kansas River are not occupied by *N. dorsalis,* although a single specimen was obtained from the lower mainstream of the Kansas River in 1955, a year of exceptionally low waterlevels.

Populations of *N. dorsalis* in Kansas are referable to the eastern subspecies, *N. d. dorsalis,* because all specimens have the predorsal area covered by exposed scales. In *N. d. piptolepis* the nape is naked, or its scales are minute and embedded. That subspecies is prevalent in the larger Plains rivers north of the Kansas River. Kansas populations of *N. dorsalis* may be relics of stocks that dispersed westward in Wisconsinan time. The small, short streams occupied by *N. dorsalis* drain highlands on the west side of the broad Missouri mainstream, and represent an "island" environment not readily accessible to kinds of fishes that predominate in prairie streams farther west. This interpretation is supported by occurrences of other eastern fishes in the same streams where the big-mouthed shiner occurs. Sand shiners and fat-headed minnows in these streams, although intergrades, more closely resemble eastern than western populations of those species (*Notropis stramineus* and *Pimephales promelas*).

Apart from its biological interest, the association of *N. s. stra-*

mineus with *N. d. dorsalis* has convenience for the beginning student of fishes in that it facilitates recognition of these species where they coexist. The big-mouthed and sand shiners look alike, occupy similar habitats, and vary geographically in parallel fashion. Western populations of both species have smaller, more deeply embedded scales than do eastern populations; *N. dorsalis* is more extreme in reduction of scale-size than is *N. stramineus.* The number of predorsal and circumferential scales in the western subspecies of the sand shiner (*N. s. missuriensis*) is about the same as in the eastern subspecies of *N. dorsalis.* Populations of *N. dorsalis* in Kansas are nearly surrounded by *N. s. missuriensis* or intergrades of the eastern and western sand shiners. But in the tributaries of the Missouri River where both species occur, *stramineus* has large scales: 13-16 rows before dorsal fin, 24-26 rows around the body. The corresponding counts in *dorsalis* from these streams are 15-20 rows, 26-33 rows. Consequently scale-size supplements the number of anal fin-rays, shape of head and of dorsal fin, and the size and position of the mouth as a distinguishing character in sympatric populations of these species in Kansas.

N. d. dorsalis spawns in June and July.

Sand shiner

Notropis stramineus (Cope)

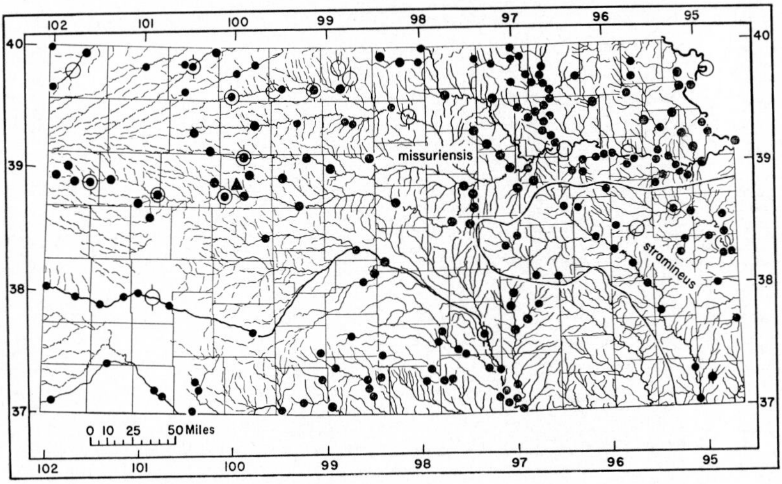

Hybopsis missuriensis Cope (1871:437 [orig. descr.], type locality Missouri River "near St. Joseph").

Cliola straminea, Gilbert (1884:12).

Notropis deliciosus, Jordan and Meek (1885:13); Hay (1887:246, 247, 249, 250, 252); Gilbert (1889:38-39); Fowler (1910:274); Hubbs and Greene (1928:375-379); Hall (1934:230).

Notropis deliciosa, Cragin (1885b:108); Graham (1885b:73); Cross (1954: 310); Greer and Cross (1956:362); Clarke, Breukelman, and Andrews (1958:167).

Notropis lineolatus, Graham (1885b:73).

Notropis lineolata, Cragin (1885b:108).

Notropis ? lateralis, Gilbert (1886:207).

Notropis deliciosus lineolatus, Gilbert (1889:38, 40).

Notropis scylla, Jordan (1891:17).

Notropis deliciosus missuriensis, Breukelman (1940a:371, 1940b:380); Jennings (1942:365); Moore and Buck (1955:22); Metcalf (1959:368); Minckley (1959:423).

Notropis stramineus, Suttkus (1958); Minckley and Cross (1959:212); Minckley and Deacon (1959:348); Deacon (1961:383); Deacon and Metcalf (1961:316); Kilgore and Rising (1965:140); Metcalf (1966: 124).

Body stout, not compressed, back slightly arched; head short, eyes lateral; snout blunt, not projecting beyond mouth; snout length more than 1.5 in postorbital length of head; mouth subterminal, slightly oblique, maxilla extending only to front of orbit; dorsal fin originating approximately over insertion of pelvics, nearer tip of snout than base of caudal fin; dorsal fin 8-rayed, not high, anterior rays not extending beyond tips of posterior rays in depressed fin; anal rays usually 7; pelvic rays 8; pectoral fins rounded, with 13-18 rays, their tips never reaching insertion of pelvics; pharyngeal teeth 0,4—4,0; intestine short, peritoneum silvery; vertebrae 33-36.

Characteristics of the two subspecies in Kansas are as follows. *N. s. stramineus*: lateral-line scales usually 32-35; scale rows around body most often 11—2—11 (total circumferential scales usually 24 or fewer); predorsal scale-rows 13-15; eye large (diameter usually more than 70% of postorbital length of head); gape narrow. *N. s. missuriensis*: lateral-line scales usually 34-37; scale rows around body most often 13—2—13 (total circumferential scales usually more than 26); predorsal scale-rows usually more than 15; eye small (diameter less than 70% of postorbital length of head); body more robust, and head and gape wider, than in *N. s. stramineus*.

Tawny to olivaceous dorsally, silvery laterally and ventrally; mid-dorsal stripe narrow, interrupted at origin and terminus of dorsal fin-base but intensified within base (black dash in base of dorsal fin); anterior lateral-line scales marked by dark flecks near pores (but no dark lateral band); fins colorless, caudal often with small, angular basal spot. *N. s. stramineus* usually darker than *N. s. missuriensis*, and more prominently cross-hatched by dark pigment on margins of dorsolateral scales. No chromatic breeding-colors.

In breeding males, granular tubercles cover upper part of head, from front of snout to occiput and, laterally, from snout to edge of preopercle; tubercles best-developed near nares; operculum sparsely tuberculate; underside of head seldom tuberculate in *missuriensis*, but in *stramineus* mandibles bearing tubercles; anterior scales of nape sparsely tuberculate; pectoral fin-rays 2-9 with multiple files of tubercles (ray 1 often with single file of tubercles, especially in *N. s. stramineus*); other fins lacking tubercles.

Length 2¾ inches or less.

The sand shiner is one of the commonest fishes in Kansas, inhabiting streams throughout the State except those of the Caney, Verdigris, and Spring river drainages. The western subspecies (*N. s. missuriensis*) abounds in shallow, sandy rivers having permanent flow, in both the Arkansas and Kansas river-basins; that subspecies is rare in streams that drain limestone uplands, and rare in highly-intermittent, muddy creeks. The eastern subspecies, *N. s. stramineus*, occupies the Osage River System, and (somewhat diluted by intergradation) the Neosho River and small, direct tributaries of the Missouri River, at least in Doniphan and Atchison counties. Populations of intergrades that resemble *missuriensis* more than *stramineus* occur now in the mainstream of the Missouri River and in some tributaries of the Blue River. *N. s. stramineus* seems to be restricted, in Kansas, to areas having soils that are derived from limestone and shale; gravels and clays instead of sand predominate in these streams, and they are generally clearer than streams occupied by *N. s. missuriensis.*

The sand shiner has an unusually long reproductive period. Tuberculate males of *N. s. missuriensis* have been taken as early as April; from May through August, males in nearly all collections of that subspecies are tuberculate. I have seen fewer tuberculate males of *N. s. stramineus,* most of them in June. A protracted reproductive season may be an important adaptation to life in Plains rivers that fluctuate widely and irregularly in volume of flow. Like *N. s. missuriensis,* several other fishes that attain great abundance in those rivers have nuptial characteristics throughout the warm part of the year.

Arkansas River shiner
Notropis girardi Hubbs and Ortenburger

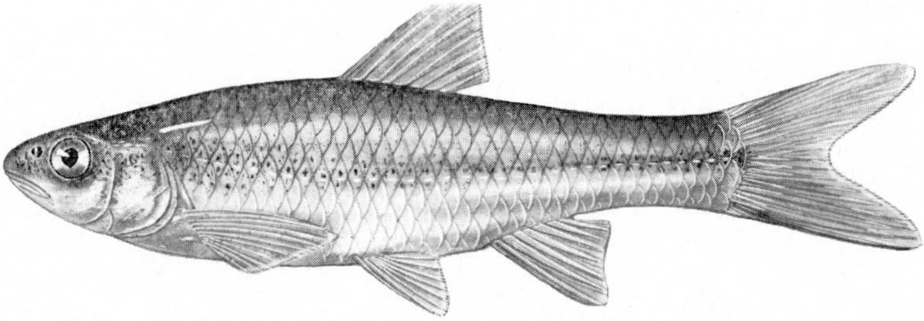

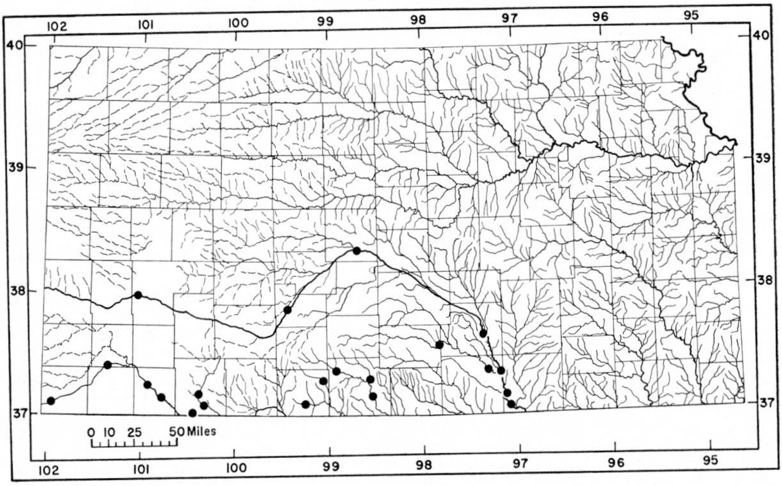

Notropis girardi Hubbs and Ortenburger (1929a:32 [orig. descr.], 1929b: 70); Cross (1953c:259); Cross, Dalquest, and Lewis (1955); Metcalf (1959:368); Kilgore and Rising (1965:140).

Body thick anteriorly, little compressed, caudal peduncle slender; back arched; head small, flattened dorsally, length 4.0 or more in standard length; snout rounded, length contained more than 1.5 times in postorbital length of head; mouth small, scarcely oblique; eye small, diameter 4.5 or more in head length; dorsal fin high, anterior rays exceeding posterior rays in depressed fin; origin of dorsal fin nearer tip of snout than base of caudal fin; dorsal, anal, and pelvic rays 8; pectoral rays usually 14; pectoral fins long and falcate in males, rounded in females; lateral-line scales 32-37, not higher than scales in adjacent rows; predorsal scale-rows 14-17; scale rows around body 13—2—11-14 (total circumferential scales usually 28); pharyngeal teeth 0,4—4,0; intestine short, peritoneum silvery; vertebrae usually 34-36.

Coloration pallid, tan dorsally and silvery laterally; dorsolateral scales scarcely pigmented, not clearly outlined; mid-dorsal stripe obscure anteriorly, distinct dark line in base of dorsal fin; mid-sides with scattered dark dots anteriorly, but lateral line not accentuated by melanophores; minute, chevron-like dark spot often present at base of caudal fin; breeding males without chromatic colors.

Nuptial tubercles of males confined to pectoral fins, in 2 or more files on rays 2-8.

Length of adults 2 inches.

Notropis girardi is endemic to the broad, sandy channels of the major streams of the Arkansas River System. In those streams, the steady, shallow flow forms series of unstable sand-ridges, analogous to dunes in a wind-swept terrestrial environment. Arkansas River shiners commonly lie in the "lee" of these transverse sand-ridges, face into the current, and feed on organisms that are exposed by movement of the sand or are washed downstream. *N. girardi* is uncommon in quiet pools or backwater, and almost never enters tributaries having deep water and bottoms of mud or stone. The species has not been found east of the Arkansas mainstream in Kansas.

N. girardi spawns in late spring or in summer, at whatever time the streams approach flood-stage. The eggs and larvae are found then in swift currents of the open channel, drifting freely near the surface. Development is rapid, in that hatching occurs and the larvae are capable of swimming horizontally within three or four days after spawning (Moore, 1944b). Seemingly, the sex-products are essentially mature by June but are not released until the rivers are filled by runoff from heavy rains. Individuals in spawning condition have been taken in Crooked Creek, Meade County, as early as June 14 and as late as August 29 in different years. Metcalf (1959:368) found females distended by eggs in the Arkansas River in late August, 1956, and subsequent collections indicated failure of reproduction in that exceptionally dry year.

The unusual reproductive habits of *N. girardi* seem adaptive to the variability of flow in Plains streams, which normally flood at some time in the warm months, but which approach intermittency at other times. The timing of reproduction insures that the young undergo their development when the amount of water and of food are greatest.

Mimic shiner

Notropis volucellus (Cope)

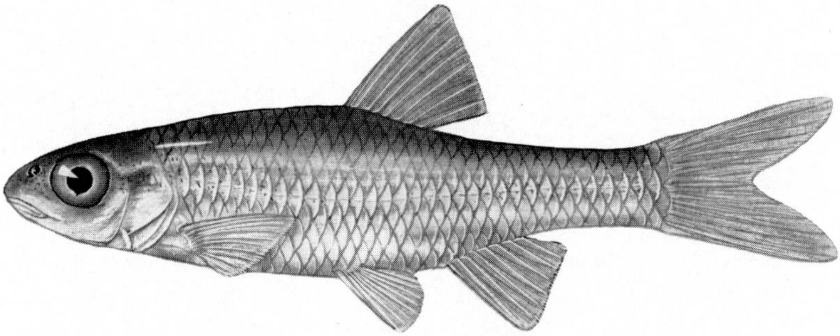

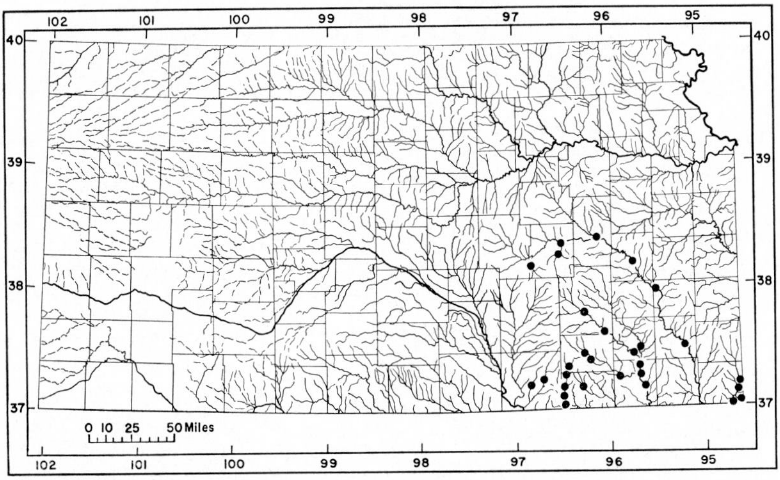

Notropis volucella, Hubbs and Bonham (1951:103); Cross (1954:310; 1955: 474); Schelske (1957:45); Clarke, Breukelman, and Andrews (1958: 168).

Notropis volucellus, Metcalf (1959:372, 393, 394); Deacon (1961:382).

Body scarcely compressed, chunky; head length 3.5-4.0 in standard length; snout rounded, shorter than eye diameter, which is 3.5 or less in head length; mouth oblique but lower jaw included; fins moderately large; dorsal fin triangular, originating almost over insertion of pelvic fins; dorsal, anal, and pelvic rays 8; pectoral rays usually 12 or 13; lateral line nearly straight, scales usually 32-34; anterior lateral line scales notably higher than scales in adjacent rows, but less extremely elevated than in *N. buchanani;* infraorbital canal complete;

scale rows around body 9—2—9-11, around caudal peduncle 5—2—5; pharyngeal teeth 0,4—4,0; intestine short, peritoneum silvery; vertebrae usually 35-37.

Coloration pallid; olivaceous dorsally; dorsolateral scales outlined by melanophores; mid-dorsal stripe weak, intensified before origin of dorsal fin and in dorsal fin base; sides silvery; lateral line scales with dark pigment adjacent to pores, or faint dusky lateral band; basicaudal spot minute or absent; fins unpigmented except for fine lines of melanophores alongside anterior pectoral rays and most principal rays of dorsal and caudal fins. No chromatic breeding colors.

In breeding males, head invested by tubercles of moderate size, densest on front of snout and below eye, but extending over all bones of opercular series and onto mandibles (no tubercles on branchiostegals or gill membranes); body lacking tubercles except for minute ones on some scales of nape; pectoral fin-rays 2 through 7 tuberculate, in 1 (basally) or 2 (distally) files on each ray; other fins lacking tubercles.

Largest Kansas specimens slightly less than 2 inches in total length.

The mimic shiner occurs in Kansas only in the eastern part of the Arkansas River System, and is nowhere abundant. Normally the species occupies the larger upland streams that have rocky bottoms. In that respect it differs from *N. buchanani,* which usually inhabits creek mouths or comparable areas where flow is sluggish in the main channels of rivers. Records of *N. volucellus* in the lower mainstream of the Neosho River were obtained in years when most tributaries were dry.

The mimic shiner spawns in July and August, later than do most Kansas species. The earliest instance of reproductive development that I have recorded is June 25. On that date in 1964, many mimic shiners were taken in Elk River (Elk County at Howard), which was unusually low and warm (83°) for June. Seemingly, spawning had just begun. Only part of the males were fully tuberculate; these males were scattered on an expansive rocky riffle. Females having abdomens distended by eggs were concentrated in a deep eddy and pool at the foot of the riffle. On other occasions, most often in August, I have found mimic shiners that seemed to be spawning on broad riffles at depths of 6 to 12 inches, where flow was moderate. Ripe specimens were captured singly or in pairs, often adjacent to large stones that littered the riffles.

The natural history of this species in an Indiana lake has been discussed by Black (1945). Black was unsuccessful in finding the reproductive sites used by mimic shiners, but he thought that spawning occurred nocturnally, in deep water among dense weed beds.

Mimic shiners in the Arkansas River System differ morphologically from those in the northeastern part of the Mississippi River System, but the taxonomic relationship of these geographic variants has not been established.

Ghost shiner

Notropis buchanani (Meek)

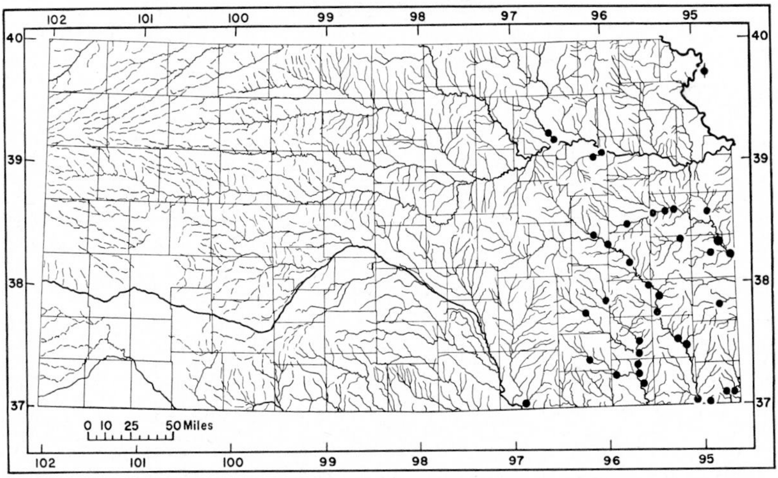

Notropis volucellus buchanani, Hubbs and Greene (1928:377).

Notropis buchanani, Cross (1955:474); Schelske (1957:45); Clarke, Breukelman and Andrews (1958:167); Metcalf (1959:366-367, 1966:123); Minckley (1959:423) Minckley and Deacon (1960:348); Deacon (1961: 382-383); Deacon and Metcalf (1961:317).

Notropis volucellus, Fisher (1962:427).

Body small, delicate, moderately compressed; head length 3.6-3.9 in standard length; snout short, rounded; mouth low, moderately oblique, lower jaw closing within upper jaw; eye large, diameter 3.5-4.0 in head length; infraorbital canal interrupted, absent below eye; fins high and fragile; dorsal fin acutely pointed, height greater than head length; dorsal, anal, and pelvic fins with 8 rays; lateral line nearly straight, its 32-35 scales conspicuously higher than scales in rows above and below lateral line; scale rows around body usually 9—2—9, occasionally 11—2—9; caudal peduncle long, 3.8-4.3 in standard length; pharyngeal teeth 0,4—4,0; intestine short, peritoneum silvery; vertebrae usually 34-36.

Coloration uniquely pallid, translucent, accounting for vernacular name; dark pigment limited to top of head, base of dorsal fin, scales of lateral-line series, and mid-ventral line from anus posteriorly; mid-dorsal stripe obsolescent, except immediately before origin of dorsal fin; dorsolateral scales not dark-outlined; bright, silvery lateral stripe; no chromatic breeding colors.

In breeding males, snout and crest of head densely tuberculate; tubercles extending backward onto scales of anterior part of nape; tubercles absent from lower part of head, behind and below eyes; pectoral fins tuberculate, in multiple files on rays 2-7; other fins lacking tubercles.

Maximum length less than 2 inches.

The ghost shiner occurs in the larger streams of eastern Kansas, attaining its greatest abundance in the Neosho, Verdigris, and Marais des Cygnes rivers. Although rare in the Kansas River Basin, *N. buchanani* has been taken in the Blue River (Pottawatomie County), Mill Creek (Wabaunsee County), and in the Missouri River in Doniphan County. Fisher (1962:427) reported *N. volucellus* from numerous localities in the Missouri River. I suspect that his specimens from the Kansas segment of that river were *buchanani.*

Ghost shiners usually occupy gentle eddies adjacent to strong currents in the main channels of rivers. I have found this fish most often in two habitats: the exact confluence of small, intermittent creeks with large rivers, where the current sweeps past backwater in the creek-mouth; and alongside the lower part of gravel-bars in the mainstream, where the direction of flow is reversed. Sometimes, ghost shiners are the dominant minnow at the lower, silted ends of gravel bars in the Neosho River, but are absent from the upper ends of the same bars. During the drought of the mid-1950's, ghost shiners were abundant in the mainstream of the Neosho River where it flowed shallowly across bedrock. Currents usually are swift at these points of limestone-outcrop, but in drought the flow was slight; ghost shiners rested behind large stones that littered the bedrock, then darted from these retreats for bits of food that were borne downstream by the current.

Trautman (1957:387) stated that *N. buchanani* is found mainly in clear water in Ohio, and that this species has declined as a result of siltation in streams of that State. His statement seems inapplicable to ghost shiners in Kansas, where they inhabit streams that are frequently turbid. *N. buchanani* is uncommon in clear, upland streams of southeastern Kansas, where it is replaced by the mimic shiner (*N. volucellus*).

The failure of early collectors to report *N. buchanani* is perplexing. Its omission may be attributable to its small size, which permits escape through seines having mesh-sizes of ¼-inch or larger.

Judging from dates when tuberculate males have been found, ghost shiners reproduce between early May and mid-August; thus, the breeding season seems longer and mainly earlier than that of the mimic shiner in Kansas.

Black-nosed shiner

Notropis heterolepis Eigenmann and Eigenmann

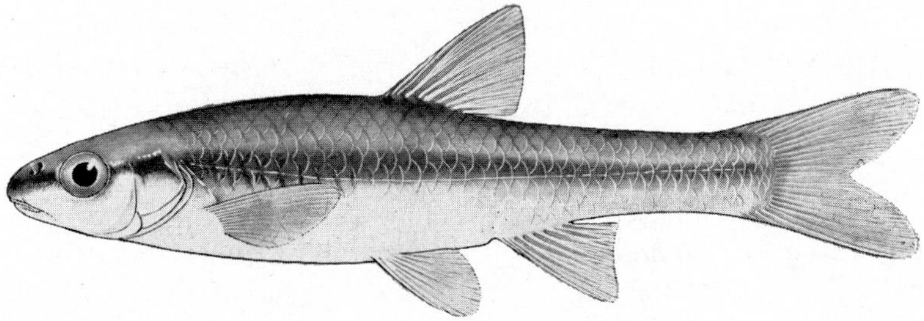

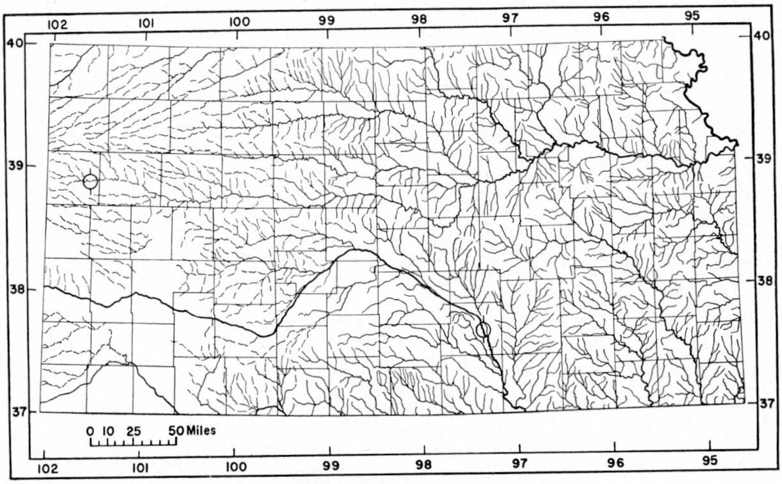

Notropis germanus Hay (1887:252-253 [orig. descr.]).
Notropis cayuga, Jordan (1891:18).
Notropis heterolepis, Hubbs (1951a); Metcalf (1966:123).

Body slender, not compressed, its depth 5.0 or more in standard length, much less than head length; head elongate, 4.0 or less in standard length; snout rounded; mouth small, oblique but subterminal; eye large, diameter 3.3-4.0 in head length, equal to or greater than snout length; dorsal fin high, acutely pointed, originating slightly behind pelvic insertion; dorsal, anal, and pelvic rays 8; pectoral rays usually 13; lateral line almost straight, with 34-36 scales; scale rows around body 11—2—11, around caudal peduncle 5—2—5; predorsal scales large, in about 15 rows; pharyngeal teeth 0,4—4,0; intestine short, peritoneum silvery or dusky; vertebrae 36-38.

Coloration generally dark, brownish or olivaceous dorsally; dorsal scales outlined by dark pigment; prominent black lateral band, extending forward across opercle, around tip of snout (above lips), and backward onto central rays of caudal fin; within dark lateral band, pigment intensified behind scale margins, forming chevronlike markings with apices directed forward; pallid longitudinal strip above lateral band; many scales below lateral line outlined; scales on venter and lower surface of caudal peduncle having dark pigment; rays of all fins outlined by melanophores.

Length 2½ inches or less.

Evidence for the former occurrence of the black-nosed shiner in Kansas consists of two early records that have been discussed by Hubbs (1951a). One of these is a single specimen, collected in 1885 from the Smoky Hill River in Wallace County by Hay (1887: 252-253), and described by him under the name *Notropis germanus* new species. Hubbs (*loc. cit.*) reidentified that specimen (USNM 3749) as a hybrid, *Hybognathus hankinsoni* × *Notropis heterolepis*. The second record is based on specimens reported from the Arkansas River at Wichita by Jordan (1891:18) as *Notropis cayuga*; Hubbs (*loc. cit.*) reidentified those specimens as *N. heterolepis*.

Jordan listed *N. cayuga* as "Abundant" in his report upon a collection, comprising 27 species, that was provided him by Mr. Sherman Davis. To my knowledge, this is the only collection by Davis that has received published mention. The number of species is large for any single locality in the vicinity of Wichita. All the species involved except *N. heterolepis* are ones well-known from Kansas, but eight of them are characteristic of upland creeks rather than large rivers. I suspect that Davis's collection was a composite of samples from streams in the Flint Hills northeast of Wichita as well as the Arkansas mainstream. This record of *heterolepis* is the only one from the Arkansas River System.

The black-nosed shiner still occurs in some tributaries of the Osage River and the Missouri River in central Missouri. Because the westernmost recent records are within 75 miles of the Kansas State-line, past occurrences of black-nosed shiners in eastern Kansas seem plausible. Decimation of this species over much of its original range has been well documented by Hubbs (*loc. cit.*). The black-nosed shiner seems to require cool, clear, weedy waters—a habitat that has been especially vulnerable to destruction in the course of agricultural development of the prairies.

Ozark minnow

Dionda nubila (Forbes)

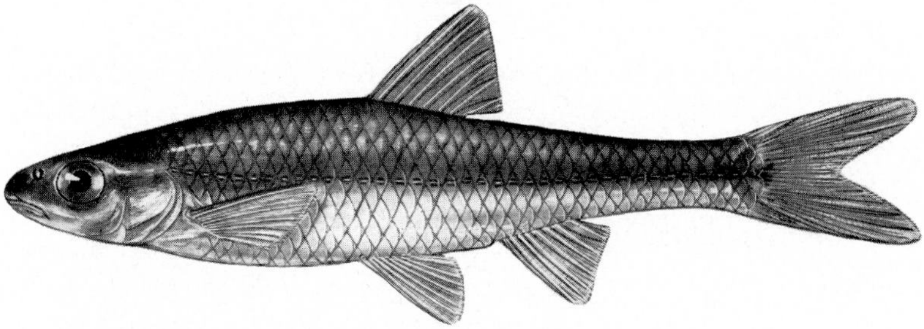

Dionda Meeki, Graham (1885b:73).
Dionda nubila, Cross (1955:473-474); Metcalf (1959:393).

Body terete, streamlined, having aspect of many species of *Notropis;* mouth nearly terminal, slightly oblique; barbels absent; intestine long, its loops forming definite coils; peritoneum black; lateral line complete, nearly straight, with 36-38 scales; scale rows around body usually 11—2—11; dorsal, anal, and pelvic fin-rays 8; pectoral rays 13-15, usually 14; pharyngeal teeth 0,4—4,0; vertebrae 36-39.

Dark olivaceous dorsally; thin mid-dorsal stripe from nape through (not surrounding) dorsal fin-base to base of caudal fin; dorsolateral scales large and dark-outlined; sides with dark dots along lateral line, often having prominent dark lateral band from base of caudal fin forward across opercle, iris, and snout; lower sides and belly silvery white; fins transparent, without prominent markings except for tiny wedge-shaped basicaudal spot. In breeding males, ventrolateral scales yellowish- or pinkish-orange, underside of head orange; all fins with yellow or orange pigment basally, fading distally; orange pigment lacking on crest of head, cleithrum above base of pectoral fins, and along lateral-line scales. Females yellowish when spawning.

Tubercles in breeding males disposed as follows: scattered over top of head, extending downward on sides of head behind and below eye; tubercles diminishing in size laterally and anteriorly, becoming obsolescent on front of snout; scales (except on venter) with marginal row of 6-10 minute tubercles; rays 1-7 of pectoral fin with single file of large tubercles, double-file on branched part of rays; rays of all other fins with minute tubercles. Spawning females slightly tuberculate.

Length 2½ to 3 inches.

In Kansas, *Dionda* now seems to be confined to Shoal Creek, Cherokee County, although Graham (1885b:73) reported this species from "Neosho river" without stating a precise locality of capture. Shoal Creek is the only truly Ozarkian stream in Kansas, and *Dionda* is rarely found west of the Ozark Upland in the

Arkansas River System. In high-gradient, clear, strongly-flowing Ozark streams, *D. nubila* often is the predominant minnow. It is abundant in the upper part of Shoal Creek in southwestern Missouri, but that is not the case in the lower course of the same stream in Kansas. Only at times of high water have I found *Dionda* commonly in lower Shoal Creek. I doubt that the species now occurs west of Spring River.

Ozark minnows in spawning-condition have been taken in Kansas in May, and in Missouri in May and June.

Brassy minnow

Hybognathus hankinsoni Hubbs

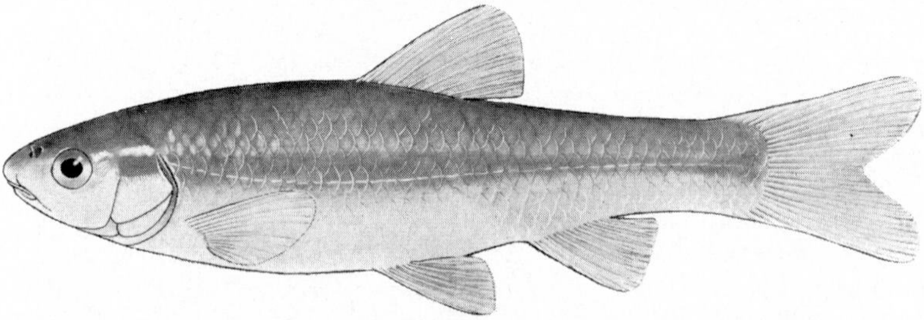

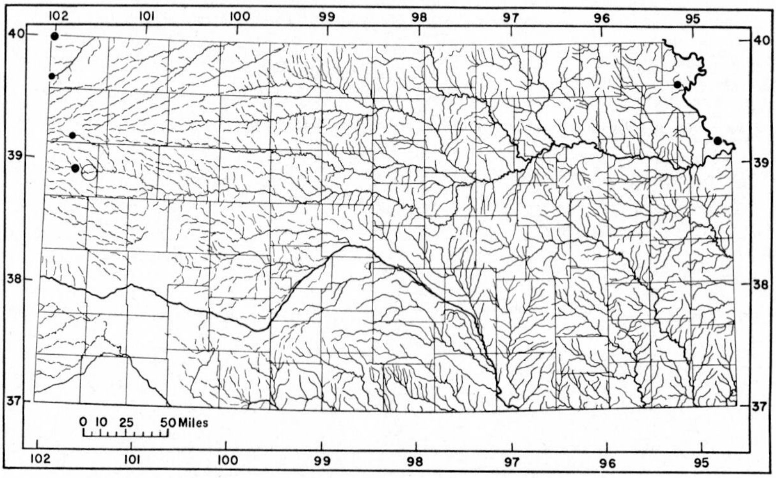

Hybognathus nuchalis, Hay (1887:253, misidentification).

Hybognathus hankinsoni, Breukelman (1940a:371); Hubbs (1951a); Bailey (1954:290); Metcalf (1966:133).

Body stout, little compressed; head short, length 3.8-4.2 in standard length; eye moderate, diameter 1.2-1.5 in snout length, more than 1/5 head length; snout blunt; mouth crescent-shaped, without barbels, somewhat oblique (more nearly terminal than in *H. placitus* and *H. nuchalis*); posterior process of basioccipital (Fig. 14) moderately broad, muscle-attachments separated by bony space; dorsal fin rounded, originating over pelvic insertion; dorsal, anal, and pelvic rays 8; pectoral rays 13 or 14; scales in lateral line 36-39; scale rows around body usually 12—2—15-17, around caudal peduncle 7—2—7; pharyngeal teeth 0,4—4,0, not hooked; intestine long, peritoneum black; vertebrae usually 37-39.

Olivaceous dorsally, with well-developed mid-dorsal stripe, continuous through base of dorsal fin; dorsolateral scales not dark-outlined; sides usually brassy, sometimes dull silvery; dusky lateral band usually evident immediately above lateral line (no such band in *H. placitus* or *H. nuchalis*); pectoral and dorsal fin-rays prominently outlined by melanophores. No chromatic breeding colors.

In breeding males, rays 2-8 of pectoral fins bearing multiple files (5 or more rows distally) of tubercles.

Length usually 3 inches or less.

The brassy minnow is known only from the headwaters of the Smoky Hill and Republican rivers, from the Missouri River, and from a tributary of the Missouri River in Atchison County. The species is rare at these localities. Its habitat in Kansas is small, clear streams having sluggish current and sandy bottom overlain by organic sediment. Perhaps the brassy minnow was formerly more widespread than at present, but was overlooked by early writers who reported it as *H. nuchalis*. Hubbs (1951a:449) found that specimens (USNM 38237) from Wallace County that were reported by Hay (1887:253) as *H. nuchalis* are instead *H. hankinsoni*, and Hay's name *Notropis germanus* was based on a hybrid having *H. hankinsoni* as one parent.

Seemingly, reproduction occurs in May in Kansas, earlier than in *H. placitus*.

Plains minnow

Hybognathus placitus Girard

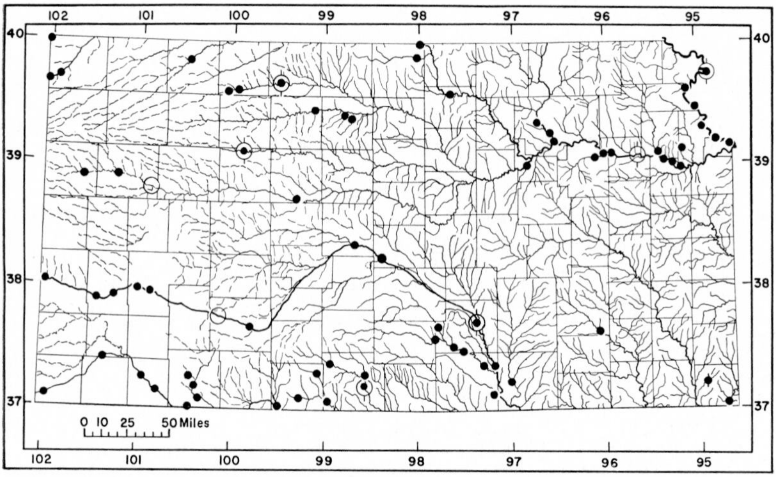

Hybognathus placitus Girard (1856:182 [orig. descr.]; type locality, "sluices of the Arkansas near Fort Makee" [approximately 8 mi. W of Dodge City, Ford Co., Kansas, according to Al-Rawi and Cross, 1964:162]); Girard (1858:236); Al-Rawi and Cross (1964); Metcalf (1966:134).

Hybognathus placitus placitus, Breukelman (1940a:371, 1940b:381); Jennings (1942:365).

Hybognathus placita, Graham (1885a:4, 1885b:72); Metcalf (1959:386, 395); Fisher (1962:427).

Hybognathus nuchalis, Gilbert (1885b:98, 1886:210, 1889:40); Cragin (1885b:108); Hay (1887:251); Jordan (1891:17); Fowler (1925:391-392); Hall (1934:230); Minckley (1959:423-426); Deacon and Metcalf (1961:317).

Hybognathus nuchalis placita, Jordan and Meek (1885:13).

Body thick, nearly terete; head short, snout blunt; mouth ventral, crescent-shaped (Fig. 12B), without barbels; eye small, less than 1/5 head length except in young; posterior process of basioccipital bone rodlike, thickened medially (convex on ventral surface), narrow to its tip, with contiguous muscle attachments (Fig. 14A); dorsal fin originating over pelvic insertion; dorsal fin 8-rayed, acutely pointed at tip; anal rays 8; pelvic rays 8; pectoral rays usually 16 or 17; lateral line scales 36-39; scales around body 11-15—2—13-19 (usually 15 or more rows ventral to lateral line); pharyngeal teeth 0,4—4,0, not hooked; intestine long, coiled; peritoneum black; vertebrae usually 37-39.

Brownish dorsally, with well-developed mid-dorsal stripe, continuous through base of dorsal fin; dorsolateral scales not outlined by melanophores; sides silvery, sometimes with dusky flecks anteriorly but lacking dark lateral band; lateral line canals not outlined by melanophores; ventral surface yellowish or white; fins colorless, pectoral rays not outlined by melanophores.

In breeding males, minute tubercles cover top and sides of head; many lateral scales with peripheral row of fine tubercles; pectoral fins with single or double file of tubercles on first ray, double or triple file on each subsequent ray; tubercles near distal ends of branched rays arranged in clusters, suggesting possible subdivision of single antecedent tubercles; all other fins sometimes having tubercles on rays, least developed on caudal fin.

Length 5 inches or less.

The plains minnow abounds in all large streams of Kansas that have broad beds of sand and shallow, braided flow. Within such streams, plains minnows are most numerous where sediments accumulate in shallow backwaters, gentle eddies, and along the deeper edges of sand "waves" that are formed on the shifting substrate by the tumbling action of the current in the mainstream. Plains minnows are seldom found in small, intermittent creeks, or in rivers where bottoms are mainly rocky or muddy.

The long, coiled intestine of *H. placitus* indicates its herbivorous habit. The crescent-shaped mouth and thin-edged lower lip may be adaptations for scooping up the film of organisms (mainly diatoms?) that accumulate on the sandy substrate in calm water. In this respect the plains minnow seems to be an ecological counterpart of the river carpsucker, which obtains similar food in deeper parts of the same rivers occupied by *H. placitus*, and of the stoneroller minnow, which scrapes its food from rocky riffles of small, shallow streams.

The reproductive habits of the plains minnow have not been described. Probably eggs are scattered over the substrate, communally, by fish that maintain no individual nest-sites or territories. I have found such aggregations of "ripe" plains minnows in shallow backwaters made so muddy by the activity of the concentrated fish that observations of their behavior were impossible. The breeding season is long, extending from April into August.

Because of its great abundance and large size, the plains minnow is one of the most commonly used bait minnows in Kansas. Large plains minnows are most often called "chubs" by anglers who use them as bait, but that name is properly reserved for other species that have barbels. A major disadvantage of *H. placitus* as bait is its lack of hardiness outside its stream environment.

Silvery minnow

Hybognathus nuchalis Agassiz

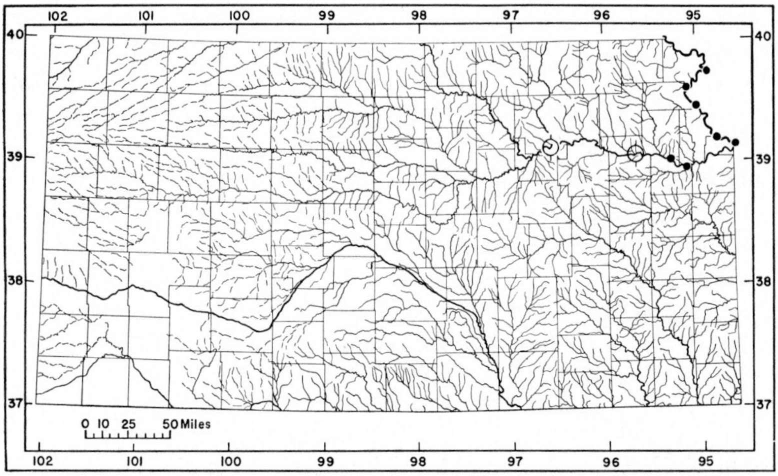

Hybognathus nuchalis, Gilbert (1884:11); Graham (1885b:73); Breukelman (1940b:381); Fisher (1962:427).

Hybognathus nuchalis nuchalis, Jennings (1942:365); Metcalf (1966:135).

Similar to *H. placitus* (p. 146) except as follows: posterior process of basioccipital bone flared posteriorly, its ventral surface thin and concave, muscle-attachments distinctly separated by a bony space (Fig. 14B); scale rows ventral to lateral line usually fewer than 15; eye diameter usually more than 1/5 head length; anterior profile nearly symmetrical, streamlined (in *H. placitus*, ventral contour usually more nearly flat than dorsal contour, back often abruptly arched at occiput).

Length 6 inches or less.

Most early reports of *H. nuchalis* probably pertain instead to *H. placitus* and are listed in the account of that species. Five reports are retained under *nuchalis* because: Gilbert's (1884:11) description indicates that his specimens from Topeka had large eyes, a characteristic of *nuchalis;* and, the other four authors included both species in their faunal lists. Both Gilbert's (1884:11) record and Jennings' (1942:365) from Riley County are farther west than *nuchalis* is now known to occur in Kansas. Graham (1885b:73) and Breukelman (1940b:381) did not specify precisely where their specimens were caught.

At present, the silvery minnow occurs commonly only in the Missouri River and in creeks and backwaters on its floodplain. The preferred habitat seems to be relatively deep water where flow is sluggish and bottoms are silted. The species rarely ascends small tributaries of the Missouri River. In the Kansas River Basin, I have found *nuchalis* only in the mainstream from Lawrence eastward. Many silvery minnows were taken in the channel of the Kansas River in 1951 and 1952, after protracted floods, but few have been obtained in subsequent years, when flow in the Kansas River was normal or below-normal. All my collections of *nuchalis* from Kansas have included *H. placitus* also, with the latter species predominating in abundance. Tabulations by Fisher (1962:427) indicate that *placitus* was approximately three times as abundant as *nuchalis* in his collections from the Missouri River at St. Joseph, Missouri.

Fat-headed minnow
Pimephales promelas (Rafinesque)

Pimephales maculosus Girard (1856:16 [orig. descr.], 1858:234).

Coliscus parietalis Cope (1871:437 [orig. descr.]).

Pimephales confertus, Gilbert (1884:11).

Pimephales promelas, Cope (1965b:85); Gilbert (1885b:98, 1886:210; 1889:40); Cragin (1885b:108); Graham (1885a:4, 1885b:73); Evermann and Fordice (1886:185); Jordan and Meek (1885:11); Fowler (1925:395); Breukelman (1940a:371, 1946:56); Minckley (1956:354); Schelske (1957:46); Clarke, Breukelman, and Andrews (1958:168); Minckley and Cross (1959:212); Metcalf (1959:374, 1966:136); Minckley (1959:426, 432); Deacon (1961:384); Deacon and Metcalf (1961:317, 319); Burrage (1962); Fisher (1962:427); Kilgore and Rising (1965:141).

Pimephales promelas confertus, Graham (1885a:4, 1885b:73); Hay (1887:247, 248, 249, 251, 253); Jordan (1891:17); Cross (1954:310-311).

Pimephales promelas: confertus × *promelas,* Breukelman (1940b:381); Jennings (1942:365).

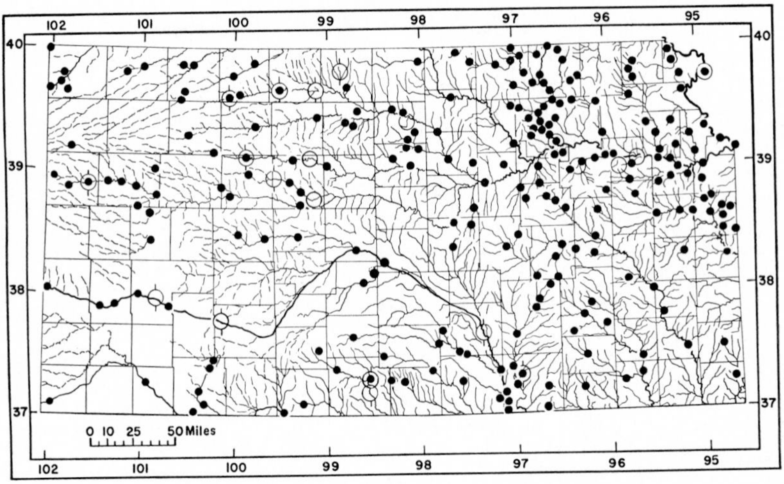

Body robust; head short, rounded, length 3.4-4.0 in standard length; snout blunt, seldom protruding beyond mouth; mouth small, slightly oblique; eye small, diameter 4.3-5.0 in head length; dorsal fin rounded, originating approximately over insertion of pelvic fins; principal dorsal rays 8; anal rays 7; pelvic rays 8; pectoral rays 15-18; lateral line often incomplete, with 44-48 scales; predorsal scales minute; scale rows around body 18-20—2—19-23, around caudal peduncle 7-9—2—7-9, total usually 18 or more; pharyngeal teeth 0,4—4,0; intestine long, with several loops crossing ventral midline, peritoneum black; vertebrae usually 36-38.

Coloration dark, brown to olivaceous dorsally, sides sometimes pallid but not glistening silvery; dorsolateral scales not dark-outlined; dark lateral band evident in specimens from clear water, but more often obscure or absent; dark spots on anterior bases of dorsal and caudal fins diffuse or absent; upper sides often having diagonal, chevronlike markings (blood vessels visible through epidermis); mid-dorsal stripe narrow, uniform in intensity before and behind dorsal fin. Breeding males nearly black, with two broad, pallid, transverse bands—one extending vertically from axil of pectoral fin, and one extending from axil of pelvic fin to dorsal origin; all fins dark, especially medially; basal spots in dorsal and caudal fins intensely dark; pectoral fin darkest along leading edge.

Crest of head in nuptial males turgid, nape greatly thickened, extreme for genus; membranes enveloping anterior rays of dorsal fin thickened, sometimes turgid, but leading edge of rudimentary and first principal rays thickened less than in other species of *Pimephales* (except at pallid, knobby tip of rudimentary ray).

Tubercles aligned in three horizontal rows across snout; number in lowermost row commonly 7 or 8 but highly variable (4-15); number in median row most often 7, in uppermost row usually 4 (counting tubercles between nostril and eye in this row); chin tubercles nearly always present in specimens from Kansas River Basin, usually absent in specimens from Arkansas River Basin;

pectoral fin with single file of tubercles on rays 2 through 5 (sometimes also rays 6 and 7), better developed than in other species of *Pimephales*.

Length 3¼ inches or less.

No other fish seems so widespread nor so nearly ubiquitous in Kansas as the fat-headed minnow. Its abundance is greatest in pools of small, intermittent creeks having bottoms of mud or firm clay. Usually, a few specimens can be obtained in the sandy main-streams of major rivers, and in clear, permanently flowing upland streams of the Flint Hills; but, the species is scarce in these environments. Minckley (1959:432) reported that *P. promelas* comprised about 29 per cent of all fishes in muddy streams of the Blue River System, whereas it comprised only 4 per cent of fish in gravelly streams, and 1 per cent in sandy streams within the same river system.

The fathead is by nature a pioneer, if any fish can be so designated. It is one of the first species to invade intermittent drainage channels after rains, and it commonly progresses upstream into farm ponds via their spillways. It is one of the last species to disappear from small, muddy, isolated pools that remain in stream channels during droughts. This species has other attributes of hardiness that enable it to flourish where few other fishes survive. It seems unusually tolerant of pollution, in streams having little oxygen as a consequence of sewage influx or barnlot drainage, and in other streams that are saline owing to effluents discharged by the petroleum industry.

The reproductive habits of *P. promelas* reflect adaptations to the variable conditions found in many prairie streams. The spawning season is long; breeding males have been taken in the same stream system in the same year from April through August in Kansas. Elsewhere, Markus (1934) has shown that individuals spawn repeatedly in the same year, and that some young that hatch in May spawn before autumn.

The nesting habits are like those of other species of *Pimephales*, in which eggs are attached to an object (usually to its undersurface) above the stream bottom, and are attended throughout their development by the male. Eggs of *P. promelas* have been found on surfaces varying from horizontal to vertical. In western streams, some of the nesting sites used are roots that project through under-cut stream banks, and stems of sunflowers or other plant debris. Material of this kind commonly enters streams with runoff, or when stream banks collapse due to undercutting. Dineen (1953) reported that fatheads deposited eggs on vertical stakes that he placed in a pond as depth markers, and male fatheads that I have put in aquaria have accepted vertical overflow pipes as nesting sites. Presumably, surfaces that are nearly horizontal are used most often, but the diversity of objects (and angles) that this species can utilize for its nests may account in part for its ubiquity and abundance. The long reproductive season and the rapid attainment of maturity are additional adaptations.

The food of fat-headed minnows is diverse, consisting of many kinds of small animals and plants, consumed opportunistically.

Starrett (1950:117-118) commented that in Iowa *P. promelas* was found most abundantly in a stream "peculiar in having emergent vegetation in pools, and a scarcity of other minnows." He stated and credited to Hubbs and Cooper (1936) a belief that *P. promelas* has limited competitive tolerance of other species. This observation is applicable in Kansas, where the fathead is least common in streams that support numerous other kinds of fish. Such streams normally have a constant flow of clear water. Perhaps the remarkable adaptability of the fathead, so advantageous in erratically fluctuating environments, is a handicap in stable habitats. There, it is replaced by a community of specialists, each one of which seems better equipped than *promelas* to utilize one persistent niche within the environment. Because variable conditions in many Kansas streams place a premium on adaptability, continued abundance of this species seems assured.

The fathead is widely cultivated in ponds as a bait minnow. Shingles or short pine boards, floated and spaced by wires or jammed into the mud, suffice as substrates for egg deposition, as do broken sections of ceramic tile that can be placed on the bottom in shallow water. Fertilization of the pond to increase the supply of food generally assures production of several hundred pounds of minnows per acre per year. The fathead will use pelleted feeds that are manufactured for trout, catfish, and farm livestock. *P. promelas* can be raised successfully in combination with channel catfish in ponds; the latter fish does not prey heavily enough on minnows to reduce their abundance severely. Excellent short-term angling for bass can be obtained by stocking fatheads one year, allowing a large population of them to develop, and introducing stocks of bass in the second year. The bass grow rapidly until they deplete the minnow population, as they surely will in clear ponds; then, ponds stocked in this way require renovation by removal of all fish that remain, and repetition of the cycle.

Bull-headed minnow

Pimephales vigilax (Baird and Girard)

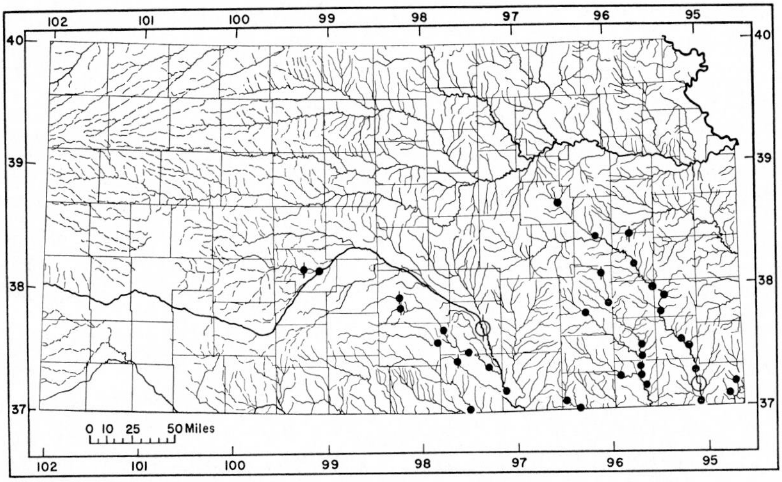

Cliola vigilax, Graham (1885b:73); Gilbert (1886:209); Jordan (1891:18).
Ceratichthys taurocephalus, Breukelman (1940b:381).
Ceratichthys perspicuus, Hubbs and Black (1947:26-31).
Pimephales vigilax perspicuus, Cross (1953b); Moore and Buck (1955:23); Schelske (1957:45-46); Metcalf (1959:374); Deacon (1961:383-384).
Pimephales vigilax, Clarke, Breukelman, and Andrews (1958:168); Breukelman (1960:34).

Body stout; head rather large, blunt, length 3.6-4.0 in standard length; eye moderately large, 3.2-4.0 in head length, nearly equal to snout length; snout not protruding; mouth slightly oblique, upper lip expanded medially; dorsal fin rounded, originating almost over (sometimes slightly behind) pelvic insertion; second rudimentary ray of dorsal fin usually prominent and separated from first principal ray; dorsal rays 8; anal rays 7; pelvic rays 8; pectoral rays 15 or 16; lateral line complete, slightly decurved anteriorly, with 38-40 scales; predorsal scales minute, sometimes embedded; scale rows around body 15-17—2—13-15, around caudal peduncle 7—2—7; pharyngeal teeth 0,4—4,0; intestine short, peritoneum silvery; vertebrae 37-39.

Coloration pallid, tan dorsally, silvery laterally; no dark lateral band (but pores of lateral-line scales often indistinctly marked by melanophores); base of caudal fin with intense, triangular dark spot; anterior base of dorsal fin having prominent dark spot, more conspicuous than in any other species of the genus; dorsolateral scales not clearly outlined by melanophores (body not cross-hatched); mid-dorsal stripe obscure or absent.

Breeding males dark, head nearly black; dark spot on dorsal fin intensely black; crotches of dorsal and caudal rays blackened; lower fins not especially darkened; anterior ray of pectoral fin dark, remainder of fin pale, its pattern opposite that in *P. tenellus* (but see also Parker, 1964:232-233).

Nuptial tubercles in two transverse rows on snout, numbering 5 in lower row, 4 in upper row; tubercles absent elsewhere; top of head and nape thickened, forming rugose pad; membranes surrounding rudimentary dorsal ray thickened, as in *P. tenellus*.

One subspecies, *P. v. perspicuus* (Girard) in Kansas.

Length 3½ inches or less.

Except for a single record from the Osage System that Hubbs and Black (1947:31) attributed to an introduction, the bullheaded minnow is known only from the Arkansas River System in Kansas. The species occurs mainly in large rivers. Its centers of abundance complement those of the other three species of *Pimephales*: *promelas* mostly in muddy, intermittent creeks, *notatus* and *tenellus* mostly in clear, permanent or semipermanent secondary streams, and *vigilax* mostly in the mainstreams of the Neosho and Arkansas rivers or the lower parts of their largest tributaries.

P. vigilax is most common in pools or backwaters that have sandy or silted bottoms, and along the lower ends of expansive gravelbars where eddies deposit silt. An avoidance of strong currents was emphasized by Hubbs and Black (1947:31), who described the habitat of this species as "sluggish muddy backwaters and bayous of large and medium-sized streams."

The reproductive habits are like those described for *P. notatus* (see pp. 158-159). Spawning takes place in June and July, beneath flat stones or debris in shallow pools or slowly-flowing water.

Parker (1964) discussed several aspects of the natural history of *P. vigilax*. Its food in a pond consisted mainly of larval insects (bloodworms, moth flies) and small crustaceans; but, the diversity of items eaten caused Parker to consider the species omnivorous. In aquaria, the fish often formed stratified schools on the bottom by day, but dispersed at night and at all times during the breeding season. Reproduction occurred at temperatures of 78° F. or higher in the aquaria and the pond.

Slim minnow
Pimephales tenellus (Girard)

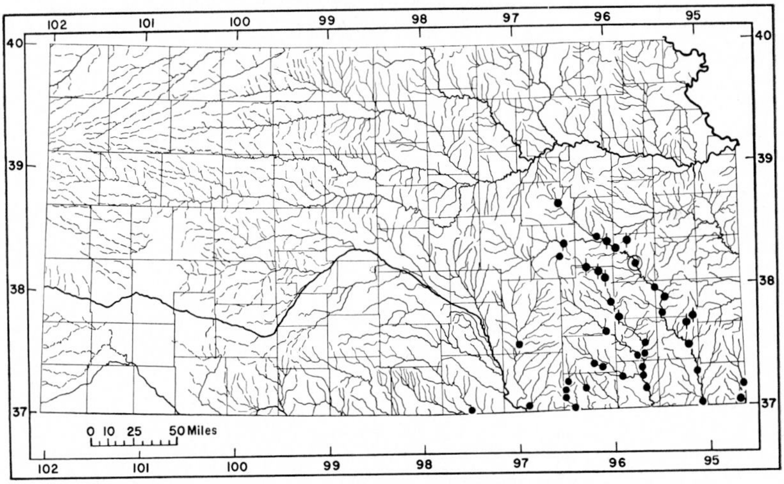

Ceratichthys tenellus tenellus, Hubbs and Black (1947:36, Map 2).
Pimephales tenellus tenellus, Cross (1954:310); Moore and Buck (1955:23); Schelske (1957:46); Clarke, Breukelman, and Andrews (1958:168).
Pimephales tenellus, Metcalf (1959:373-374, 393); Deacon (1961:383).

Body slender, terete or squared; head flattened dorsally, blunt anteriorly, length 3.6-4.0 in standard length; eye of moderate size, 3.5-4.5 in head length, slightly shorter than or equal to snout length; snout blunt, not protruding; mouth slightly oblique, upper lip widest medially (expanded at center); lower jaw closing inside upper jaw; dorsal fin rounded, originating over or slightly behind pelvic insertion, having second rudimentary ray prominent and slightly separated from first principal ray; principal dorsal rays 8; anal rays 7; pelvic rays 8; pectoral rays usually 14 or 15; lateral line complete, nearly straight, with 37-41 scales; predorsal scales small, sometimes embedded; scale rows around body 13-15—2—12-14, around caudal peduncle 7—2—5-7; pharyngeal teeth 0,4—4,0, hooked; intestine short, peritoneum silvery; vertebrae 36-38.

Dark olivaceous dorsally, creamy ventrally; well-defined, narrow, dark lateral band usually present, terminating in small spot at base of caudal fin (spot usually attenuated vertically); dorsolateral scales outlined by melanophores (body cross-hatched); mid-dorsal stripe indistinct or absent; dorsal fin with dark spot anteriorly, immediately above base; fin-rays, especially those of caudal, often tinged with orange. Breeding males dark, head and lateral band intensely black; central areas of all fins black (light basally and peripherally); leading edges of fins white, contrasting sharply with black pigment posteriorly.

Tubercles in breeding males aligned in three rows on snout, numbering 5 in lowermost row, 4 in second row, and two (between nostrils) to four in upper row (alternatively, tubercles on head might be counted as 9 in one curving row across snout, extending dorsolaterally between nostril and eye on each side, plus 4 forming a rectangle between nostrils); tubercles absent elsewhere except on pectoral fin-rays 2-5; each ray bearing single file of weak tubercles concealed by swollen membranes. Top of head somewhat turgid and skin on nape thickened, obscuring predorsal scales; membranes enveloping anterior dorsal rays (especially second rudiment) thickened, but interradial membranes not swollen and not forming cushion receiving and concealing second rudiment.

One subspecies, *P. t. tenellus,* in Kansas.

Maximum length 2½ inches.

The slim minnow is confined to the eastern part of the Arkansas River System in Kansas. Hubbs and Black (1947:36) published one record from the Osage River System, but thought that it "doubtless represents an introduction from the Neosho system into an artificial pond." I have never obtained *P. tenellus* from the Osage Drainage. Collections from the upper parts of Caney, Elk, Fall, and Verdigris rivers regularly contain this species, but nowhere in Kansas have I found it abundantly. The slim minnow has a decided preference for clear, flowing water over rocky bottoms.

Deacon (1961:383) reported substantial numbers of *P. tenellus* in the lower mainstream of Neosho River, along clean gravel-bars, in 1957 and 1958. Prior to the lengthy drought of the early 1950's, this species was rare in the Neosho mainstream. The bull-headed minnow, *P. vigilax perspicuus,* is the dominant representative of the genus *Pimephales* in that river when rainfall and stream-flow are normal in amount.

Nuptial males of *P. tenellus* have been taken in Kansas as early as May in some years, and as late as July in others. I think that the breeding season is brief, but varies in its timing depending on seasonal temperatures. Certainly spawning occurs only in relatively warm water (high 70's and low 80's, ° F.). Moore and Buck (1955:23) indicated that the nest-sites are "among rocks in very fast water." Most of the reproductively-active males that I have found in Kansas occupied swift riffles more than 18 inches deep, and were obtained in June.

Blunt-nosed minnow

Pimephales notatus (Rafinesque)

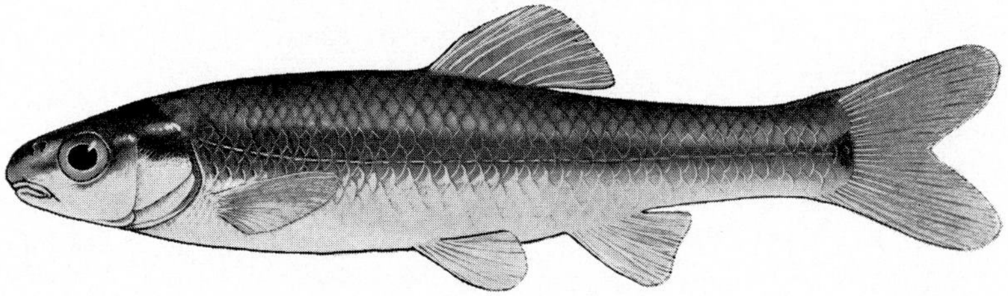

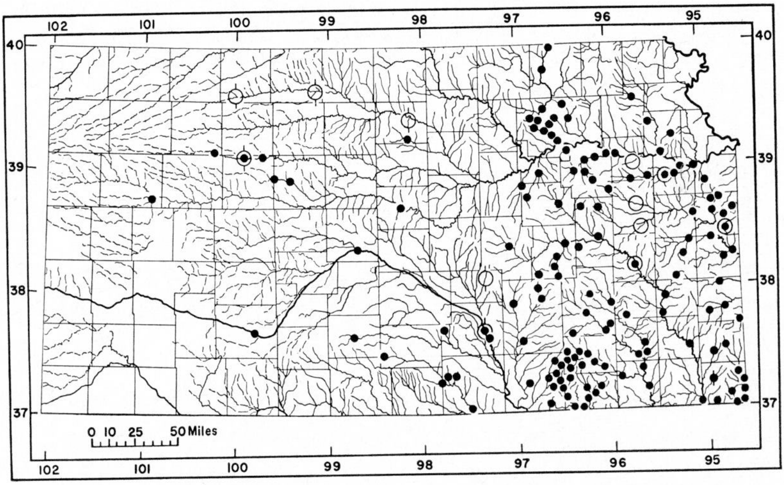

Pimephales notatus, Gilbert (1884:12, 1885b:98); Cragin (1885b:108); Graham (1885b:73); Evermann and Fordice (1886:185); Hay (1887: 246, 248, 249, 251); Jordan (1891:18); Fowler (1925:395); Cross (1953b:93, 1954:310); Moore and Buck (1955:23); Minckley (1956: 354); Schelske (1957:46); Clarke, Breukelman, and Andrews (1958: 168); Minckley and Cross (1959:212); Metcalf (1959:372-373, 393, 1966:135); Minckley (1959:426, 433); Deacon (1961:384); Deacon and Metcalf (1961:317).

Hyborhynchus notatus, Hall (1934:230); Breukelman (1940a:371; 1940b: 381); Jennings (1942:365).

Body slender, almost squared in cross-section; head flattened dorsally, blunt anteriorly, length 3.6-4.4 in standard length; eye small, 4.0-5.5 in head length, shorter than snout; snout blunt, thick, protruding beyond mouth; mouth small, ventral and horizontal, upper lip not expanded at center; dorsal fin rounded, originating slightly behind pelvic insertion, second rudimentary ray usually prominent and separated from first principal ray; principal dorsal rays 8; anal rays 7 (rarely 8); pelvic rays 8; pectoral rays usually 16; lateral line complete, nearly straight, with 39-44 scales; predorsal scales small, sometimes embedded; scale rows around body 13-15—2—13-15, around caudal peduncle 7—2—5-7; pharyngeal teeth 0,4—4,0; intestine variable in length, usually having more than one longitudinal S-shaped loop; peritoneum black; vertebrae usually 37-39.

Olivaceous dorsally, cream color ventrally; narrow, dark lateral band terminating in discrete black spot at base of caudal fin; predorsal scales and most lateral scales clearly outlined by melanophores (body cross-hatched); mid-dorsal stripe indistinct or absent; dorsal fin with diffuse dark blotch near anterior base, or colorless. Breeding males dark, nearly black, head darkest; rays of dorsal fin blackened; most rays of caudal fin dark, but procurrent rays of dorsal fin blackened; most rays of caudal fin dark, but procurrent rays and basal parts of central rays pallid; posterior anal rays and anterior pectoral rays darkened, but lower fins generally paler than in *P. tenellus,* without sharply contrasting pigment on leading edges.

Tubercles in breeding males disposed in three transverse rows on snout, numbering 7 in lowermost row, 7 in second row, and 2 in uppermost row (between nostrils); pectoral rays 3 through 8 tuberculate, each ray with single file of tubercles, best-developed on rays 4-6; top of head turgid, skin of nape thickened and pallid in nuptial males; membranes surrounding anterior (rudimentary) rays of dorsal fin swollen, turgid, forming an expanded cushion into which rudimentary rays fit.

Length 4 inches or less.

The blunt-nosed minnow occurs widely in Kansas, but is uncommon in the west. Because small streams having permanent flow and rocky bottoms are its principal habitat, *P. notatus* is replaced in most intermittent western streams by *P. promelas.* The two species are found together at many localities, but I have never obtained both in abundance from the same stream.

Most writers who mentioned *P. notatus* in Kansas have reported it from pools of clear streams. Metcalf (1959:373) found schools of blunt-nosed minnows in the shallow parts of a large pool over bedrock in spring, and in the deeper, shaded part of the same pool in summer. Deacon (1961:384) stated that *P. notatus* increased in abundance in the Neosho and Marais des Cygnes rivers in 1957-1959, as flow of those streams increased and then stabilized subsequent to prolonged drought.

The several records by Hay (1887) from streams in northwestern Kansas, where this species is now rare, indicate a recent reduction in its abundance in that part of the State. The decline probably resulted from changes in stream-habitat, toward increased siltation and intermittency, that proved unfavorable to this and some other kinds of minnows.

P. notatus spawns from late May through early July, at temperatures higher than 70° F. Like other species of *Pimephales,* the blunt-nosed minnow attaches its eggs to the underside of stones, or to miscellaneous debris such as clamshells, boards, or scrap-metal. I think, however, that the blunt-nosed minnow is less resourceful than the fat-headed minnow in adapting diverse objects to its needs as substrates for spawning. Most nests of *P. notatus* seem to be beneath small slabs of limestone or shale that lie almost horizontally on the stream-bottom.

The male prepares the nest site by cleaning a small cavity beneath the stone. The soft, fleshy pads that develop on the head, nape, and anterior dorsal fin-rays of breeding males are adaptations for cleaning the surfaces to which eggs are attached, and for subsequent attention to eggs during their development. The male guards its nest until all young fish have dispersed from it. According to Westman (1938), new batches of eggs are deposited in a nest by the same or different females at intervals of two to seven days. The duration of nesting never exceeded two months in the populations studied by Westman in New York State. Maturity is attained at ages of one to three years, depending on the time of hatching, the amount of food available, and the length of the growing season (locally).

Stoneroller

Campostoma anomalum (Rafinesque)

Campostoma anomalum, Gilbert (1884:11; 1885b:98; 1886:210; 1889:40); Cragin (1885b:108); Graham (1885a:4, 1885b:72); Evermann and Fordice (1886:185); Hay (1887:247, 250, 251, 253); Jordan (1891:17); Minckley (1956:353-354); Clarke, Breukelman, and Andrews (1958: 167); Minckley and Cross (1959:212); Metcalf (1959:375-376; 1966: 137); Breukelman (1960:34); Deacon (1961:385); Deacon and Metcalf (1961:317).

Campostoma anomalum pullum, Breukelman (1940b:380); Jennings (1942: 365); Cross (1954:311); Moore and Buck (1955:23); Schelske (1957: 46).

Campostoma anomalum plumbeum, Breukelman (1940a:371; 1940b:380); Jennings (1942:365); Minckley (1959:426); Cross and Minckley (1960: 7-11).

Campostoma sp., Crevecoeur (1908).

Body nearly terete, back arched; head length 3.6-4.0 in standard length; eye small; snout blunt and rounded, protruding slightly beyond mouth; mouth ventral (Fig. 12D), broadly rounded, lower lip having distinctive cartilaginous

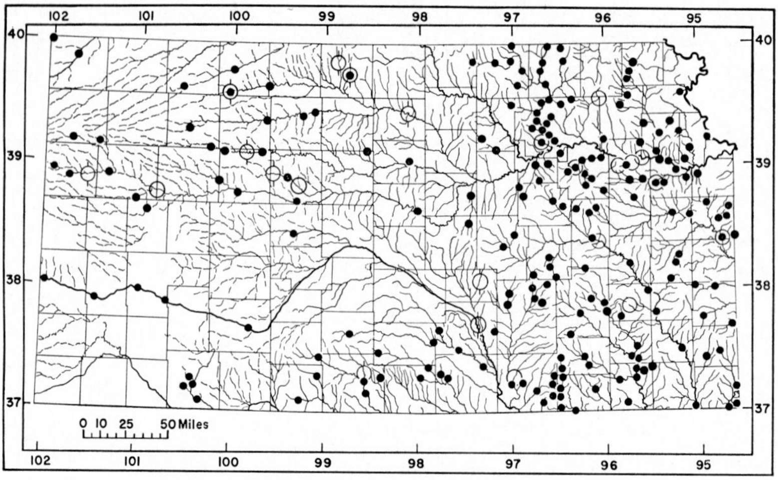

edge not covered by skin (revealed by opening mouth!); barbels absent; fins small, rounded; dorsal fin 8-rayed, originating approximately over insertion of pelvic fins; anal rays 7; pelvic rays usually 8; pectoral rays usually 15; lateral line complete, nearly straight, with 48-64 (usually 51-56) scales; circumferential scales (scale rows around body) 36-50; intestine long, loops transverse, forming unique coil enclosing air bladder; peritoneum black; pharyngeal teeth 0,4—4,0, without hooks; vertebrae 40-42.

Olivaceous or gray dorsally, white ventrally, dark pigment diminishing abruptly along mid-sides; young with dark lateral band and small basicaudal spot; sides of adults usually with scattered dark flecks indicative of replacement scales (hence flecks form no consistent pattern); fins usually transparent except in breeding males. Breeding males dark slate-gray except ventrally; sides with brassy sheen, belly white; dorsal fin orange colored basally and with broad black slash medially; caudal fin with basal suffusion of orange surrounded by diffuse dark pigment, dusky distally; anal fin often orange basally, membranes with black blotches medially, rays and distal edge of fin creamy or yellow; pelvics with black slashes on membranes, yellowish distally; pectorals dusky, suffused with yellow; cleithrum and opercular membrane dark.

Breeding tubercles large, atop head above level of eye, extending forward between nostrils in *C. a. pullum;* sides of head mostly lacking tubercles; lower edge of operculum and gill membranes covered by minute tubercles; most scales above lateral line bearing one tubercle per scale, arising medially from exposed surface of scale; scales on caudal peduncle below lateral line often similarly tuberculate; dorsal fin tuberculate along leading edge, branches of rays 2 through 6 tuberculate; upper rudimentary rays of caudal fin tuberculate; pectoral rays 2-4 with single file of tubercles basally, double file distally; 5th pectoral ray with single file of tubercles, 6th and 7th rays sometimes sparsely tuberculate; pelvic and anal fins lacking tubercles.

Maximum length about seven inches.

The stoneroller inhabits most small streams of Kansas and occurs occasionally in rivers. Its abundance is greatest in permanent, clear creeks in the Flint Hills, and in other streams where exposed rock-strata cause high gradients, clean stream bottoms, and frequent small riffles. Nevertheless, stonerollers seem tolerant of moderate siltation and turbidity. The species occurs westward onto the high plains wherever springs maintain stream flow during winter and early spring, and where some shallow riffles insure the availability of gravel or coarse sand needed for spawning.

The stoneroller is a gregarious minnow that becomes enormously abundant in favorable habitat. Large schools of *Campostoma* cruise slowly about the bottoms of shallow pools and slow riffles, feeding on minute bottom-dwelling organisms. Miller (1962:407) stated that stonerollers subsist mainly on diatomaceous scum scraped from the stream bottom. The thick-lipped, ventral mouth and chisel-edged lower jaw are adaptations for removing the thin film of organic material from a firm (normally rocky) substrate.

An early account of the striking breeding coloration and the interesting reproductive habits of *Campostoma* was published by Crevecoeur (1908), based on observations of stonerollers in a small stream on his farm in Pottawatomie County. *Campostoma* spawns earlier than most fishes in Kansas, from March until May. Males develop tubercles and other reproductive characteristics in winter. Stonerollers held in a pond at the University of Kansas had fully-developed tubercles in mid-February, although that pond had a thin layer of ice when the fish were examined, and water temperatures in previous weeks were mostly 32° to 40° F. Stonerollers having a full complement of small tubercles, developed preparatory to the spring breeding season, have been taken from streams in Kansas as early as November 28.

Construction of nests begins when water in the shallows warms to 60° F. Miller (1962:409) describes sites used for nests as "gravel bottom and moderately clear water with a deeper pool nearby." Nests are most often at the lower ends of pools, where the current quickens, exposing coarse bottom materials at the heads of riffles. Some elasticity in selection of nest sites by stonerollers is indicated, however, by Miller's report (*loc. cit.*) of spawning in "a small backwater pool" where the "gravel bottom was covered by one-half to one and one-half inches of soft silt."

Males prepare nests by digging into the bottom with their snouts, pushing stones aside, and by lifting pebbles in their mouths. Pebbles removed are deposited at the periphery of the nest, and a shallow pit floored by clean, coarse gravel is formed. Miller (1962) points out that most authors have stressed the apparent communal nature of nest-construction by *Campostoma.* To demonstrate that a degree of territoriality exists in stonerollers, Miller emphasizes in the account of his own observations that males independently undertake excavation of isolated pits in the incipient stages of nest-construction. Individual combat occurs and large males dominate smaller ones. The territory is not fixed, however, because large males move from one pit to another at short intervals, and the pits often coalesce by enlargement. Miller states that the territorial system seems to break down where large numbers of males work over a limited spawning area.

I have seen dozens of stonerollers crowd into a single large, linear nest, where each fish vigorously picked up pebbles and threw them sideways and upward by rapid lateral movement of the head. Many pebbles struck adjacent fish. The pebbles then were carried or rolled downstream by the current, so that part of the riffle below the nest was strewn with sand and gravel displaced by *Campostoma.* When alarmed, the stonerollers scurried upstream into the adjacent pool, but soon returned to the nest-area, more or less as an organized school composed exclusively of males. Usually the school drifted downstream past the offshore end of the nest, swung onto the riffle below the nest, and re-entered it in small groups (not singly) until the cavity was essentially filled by fish.

Females remain in separate schools, in pools near the nest-sites, when not actually spawning. Then, they enter the pits individually, depositing eggs in the company of males, several of which usually converge on a female that moves into a nest (Miller, 1962:415).

I suspect that widespread occurrence of stonerollers where few other riffle-fishes are found in Kansas results from the following ecological adaptations of this species: First, it occupies pools through much of the year so permanent flow is not essential for its persistence. Second, it reproduces early in the year, while streams are fed by groundwater untapped by growing vegetation, and before the normal cycle of heavy rainfall in May and June greatly alters the volume and clarity of the water in most streams. Finally, the stoneroller is a "primary consumer"—that is to say, it takes its meals at the very base of the food-chain; and, its gregarious tendencies permit development of especially high populations. Therefore, unless the species is entirely eliminated from extensive areas, substantial local reservoirs of stonerollers exist for replenishment of stock at localities where the habitat is not perpetually suitable. Although Deacon (1961:417) found that stonerollers are mainly sedentary over short periods of time when stream-conditions are relatively stable, Metcalf (1959:375) reported rapid dispersal by this species when flow commenced in stream-channels that previously had been dry.

Variation in scale-size among stonerollers in Kansas has led some authors to recognize two subspecies, *C. a. pullum* (Agassiz) and *C. a. plumbeum* (Girard), within the State. Metcalf (1966:137) has discussed this matter, and I agree with him in rejecting *plumbeum* as a meaningful taxonomic entity. In explanation of that opinion, the following resumé and supplementary remarks seem appropriate. *Chondrostoma pullum* was described by Agassiz in 1854, from specimens obtained at Burlington, Iowa. *Dionda plumbea* was described by Girard in 1856, from specimens obtained in "head waters of the Canadian River (Llano Estacado)"; in Girard's (1856:14) brief account the only diagnostic character given for *D. plumbea* was "the size of its scales, which are the smallest in the genus." Hubbs and Ortenburger (1929b:95) referred *D. plumbea* to the synonymy of *Campostoma anomalum*, on the basis of "a type" in the Museum of Comparative Zoology and other evidence. Girard's name appears to be the oldest one available for a fine-scaled southwestern subspecies of *C. anomalum*, if stonerollers from that region are in fact different from *C. a. pullum*.

Authors who have recognized *plumbeum* have generally done so on the basis of circumferential scale-counts. Knapp (1953:51), in his keys to the fishes of Texas, referred to *pullum* those specimens having 41-43 circumferential scales, and to *plumbeum* those specimens having 45-50 circumferential scales. In Oklahoma, Moore and Buck (1957:23-24) assigned to *pullum* all *series* of specimens (from single localities) having *mean* counts of 42.6 circumferential scales or less; they reported as intergrades those series having mean counts of 42.6 to 44.8 scales, and identified as *plumbeum* a single series from the upper Cimarron River having a mean count of 51.1 scales.

In regions remote from the assumed range of *plumbeum*, higher scale-counts have been reported in *C. a. pullum* than those ascribed to that subspecies by Knapp and by Moore and Buck. Hubbs and Greene (1935:90) gave the "extreme range" of circumferential scales in *pullum* from Wisconsin as 38-50, the "usual range" as 39-46, and the average as 42.3. Trautman (1957:411) recorded high counts (39-54) in *pullum* from Ohio, and Ross (1958) ascribed counts of 37 to 54 circumferential scales to *pullum* over its general range.

Circumferential scales are not always numerous in southwestern stonerollers. In specimens from four localities in the headwaters of the Canadian River (KU 4221, 4232, 4236, and 8344, from Colfax and Mora counties, New Mexico) my counts are as follows: 40 circumferential scale-rows in one specimen, 41 in three, 42 in six, 43 in five, 44 in seven, 45 in three, 46 in three, 47 in two, 48 in one, and 50 in one (mean 43.8). In six series from Texas (Menard, Bandera, Kendall, Uvalde, and Real counties, in the San Saba, Medina, Guadalupe, Nueces, and Frio drainages, respectively) I count 37 to 45 circumferential scale-rows in 55 specimens (mean 40.5).

Suckers

FAMILY CATOSTOMIDAE

KEY

1. Dorsal fin-rays more than 20 2
   Dorsal fin-rays 10-15 8

2. Lateral-line scales more than 50; lips papillose (Fig. 15C); eye closer to back of head than tip of snout, blue sucker, *Cycleptus elongatus*, p. 166
   Lateral-line scales fewer than 50; lips plicate or smooth (Fig. 15A or B); eye closer to tip of snout than back of head 3

3. Color usually dull bronze or olivaceous; lower fins dark-pigmented; anterior fontanelle (on midline of top of head, between nostrils and eyes) closed in adults; lower margin of subopercle evenly curved, not angular (widest at midpoint of its length); pelvic rays usually 10 or 11, anal rays 8 or 9, sum of pelvic and anal rays 18 or more 4
   Color silvery white; lower fins cream-colored or clear; anterior fontanelle open in adults; marginal curvature of subopercle somewhat angular (widest anterior to midpoint of its length); pelvic rays usually 8-10, anal rays 7-9, sum of pelvic and anal rays usually 17 or fewer except in *C. velifer* 6

4. Mouth terminal and oblique; anterior tip of upper lip nearly level with lower edge of eye; lips thin; upper jaw about as long as snout, big-mouthed buffalo, *Ictiobus cyprinellus*, p. 169
   Mouth ventral and horizontal; tip of upper lip far below level of eye; lips fleshy; upper jaw shorter than snout 5

5. Distance from tip of lower jaw to end of maxilla equal to or greater than eye diameter in young, about twice eye diameter in adults; height of anterior rays in dorsal and anal fins often less than ⅔ head-length; greatest depth of body 2.6-3.2 in standard length; not notably ridge-backed . . . . black buffalo, *Ictiobus niger*, p. 171
   Distance from tip of lower jaw to end of maxilla less than eye diameter in young, about equal to eye diameter in adults; height of anterior dorsal and anal fin-rays greater than ⅔ head-length; greatest depth of body 2.2-2.8 in standard length; back highly arched, ridgelike, small-mouthed buffalo, *Ictiobus bubalus*, p. 173

6. Mouth farther forward than nostrils; front of lower lip rounded; distance from tip of snout to anterior nostril greater than diameter of eye; lateral-line scales usually 37 or more, quillback, *Carpiodes cyprinus*, p. 175
   Mouth almost directly below nostrils; front of lower lip with small, median, nipplelike projection; distance from tip of snout to anterior nostril less than diameter of eye; lateral-line scales 34-36 7

7. Anterior (longest) rays of dorsal fin exceeding basal length of fin; body depth less than 2.7 in standard length; anal rays 8 or 9, pelvic rays usually 10 . . high-finned carpsucker, *Carpiodes velifer*, p. 179
   Anterior (longest) rays of dorsal fin shorter than basal length of fin; body depth 2.7 or more in standard length; anal rays 7 or 8, pelvic rays usually 9 . . . . river carpsucker, *Carpiodes carpio*, p. 177

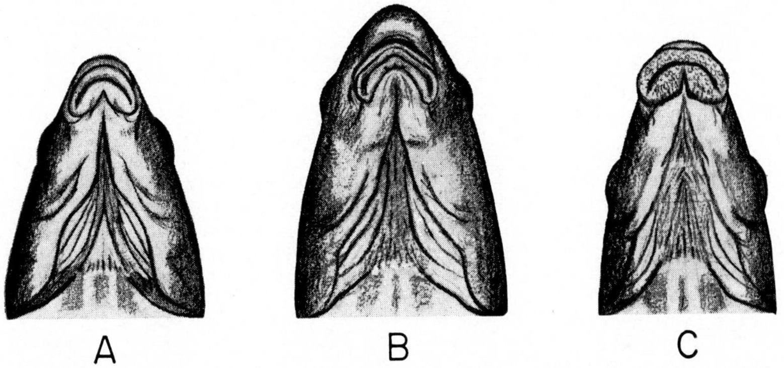

FIG. 15. Mouths in three genera of suckers (*Ictiobus, Carpiodes, Catostomus*).
A. Small-mouthed buffalo: Note moderately thick lips and rounded mouth.
B. Plains carpsucker: Note relatively thin lips and angular mouth; lower lip with median nipplelike projection.
C. Common sucker: Note thick, papillose lips.

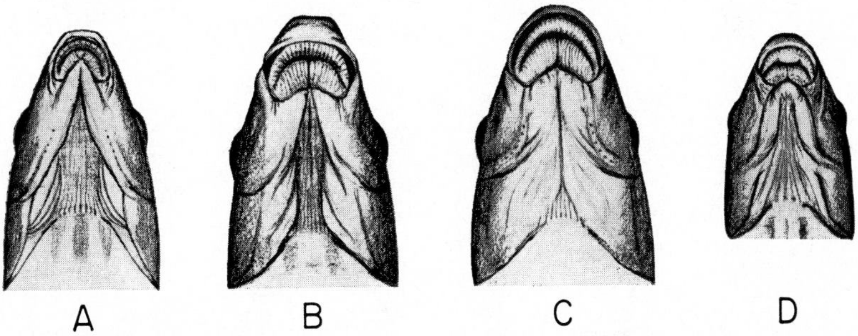

FIG. 16. Differing forms of mouths in suckers having plicate lips. A. Spotted sucker; B. Black redhorse; C. Golden redhorse; D. Northern redhorse (southwestern subspecies).

8. Lips papillose (Fig. 15C) 9
Lips plicate (Fig. 16) 10

9. Lateral-line scales 45-54; distance from hind margin of orbit to upper end of gill cleft contained 2.0 or more times in snout length; pelvic rays usually 9 ....hogsucker, *Hypentelium nigricans*, p. 191
Lateral-line scales more than 55; distance from hind margin of orbit to upper end of gill cleft contained less than 2.0 times in snout length; pelvic rays usually 10,
white sucker, *Catostomus commersoni*, p. 193

10. Lower lip thin, not coarsely striated, its width at center contained 2.5 or more times in width of gape (Fig. 16A); sides usually striped by rows of dots; air bladder divided into 2 chambers,
spotted sucker, *Minytrema melanops*, p. 181
Lower lip thick, coarsely striated, its width at center contained less than 2.5 times in width of gape; sides never conspicuously striped by rows of dots; air bladder divided into 3 chambers 11

11. Pharyngeal arch heavy, with molarlike teeth (Fig. 9B); last caudal scales outlined by melanophores, forming a semicircular line of pigment on each lobe of caudal fin; caudal fin red in life,
river redhorse, *Moxostoma carinatum*, p. 187

Pharyngeal arch fragile, with slender teeth in comblike series (Fig. 9A); no semicircular line of melanophores on caudal lobes; caudal fin red or not 12

12. Posterior margin of lower lip straight or convex (Fig. 16D); plicae of lower lip partly broken by transverse grooves; upper lip thickened medially in most examples; caudal fin red in life,
northern redhorse, *Moxostoma macrolepidotum*, p. 189

Posterior margin of lower lip notched rather than straight across, the right and left halves meeting at an obtuse angle (Fig. 16B or C); plicae of lower lip not broken by transverse grooves; upper lip not thickened at center; caudal fin not red 13

13. Lateral-line scales fewer than 45; pelvic rays 9,
golden redhorse, *Moxostoma erythrurum*, p. 184

Lateral-line scales usually 45 or more; pelvic rays usually 10,
black redhorse, *Moxostoma duquesnei*, p. 183

Blue sucker

Cycleptus elongatus (LeSueur)

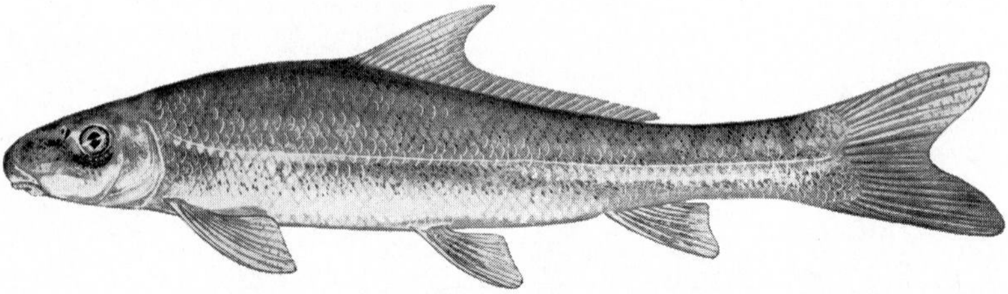

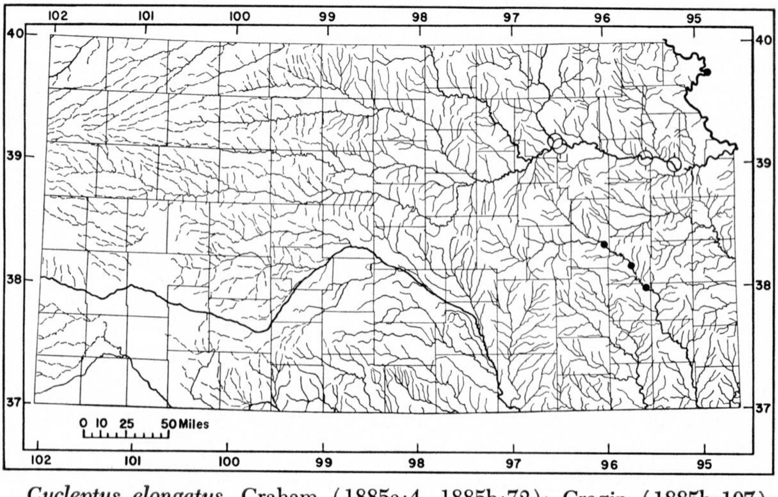

Cycleptus elongatus, Graham (1885a:4, 1885b:72); Cragin (1885b:107); Clarke, Breukelman and Andrews (1958:167); Metcalf (1959:393, 1966: 139); Minckley (1959:416); Breukelman (1960:20, 21, 33); Branson (1962:360).

Blue sucker—Snow (1875:141); Breukelman (1946:61).

Body elongate, depth less than 1/4 of standard length; head small, slender, snout acute; eye small, in posterior half of head; mouth ventral, lips thick and coarsely papillose; dorsal fin long, falcate, with 28-33 rays; anal rays usually 7; pelvic fins large, with 10 or 11 rays; pectoral fins large, falcate, with 16 or 17 rays; lateral line well developed, with 53-56 scales; vertebrae 49 or 50.

Adults dark gray or blue-black, paler ventrally than dorsally; all fins dark. Young (62-80 mm. in standard length) from Neosho River pigmented as follows: *Head*—top mottled by melanophores, dark brown over olive background, parietal spot obscure; side dark on upper half, snout dark above level of lower margin of pupil, silvery below that level; suborbital area densely dotted by melanophores; upper half of opercle with scattered melanophores, lower half and subopercle scarcely pigmented, somewhat brassy; ventral surface unpigmented. *Body*—back and upper sides heavily pigmented by melanophores over dull olive or brownish background, melanophores fewer and more widely scattered ventrally; sides of caudal peduncle mostly dark, lower third of sides anterior to pelvic fins scarcely pigmented, white or dull silvery; breast and belly white; anal region white; base of anal fin unpigmented; several melanophores on undersurface of caudal peduncle forming obscure line from anal base to caudal fin. *Dorsal fin*—leading edge and distal tip black, otherwise unpigmented except for suffusion of dull orange (in one specimen, 5th principal ray of dorsal fin and adjoining membranes streaked by melanophores). *Caudal fin*—dorsal margin (rudiments and 1st principal ray) jet-black, tip of dorsal lobe black; remainder of upper lobe transparent, devoid of melanophores but suffused with dull orange; lower lobe of caudal (and sometimes lowermost 1 or 2 rays of upper lobe) black from base to distal margin; lowermost scales on caudal peduncle and base of fin black-pigmented. *Anal fin*—mostly dark (melanophores dense on rays and membranes), distal tip unpigmented. *Pelvic and pectoral fins*—basal 2/3 of upper surface of fin bearing scattered melanophores (moderately dark), distal 1/3 of fin unpigmented; both fins tinged with orange pigment.

In breeding males, minute tubercles covering most of head, scales, and rays of all fins.

Maximum size 36-40 inches, 12-15 pounds (Trautman, 1957:221); largest Kansas specimen 27 inches long.

In recent years, the blue sucker has been found only in the mainstreams of the Missouri and Neosho rivers. Formerly, the species occupied the lower Kansas River, as indicated by Cragin (1885b: 107): "Neither rare nor abundant in Kansas R. I have known of a fisherman taking twenty specimens or thereabout in a trip from Manhattan to Topeka. It is rarely taken except in spring and autumn, and is said to be one of the finest of Kansas food-fishes." Snow (1875:141) and Graham (1885a:4, 1885b:72) likewise reported blue suckers from the Kansas River, and a specimen (KSU 2917) obtained from the Blue River by Graham is extant at Kansas State University (Minckley, 1959:416).

All blue suckers that I have collected in the Neosho River were found in strong currents over bottoms of bedrock or rubble and gravel. Juveniles occupied the broader, less turbulent riffles; most adults were taken from narrow chutes where exposure of a major rock-stratum caused flow to be funneled through a constricted channel. Throughout their range, blue suckers characteristically inhabit large, deep rivers, and the deeper zones of large lakes (reservoirs).

Blue suckers that were in breeding condition have been taken in Kansas in April, at water temperatures of 50° to 60° F. Probably the adults overwinter in deep pools and move upstream to spawn on riffles.

Carlander (1954:23), Trautman (1957:221-222), and others have called attention to depletion of blue suckers in the upper Mississippi and Ohio rivers and their tributaries during the early part of this century. Pollution (including silt) and dams (which inundate rapids and block spawning migrations) are suspected causes of the decline. I doubt that the decimation of populations in the lower Kansas River resulted from dams, or from domestic or industrial pollution; change in the physical character of the lower mainstream seems more likely. Parts of the channel must originally have been narrow, and the water deeper than now. These areas were later converted to an essentially uniform, sand-choked channel, perhaps by the major flood of 1903. Other ichthyological evidence supports this conclusion (see accounts of the lake sturgeon, burbot, and blue catfish).

Buffalofishes

Genus **Ictiobus** Rafinesque

The buffalofishes are dull gray or bronze-colored and have deep bodies and long, falcate dorsal fins. The anterior fontanelle (on dorsal midline of head, between nares and eyes) is closed in adults. The head is ovoid or subtriangular, its lower margin nearly straight in *I. bubalus* and *I. niger*, but not so precisely horizontally aligned with the ventral body contour as in the related carpsuckers. The subopercle is rounded; its hind margin forms a nearly perfect arc, the bone being widest at the midpoint of its length. The mouth, if horizontal, has lips thicker than those of carpsuckers (Fig. 15 on page 165). The pharyngeal bones are thin, but less fragile than in carpsuckers. The intestinal tract is long. The lower fins usually bear considerable dark pigment.

PLATE 1

Northern redhorse
x 0.25

Red-bellied dace
x 1.00

Red shiner
x 0.90

Topeka shiner
x 1.20

Dusky-striped shiner
x 0.70

Black-striped topminnow
x 0.80

PLATE 2

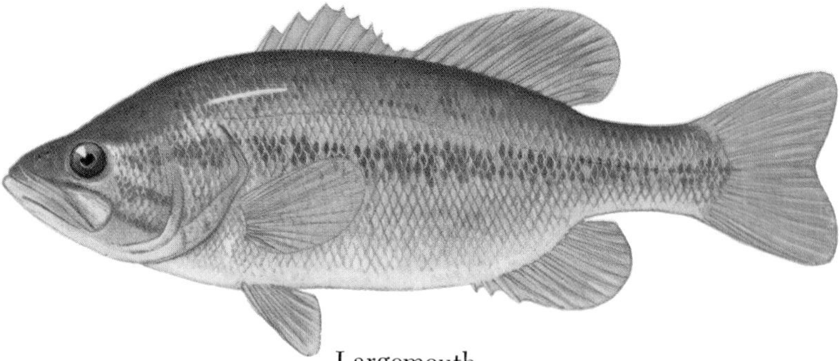

Largemouth
x 0.25

White bass
x 0.25

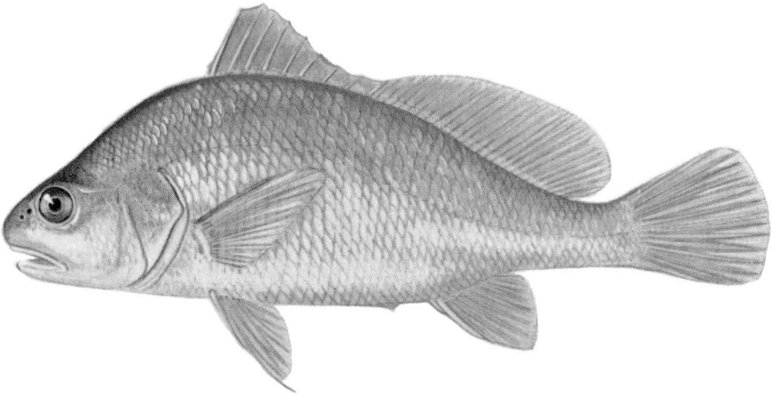

Freshwater drum
x 0.25

PLATE 3

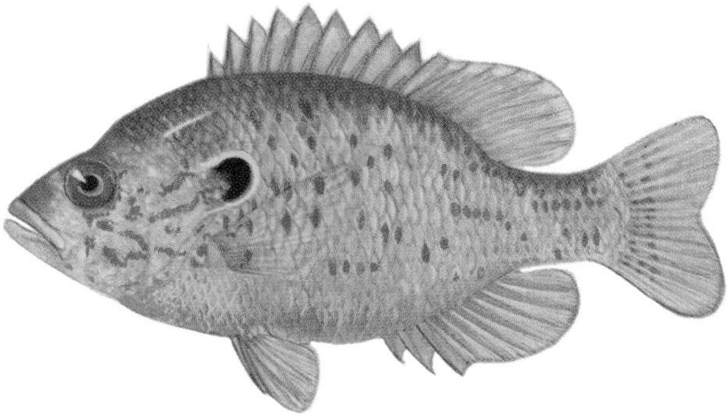

Orange-spotted sunfish
x 0.80

Longear
x 0.60

Green sunfish
x 0.50

PLATE 4

Orange-throated darter
x 1.4

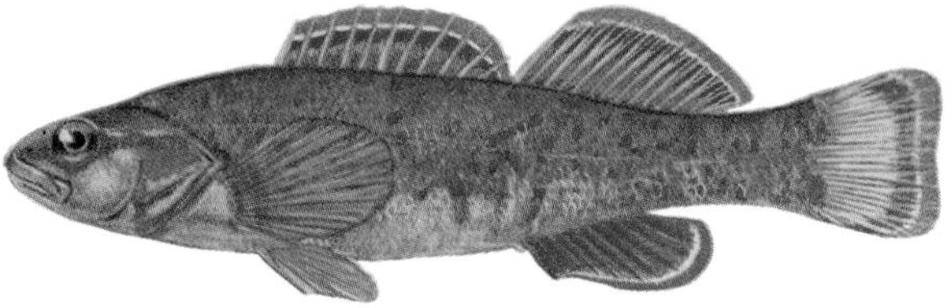

Red-finned darter
x 0.9

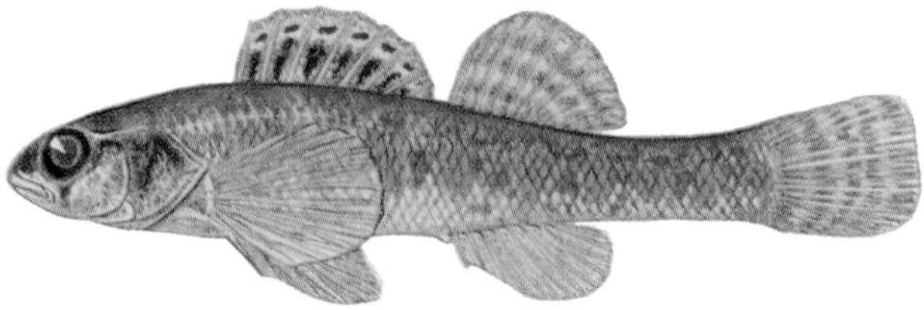

Slough darter
x 1.5

Green-sided darter
x 0.75

Banded darter
x 1.4

Big-mouthed buffalo

Ictiobus cyprinellus (Valenciennes)

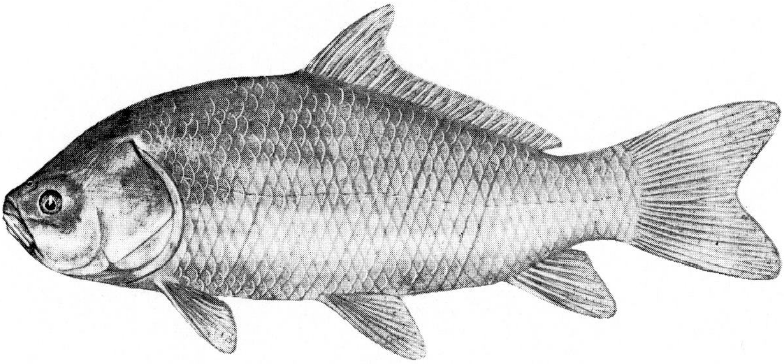

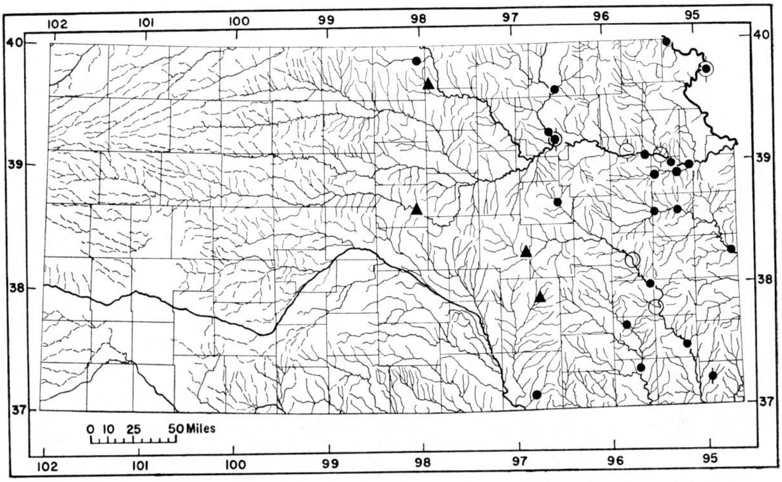

Ictiobus cyprinella, Cragin (1885b:107); Graham (1885b:72); Jordan and Meek (1885:13); Greer and Cross (1956:359-360); Clarke, Breukelman, and Andrews (1958:167); Metcalf (1959:364); Minckley (1959: 416); Breukelman (1960:33); Deacon (1961:375); Deacon and Metcalf (1961:315).

Megastomatobus cyprinella, Hall (1934:230); Breukelman (1940b:379); Jennings (1942:364).

Ictiobus cyprinellus, Schelske (1957:39); Fisher (1962:428); Metcalf (1966:140).

Body robust, thick, ventral contour curved upward anteriorly; head large, ovoid, length 3.0-3.4 in standard length; snout bluntly rounded; mouth large, oblique, thin-lipped; top of upper lip (at front of snout) nearly level with lower edge of orbit; length of upper jaw nearly equal to snout length; eye small, near front of head; fins low, rays short; gill rakers on first arch more than 60 (average 72); lateral-line scales 36-39, most often 37; scale rows around body 30-39, most often 32; dorsal fin-rays 23-30, most often 26; anterior rays in dorsal fin much shorter than fin-base, 1.4-2.0 in head length; anal fin-rays 8-10, usually 9; pelvic rays 10 or 11; vertebrae usually 36 or 37.

Maximum size 80 pounds (Harlan and Speaker, 1956:72-73).

The big-mouthed buffalo occurs mainly in calm water in or adjacent to large, lowland rivers of eastern Kansas. If size as well as number of individuals is considered, the species is sometimes almost incredibly abundant. Following concentration of fishes by drought in the 1950's, the surviving populations of *I. cyprinellus* amounted to more than 1000 pounds per acre in some oxbow lakes and pools along the Kansas, Marais des Cygnes, and Neosho rivers. Occasionally, the species becomes established in artificial lakes and ponds. The El Dorado City Lake yielded more than 200 pounds per acre of buffalo (*I. cyprinellus* and *I. niger*) to commercial nets in 1954, and thousands of buffalofish remained when that 265-acre lake was drained later in the same year. Big-mouthed buffalo commonly attain weights of eight to 12 pounds in Kansas, but larger individuals seem rare.

This species is used commercially along the Missouri River but is not highly regarded as a table-fish, being considered inferior to catfish and small-mouthed buffalo although superior to carp. Pond-culture of *I. cyprinellus* has economic potentialities, and methods for its production have been summarized by Swingle (1957). A single trial of the species in a 1/10 acre pond at the University of Kansas in 1961 resulted in a yield of 256 pounds per acre, without fertilization of the pond or feeding of the fish. This is about twice the production obtained using channel catfish under similar conditions.

The big-mouthed buffalo is partly pelagic in habit, differing in this respect from other deep-bodied suckers (*Ictiobus* and *Carpiodes*), all of which are essentially bottom-dwellers. The relatively large, oblique, and thin-lipped mouth of *I. cyprinellus*, coupled with its numerous elongate gill-rakers, indicates that it depends in substantial measure on plankton as food. Investigations of the feeding habits of *cyprinellus* prove that this is the fact inasmuch as organisms that are mainly planktonic (copepods and cladocerans) predominate in the intestinal contents of fish examined. The remaining food-items are organisms found mainly on the bottom.

The big-mouthed buffalo spawns in spring, after runoff raises waterlevels in streams. Females that had not spawned have been taken as late as May 25. The eggs are scattered and abandoned, in shallow water over plant-debris, without prior preparation of a nest-site by the parental fish. Young-of-the-year in Kansas usually make their first appearance in collections in mid-June or later when they are taken in seines.

A comprehensive account of the life-history and ecology of *I. cyprinellus* has been published by Johnson (1963).

Black buffalo

Ictiobus niger (Rafinesque)

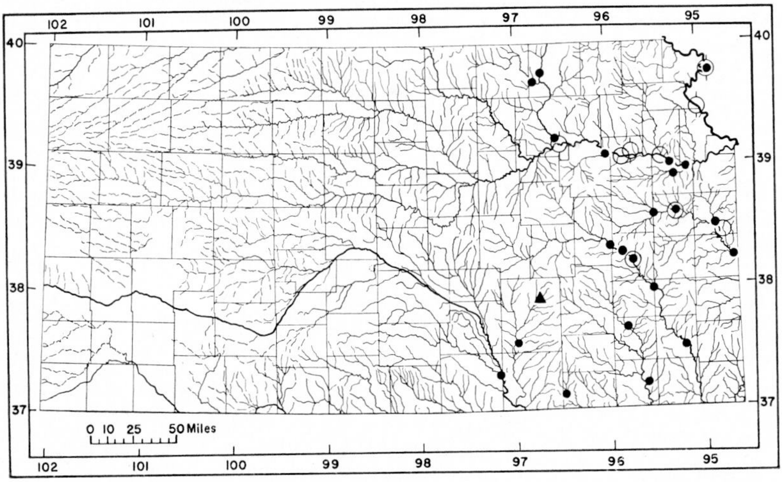

Bubalichthys niger, Wheeler (1879:33).

Ictiobus urus, Graham (1885a:4, 1885b:72); Cragin (1885b:107); Jordan and Meek (1885:13).

Ictiobus niger, Breukelman (1940b:379); Jennings (1942:364); Greer and Cross (1956:359-360); Clarke, Breukelman, and Andrews (1958:167); Metcalf (1959:363-364, 1966:140); Minckley (1959:416); Breukelman (1960:33); Deacon (1961b:375).

Body compressed but stout, back not prominently arched, ventral contour straight; width of body behind head 1.6-2.2 in distance from origin of dorsal fin to insertion of pelvic fins; head large, conical, length 2.9-3.8 in standard length; snout blunt; mouth ventral, slightly oblique, tip of upper lip far below level of orbit; lips thick and fleshy; upper jaw shorter than snout; distance from anterior tip of mandible to posterior end of maxilla 0.6-1.0 in eye diameter (eye small); gill rakers on first arch fewer than 60; lateral-line scales 36-39; scale rows around body 32-34 (15-16—2—15-16); dorsal fin-rays 27-31; anterior rays of dorsal fin shorter than in *I. bubalus,* length 1.3-1.8 in head length; anal fin-rays 8 or 9; height of anal fin 1.4-1.7 in head length; pelvic rays 9-11; vertebrae usually 37.

Slate-gray or dark olivaceous dorsally, bronze color laterally; all fins with much dark pigment.

Largest Kansas specimen 41 inches long, weight 28 pounds [Kansas Fish and Game, 23(1):11, 15, December, 1965].

Like other buffalofishes, *I. niger* occurs mainly in the larger rivers of eastern Kansas. Most black buffalo that I have caught were taken in deep, fast riffles where the channel narrows; the species seems to prefer stronger currents than either *I. bubalus* or *I. cyprinellus.* Sometimes black buffalo and small-mouthed buffalo are found together on shallow riffles, where their fins and backs break the surface as they forage for insects and epiphytes on stones. Despite their predilection for currents in streams, black buffalo adapt to impounded conditions and are common in some lakes. Growth-rates of black buffalo in one lake were reported by Greer and Cross (1956:359).

The black buffalo is less abundant than the big-mouthed buffalo and small-mouthed buffalo, and therefore has less importance commercially than the other two species. On the other hand, the black buffalo seems to be caught most often by anglers, who use worms or doughballs as bait.

Small-mouthed buffalo

Ictiobus bubalus (Rafinesque)

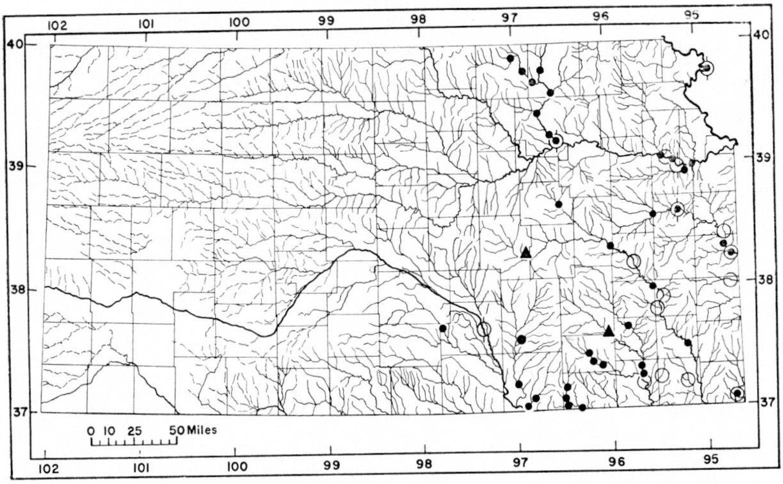

Bubalichthys Bubalus, Snow (1875:141).

Icthyobus bubalus, Wheeler (1879:33).

Ictiobus bubalus, Cragin (1885b:107); Graham (1885b:72); Jordan and Meek (1885:13); Jordan (1891:17); Breukelman (1940b:379); Jennings (1942:364); Schelske (1957:39); Clarke, Breukelman, and Andrews (1958:167); Metcalf (1959:363, 1966:140); Minckley (1959: 416); Breukelman (1960:33); Deacon (1961:375-376); Deacon and Metcalf (1961:315); Fisher (1962:428).

Smallmouth buffalo—Schoonover and Thompson (1954:176-177).

Body highly compressed, back arched and ridgelike, ventral contour straight; width of body behind head 2.1-2.6 in distance from origin of dorsal fin to insertion of pelvic fins; head small, conical, length 3.4-4.1 in standard length; snout blunt; mouth small, ventral (Fig. 15A), tip of upper lip far below level of orbit; upper jaw much shorter than snout; distance from anterior tip of mandible to posterior end of maxilla 0.9-1.3 in eye diameter (eye large); gill rakers on first arch fewer than 60; lateral-line scales usually 36-38; scale rows around body 32-36 (15-17—2—15-17); dorsal fin-rays 26-31; anterior rays of dorsal fin high, length 0.8-1.4 in head length; anal fin-rays usually 9; height of anal fin 1.2-1.4 in head length; pelvic rays 9-11; vertebrae usually 36 or 37.

Maximum weight 28½ pounds, length about 35 inches [Reelfoot Lake, Schoffman (1944:4); probably less in Kansas].

The small-mouthed buffalo occurs in various habitats in the larger streams of eastern Kansas. Usually, *I. bubalus* occupies shallower water over firmer bottoms than the big-mouthed buffalo, and less rapid current than the black buffalo. *I. bubalus* commonly is found in pools, oxbow lakes, and backwaters in the mouths of tributaries, but it sometimes forages on swift, shallow riffles. Small-mouthed buffalo occasionally are found in creeks, whereas *I. cyprinellus* and *I. niger* are more nearly confined to major rivers.

The small-mouthed buffalo has considerable commercial value, although it does not grow so large as the big-mouthed buffalo or the black buffalo. I have seen no *I. bubalus* from Kansas that weighed more than ten pounds. But, Snow (1875:141) stated that this fish was "very abundant, ordinarily weighing from 4 lbs. to 20 lbs.; maximum weight, 40 lbs." in the Kansas River at Lawrence. Snow mentioned only one species of buffalofish, but more than one kind probably was involved in the catches and the weights reported.

Mr. Roy Smith of Lawrence, who fished commercially with his father in the lower Kansas River during the early 1900's, thinks buffalofish were much more common formerly than now. One of Smith's most vivid recollections relates to the decline of buffalofishes "in the 'teens." His comments referred mainly to the small-mouthed buffalo, and he thought some change in the river accounted for their reduced abundance. Another possible cause for a decline of buffalofishes is competition with carp, which were not present in the Kansas River at the time of Snow's (1875) observations. Carp were released in Kansas in the 1880's and by the early 1900's were abundant in the lower Kansas River.

Small-mouthed buffalo eat bottom-dwelling organisms, mostly larval insects. The species spawns in spring, probably most often in May. Young two or more inches long usually are present by mid-June. Growth-rates of *I. bubalus* in a reservoir have been reported by Schoonover and Thompson (1954:177), and in a stream by Minckley (1959:416).

Carpsuckers

Genus **Carpiodes** Rafinesque

Carpsuckers are bright silvery fishes having deep bodies and long, falcate dorsal fins. The anterior fontanelle (on midline of top of head, between nares and eyes) persists throughout life. The head is subtriangular and its lower margin is nearly straight and horizontal, in line with the ventral body contour. The subopercle is angular, its hind margin not forming a perfect arc; the widest part of the subopercle is slightly anterior to the middle of its length. The mouth is small and horizontal, with thin, weakly plicate lips (Fig. 15B). The pharyngeal arch is unusually thin and fragile. The intestinal tract is exceptionally long, with numerous loops. The lower fins usually lack dark pigment.

Quillback

Carpiodes cyprinus (LeSueur)

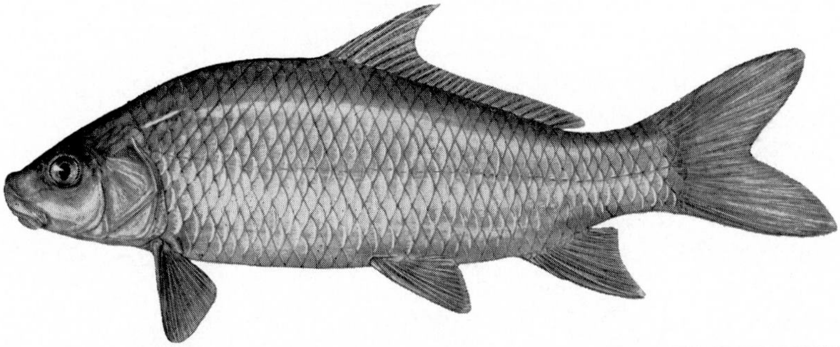

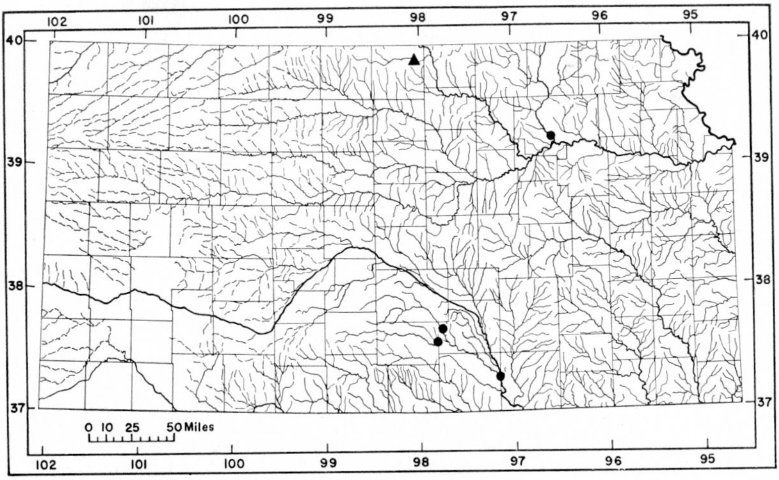

Carpiodes cyprinus, Breukelman (1940a:369); Metcalf (1966:140).
Carpiodes forbesi, Eddy (1957:68); Minckley (1959:416).

Body compressed but relatively slender, its depth 3.0 or more in standard length; head large, its length nearly equal to body depth; snout long, greatly exceeding eye diameter; snout length 4.5 or less in body depth; mouth mostly anterior to vertical line through nostril; lower lip not notably angular, without median knobby projection; dorsal fin long, falcate, usually with 26-28 rays, anterior rays shorter than fin base; anal fin-rays 7 or 8; pelvic rays 9 or 10; lateral line with 35-38 scales; vertebrae usually 38 or 39.

Coloration pallid, tan dorsally, silvery laterally, white ventrally; fins transparent.

Size 24 to 26 inches, 9 to 12 pounds (Trautman, 1957:233); largest Kansas specimen 17 inches long.

Although the quillback is known from both the Kansas and Arkansas river systems in Kansas, the localities of record are few. One specimen was taken by Minckley (1959:416) in the Blue River, and Frank Schryer, biologist for the Kansas Forestry, Fish and Game Commission, told me that he has found this species in Lovewell Reservoir, Jewell County. Since 1963 numerous specimens have been caught from two sites on the Ninnescah River, and one large specimen was taken in 1964 from a drainage channel leading into the Arkansas River below the mouth of the Ninnescah River. Possibly the occurrences in the Arkansas River System in Kansas result from introduction into the State Fish Hatchery on the headwaters of the Ninnescah River, although no such introduction is known to have been made there.

All specimens that I have seen from Kansas have the body-form characteristic of the nominal species *Carpiodes forbesi* Hubbs, which Bailey and Allum (1962:80-82) consider to be conspecific with *C. cyprinus.*

River carpsucker

Carpiodes carpio (Rafinesque)

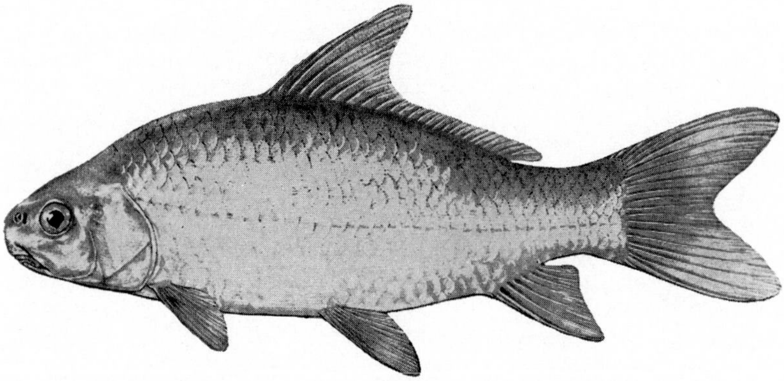

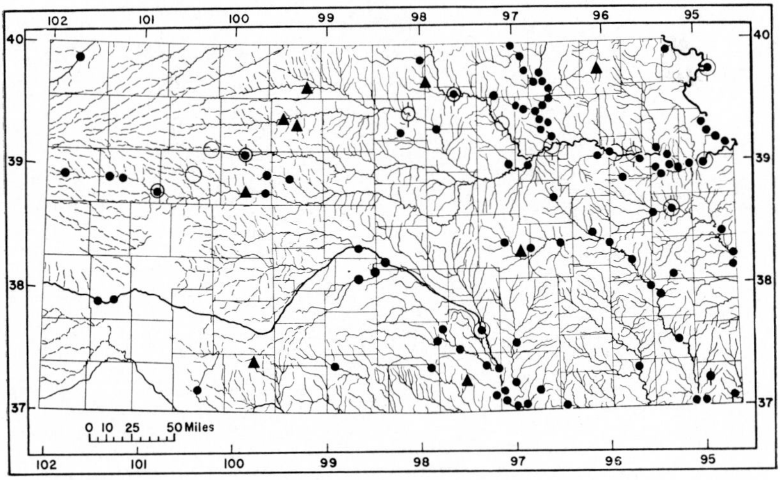

Carpiodes damalis, Cope (1865b:85).

Carpoides bison, Wheeler (1879:33).

Ictiobus carpio, Gilbert (1884:10, 1885:97); Cragin (1885b:107); Graham (1885a:4, 1885b:71); Jordan and Meek (1885:13).

Ictiobus velifer, Hay (1887:242, 247, 251) (probable misidentifications).

Ictiobus difformis, Jordan (1891:17).

Carpiodes carpio, Hall (1934:230); Breukelman (1940a:369, 1940b:379, 1960:33); Jennings (1942:364); Cross (1954:307); Schelske (1957: 39); Clarke, Breukelman, and Andrews (1958:167); Cross, Deacon, and Ward (1959:163); Metcalf (1959:363, 1966:142); Minckley (1959: 416-417); Minckley and Deacon (1960:348); Deacon (1961:376-377); Deacon and Metcalf (1961:315).

Body compressed, back arched, ventral line nearly straight; body depth 2.7 or more in standard length; head small, length 1.3 or more into body depth;

snout short, rounded, length about equal to eye diameter in young but exceeding eye diameter in adults; snout length usually 5.0 or more in body depth; mouth distinctly ventral, transected by vertical line through nostril; lower lip thin, angular (Fig. 15B), with small median knob (nipplelike projection); dorsal fin long, falcate, 23-27 rays, anterior rays shorter than basal length of fin; anal fin-rays 7 or 8; pelvic rays 8-10, most often 9; lateral-line scales usually 34-36; scales above lateral line usually 7, often 8; vertebrae 36 or 37.

Entire coloration pallid; back usually light brown, sides bright silvery or white, belly white; fins colorless to pinkish-orange, almost lacking dark pigment.

Breeding males with minute tubercles on top and sides of head, scales of nape, and upper surfaces of pectoral and pelvic fin-rays.

Length 25 inches, weight 10¼ pounds (Trautman, 1957:238); seldom more than 20 inches long in Kansas.

The river carpsucker is the most abundant and most widely-distributed sucker in Kansas. Its range is almost statewide, in small and large streams, regardless of gradient, turbidity, or bottom-type. This seemingly ubiquitous occurrence obscures the rather well-defined habitat-preference of the species, which is calm pools, backwaters, or gentle eddies where flocculent sediments accumulate, rather than the main channels of streams. Sometimes, enormous numbers of carpsuckers are captured by seining pools at the mouths of tributaries, and small embayments at the ends of sand-bars or gravel-bars that project into river-channels. Seining of the mainstreams where currents are strong, at the same localities, yields few river carpsuckers.

C. carpio feeds on microorganisms—mainly diatoms, desmids, small crustacea, larval dipterans, rotifers, and filamentous algae according to Buchholz (1957:598-599). Although currents restrict the abundance of these organisms, they are concentrated and deposited in sluggish eddies and backwaters; likewise, profuse blooms of plankton often develop in the more stable backwaters of nutrient-rich prairie-streams, providing an ecological niche that is well occupied by *C. carpio.*

River carpsuckers seemingly have a protracted spawning season in Kansas, extending from late May to July or later. I found a concentration of adults that shed eggs and milt freely, in the Smoky Hill River at Elkader, Logan County, on June 18, 1958, when the water-temperature was approximately 80° F. "Ripe" fish were confined to a narrow zone along a bank that was being eroded by the current, and was overgrown by rushes. Roots and some fallen stems of rushes, exposed by undercutting, provided substrates for deposition of the eggs. Constriction of stream-flow along this bank caused water to be deeper than in the broad, sand-filled channel elsewhere in the mainstream.

River carpsuckers mature at a length of 10 or 11 inches, and seldom grow larger than 16 inches (approximate weight two pounds). Rarely, specimens that weighed six to eight pounds have been taken from ponds and lakes in Kansas. Minckley (1959:417) reported carpsuckers as old as 11 years in the Blue River, with correspondingly slow growth-rates. During the same years covered by Minckley's report on the Blue River, Deacon (1959:377) found that length-frequency data obtained from periodic collections of carpsuckers in the Neosho River indicated more rapid growth and a shorter life-span in carpsuckers from that stream.

High-finned carpsucker
Carpiodes velifer (Rafinesque)

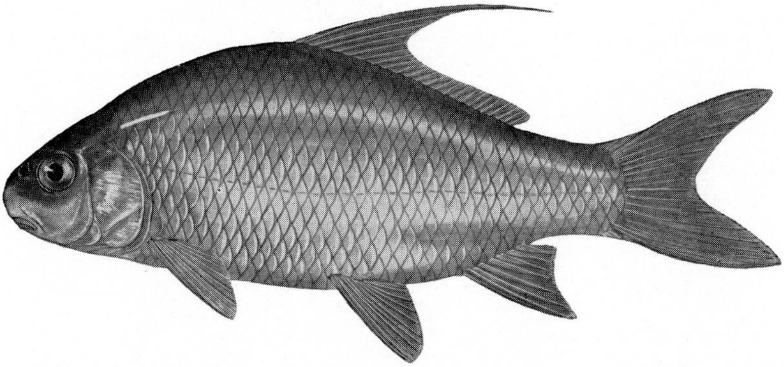

Ictiobus velifer, Graham (1885a:4, 1885b:72); Cragin (1885b:107).

Carpiodes velifer, Hay (1887:242, 247, 251, probably erroneously); Breukelman (1940a:369, erroneously; 1940b:379, in part; 1960:20, 21, 33); Jennings (1942:364); Clarke, Breukelman, and Andrews (1958:167); Metcalf (1959:363, 1966:142); Minckley (1959:417-418); Deacon (1961:377-378); Deacon and Metcalf (1961:315).

Body highly compressed, its greatest depth contained less than 2.5 times in standard length of adults and large juveniles; head small, length 1.5 or more in body depth; snout blunt and rounded, shorter than eye diameter; snout length more than 5.0 in body depth; mouth ventral, transected by or mainly posterior to vertical line through nostril, latter almost at front of snout; lower lip angular, with median "nipple" as in *C. carpio;* dorsal fin long, falcate, with 23-27 rays, anterior rays (if unbroken) longer than basal length of fin; anal fin-rays 8 or 9; pelvic rays 9 or 10; lateral-line scales usually 33-35; scales above lateral line 7-9, usually 8; vertebrae 35 or 36.

Entire coloration pallid, like *C. carpio* (the species which *velifer* most resembles, but from which it can be distinguished by its longer anterior dorsal rays, deeper body, and by having, on the average, one less scale in the lateral

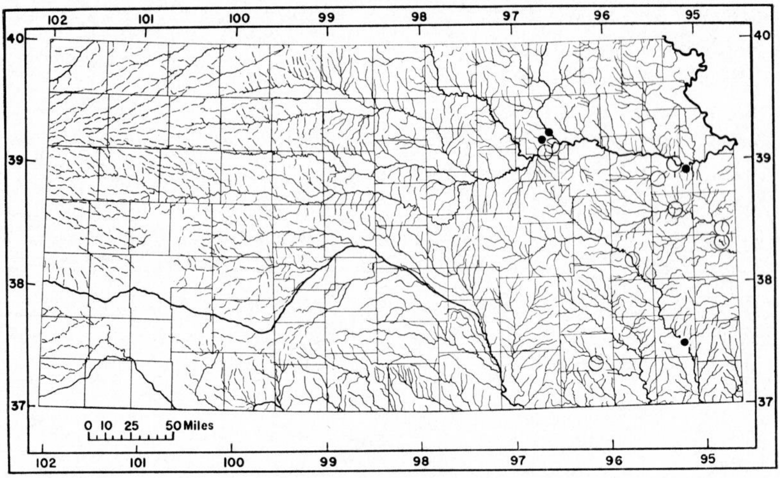

line, one more scale row above the lateral line, one more anal ray, and one more pelvic ray).

Maximum size 15 inches, 2 pounds (Trautman, 1957:242); longest Kansas specimen 13 inches.

The high-finned carpsucker is almost extirpated in Kansas. To my knowledge, only one specimen has been taken since 1940; that one was caught in the Neosho River in 1958 (Deacon, 1959:377-378). Published records based on early collections suggest that *C. velifer* occurred throughout the Kansas River Basin prior to 1900, but the reports by Hay (1887) and Breukelman (1940a, 1940b) are at least partly erroneous. Metcalf (1966:142) examined one of Hay's specimens (USNM 37936) and found it to be *C. carpio.* Hay's description (1887:242) of his "*Ictiobus velifer*" from Concordia fits the river carpsucker better than the high-finned carpsucker in scale-counts, body depth, and height of anterior dorsal rays; only in size of eye (3¾ in head) does Hay's description agree more closely with *velifer* than with *carpio,* and the value given is unusually low for either species, considering the stated length (8 inches) of his specimen. Furthermore, *C. carpio,* unreported by Hay, has subsequently been taken at or near the localities where he recorded *C. velifer.* I identify as *C. carpio* the specimen that Breukelman (1940a:369, 1940b:379) reported from northwestern Kansas as *C. velifer* (KU 165, collected in Hackberry Creek, Gove County, on June 27, 1910).

Although no western records of *C. velifer* seem valid, the highfin certainly occurred in eastern Kansas, more commonly several decades ago than at present. Collections that were made by the State Biological Survey between 1898 and 1912 contained many highfins (specimens in the University of Kansas Museum of Natural History). Records since 1912 are few, despite the statement by Breukelman (1960:20) that the highfin is common in Kansas.

Reasons for the decline are unknown. Published descriptions of the habitat of *C. velifer* are confusingly inconsistent: "clearer rivers and lakes" (Moore, 1957:80, general distribution); "large, silty rivers . . . over weedless, sandy bottoms, sometimes with an admixture of mud" (Gerking, 1945:39, Indiana); "moderately deep waters of the Ohio River and the lower halves of its larger tributaries" (Trautman, 1957:242-243, Ohio); "the shallow waters of the smaller streams (Forbes and Richardson, 1920:78 [as *C. difformis*], Illinois); "primarily in the large inland rivers" (Harlan and Speaker, 1956: 75-76, Iowa). Vanicek (1961:238) stated that when waterlevels were high in the Des Moines River, Boone County, Iowa, in 1960, the highfin and other carpsuckers occurred mainly "in shallows along the shore and in flooded weedy places"; later, after the streamlevel receded, "the highfin was generally found in riffle areas."

Spotted sucker

Minytrema melanops (Rafinesque)

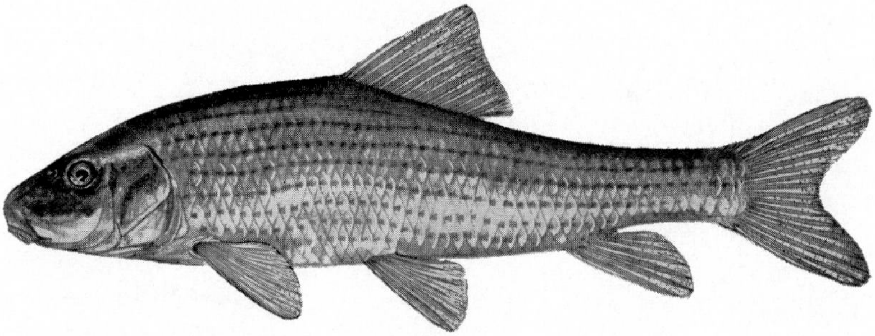

Erimyzon melanops, Wheeler (1879:33).
Minytrema melanops, Graham (1885a:4, 1885b:72); Cragin (1885b:108); Breukelman (1940b:379); Jennings (1942:364); Cross (1954:308); Metcalf (1959:365, 1966:166); Breukelman (1960:22,23,33); Branson (1962:366-367).

Body slender, scarcely compressed, greatest depth about equal to head length, ¼ of standard length; air bladder two-chambered; mouth subterminal, small, lips exceptionally thin (for a sucker), plicate (Fig. 16A); dorsal fin short, with 11-13 rays; anal fin-rays 7; pelvic rays 9 or 10; lateral line scarcely evident, 42-46 scales to base of caudal fin; air bladder two-chambered; vertebrae usually 43 or 44.

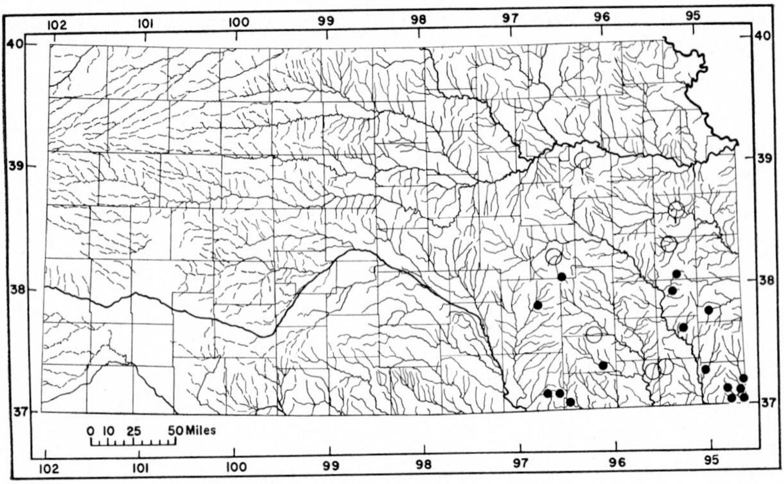

Color olivaceous to slate-gray dorsally, grading to silvery on sides and white on belly; each lateral scale with dark basal spot, imparting weakly striped appearance.

Breeding males bearing tubercles on anal and caudal fin-rays and on head: front of snout, immediately above eyes, lower cheeks, and ventral surface.

Length 18 inches or less.

The spotted sucker is scarce in Kansas, but is found occasionally in pools of small, sluggish creeks in the southeastern part of the State. Some of the streams where *Minytrema* occurs are intermittent, and become turbid after rains. The stream-bottoms vary from bedrock to mud, but are firm. The locality in Kansas where I have taken the largest number of spotted suckers is an overflow-pool in the floodplain of Spring River, east of the main channel and immediately north of U. S. Highway 66 in Cherokee County. This pool, unlike most oxbows along Kansas rivers, has clear water, considerable aquatic vegetation, and firm bottom beneath a layer of decaying leaves. Several writers have mentioned oxbow lakes, sloughs, and similar base-level environments as a principal habitat of the spotted sucker in other parts of its range. The species has been reported from major rivers (Mississippi) and lakes (Lake Erie), and it sometimes inhabits impoundments.

Trautman (1957:275-276) indicated that the spotted sucker has declined in abundance in Ohio, and is "particularly intolerant to turbid waters, various industrial pollutants, and to lake and stream bottoms covered with flocculent clay slits." Reduced abundance in Kansas is suggested by the larger number of specimens obtained in 1910-1912 (by personnel of the State Biological Survey, specimens in University of Kansas Museum of Natural History) than obtained in recent collections.

The habitat of *Minytrema* has been especially vulnerable to unfavorable change (mainly siltation) because of intensive cultivation of watersheds along the low-gradient streams that are preferred by this species.

To my knowledge, no *Minytrema* have been taken in the Kansas River Basin other than those reported by Cragin (1885b:108); his specimens are not extant. Wheeler's record (1879:33) from the Marais des Cygnes is supported by other specimens from the Osage System in Kansas, although these are few. I have verified the identity of three specimens listed by Jennings (1942:364) as having been taken in Rock Creek, Chase County, by I. D. Graham in 1885; these bear catalog number 2843 in collections at Kansas State University, Manhattan. Juvenile spotted suckers have since been taken from two other localities in the Cottonwood River Drainage of Chase County; one of these records, in section 22, Township 20S, Range 8E, is not shown on the map above.

A tuberculate male obtained in Elk River, Elk County, in early July of 1956, indicates that reproduction by this species occurs in summer in Kansas.

Black redhorse

Moxostoma duquesnei (LeSueur)

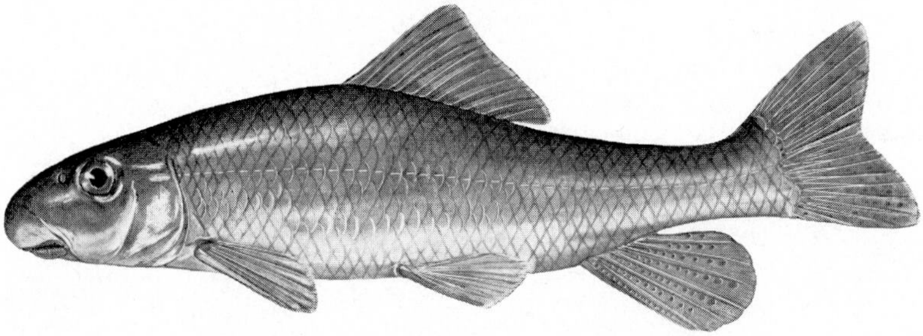

Moxostoma duquesnei, Wheeler (1879:33); Jordan (1891:17); Metcalf (1959:393); Breukelman (1960:33).

Body slender, head and trunk nearly terete; head length 3.8-4.4 in standard length in most adults, about equal to body depth; snout more tumid than in other redhorses, almost concealing upper lip; mouth large, upper lip not swollen medially, lower lip thick and coarsely plicate (Fig. 16B); caudal peduncle slender, depth less than ⅔ its length; dorsal rays usually 13 or 14; anal rays 7; pelvic rays usually 10; lateral-line scales 45-48; pharyngeal teeth thin and comblike; air bladder three-chambered; vertebrae 44 or 45.

Dark gray or olivaceous dorsally, fading to white ventrally, without contrasting markings; dorsal and caudal fins dusky, never red.

Breeding males with prominent tubercles on rays of anal fin and lower lobe of caudal fin; minute tubercles on upper lobe of caudal fin and anterior rays of pelvic fins; head never tuberculate.

Longest Kansas specimen 16 inches.

The black redhorse seems now to be confined to the Spring River System in Cherokee County, but has been reported from the Marais des Cygnes River at Ottawa, Franklin County, by Wheeler (1879: 33) and from the Arkansas River at Wichita by Jordan (1891:17). Probably those two records are referable to *M. erythrurum* (see below), but Wallen (1958:11) reported that *M. duquesnei* has been taken as far westward as the Caney River System in northeastern Oklahoma.

The preferred habitat of the black redhorse is in clear streams that have a high gradient and rocky bottoms. The species is most common in tributaries of moderate size; it is seldom found in the lower mainstreams of major rivers, or in their headwaters.

Reproduction occurs in April and early May in Kansas, on deep, swift riffles. Water-temperatures on dates when reproductively-active males were taken have been in the lower 60's (°F.). As Hubbs (1930:23-24) has indicated, this species spawns earlier than the golden redhorse where the two occur together.

Golden redhorse
Moxostoma erythrurum (Rafinesque)

Ptychostomus bucco Cope (1871 [orig. descr.]).

Myxostoma congestum, Jordan (1878:133).

Moxostoma duquesnei, Wheeler (1879:33); Jordan (1891:17) [misidentifications?].

Moxostoma erythrurum, Hall (1934:230); Breukelman (1940b:379, in part; 1960:33); Jennings (1942:364, in part); Cross (1954:307); Moore and Buck (1955:21); Greer and Cross (1956:360); Schelske (1957:39); Clarke, Breukelman, and Andrews (1958:167); Metcalf (1959:364-365, 1966:142); Deacon (1961:378).

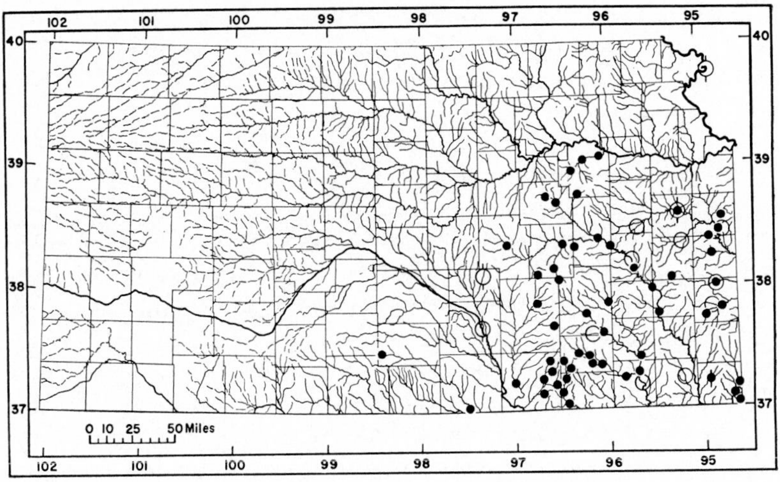

Body stout, compressed; head length 3.6-4.1 in standard length, usually slightly less than body depth; mouth large, lips coarsely plicate; upper lip uniform in thickness; lower lip narrower than in other redhorses, right and left halves forming pronounced median angle (Fig. 16C); depth of caudal peduncle more than ⅔ its length; dorsal rays 12-14; anal rays 7; pelvic rays 9; lateral-line scales usually 40-43; pharyngeal teeth thin, comb like; air bladder three-chambered; vertebrae 40-44.

Olivaceous dorsally, yellowish or bronze laterally, white ventrally, without contrasting markings (except in young-of-year, which have dark blotches); fins dusky, sometimes yellowish; dorsal and caudal fins never red or orange.

Breeding males with large tubercles, often coalescent, on snout; smaller tubercles scattered over top of head and suborbital area; operculum and ventral surface of head with few or no tubercles; breast sometimes with minute tubercles; lateral scales, especially posteriorly, with several small tubercles, in marginal row or scattered over exposed surface of each scale; rays of anal and caudal fins strongly tuberculate; pectoral and pelvic fins sometimes with minute tubercles, especially distally, on both upper and lower surfaces of rays.

Length 18 inches or less in Kansas; elsewhere reported to attain length of 26 inches and weight of 4½ pounds.

In the Arkansas System from the Walnut River eastward the golden redhorse is the most common sucker excepting *Carpiodes carpio*. *M. erythrurum* is less abundant in the Marais des Cygnes than in the Neosho Drainage; in the Kansas River Basin, this species is known only from Mill Creek in Wabaunsee County.

Nomenclatural confusion of redhorses, especially in the last 19th century, causes doubt as to the proper allocation of some of the older records in Kansas (see Hubbs, 1930:23). The fish reported as *M. macrolepidotum* by Evermann and Fordice (1886:185, Harvey County) and as *M. duquesnei* by Wheeler (1879:33, Franklin

County) and Jordan (1891:77, Sedgwick County) probably were *erythrurum*. The syntypes of *Ptychostomus bucco* Cope (catalogue numbers 6961-64 in Academy of Natural Sciences of Philadelphia) were reexamined recently by A. L. Metcalf and found to be *M. erythrurum*.

The golden redhorse inhabits pools in streams that drain soils of limestone origin, and that have a moderate to high gradient. Most of the streams occupied have permanent flow and firm bottoms of bedrock, gravel, or clay. In Mill Creek, golden redhorses are more common in the mainstream than in headwater-tributaries, where *Catostomus commersoni* is the predominant sucker. In the Osage System, most records of *erythrurum* are from tributaries of moderate size. Deacon (1961) failed to find the golden redhorse in the mainstream of the Marais des Cygnes, where the northern redhorse prevailed during his surveys in 1957-1959; *erythrurum* has been taken from the mainstream of that river in other, dryer years. In the Arkansas River System, golden redhorses are most numerous in upland tributaries, but the localities of greatest abundance vary with stream-conditions as affected by weather-cycles. Deacon (1961:408) reported that the relative abundance of *M. erythrurum* in the headwaters of Neosho River (Morris County) increased from less than 0.5 per cent to 5.7 per cent of the total fish-population in the first three years of a "wet" cycle following a five-year drought. During that drought, the golden redhorse was taken often in the lower mainstream of the Neosho River, but became scarce there when flow increased in 1957-1959.

When stream-levels are stable, the golden redhorse seems sedentary in habit except in the breeding season. Most individuals that Deacon marked in 1959 were recaptured in the areas of original capture and release. Meyer (1962) reported information on movements and other aspects of the ecology of the golden redhorse in Iowa, and cited additional literature on the natural history of this species. The food of *M. erythrurum* consists mainly of larval insects.

Reproduction occurs most often in May in Kansas, when the temperature of the water is 70° F. or higher at mid-day. Adults congregate on spawning sites over rocky bottom, presumably after short migrations upstream. Reproductively-active males usually occupy shallow water having moderate current—small "pools" between short riffles in small streams, or areas having streaming flow adjacent to riffles in large streams. Females remain in pools, or in deep water alongshore, entering the shallows occupied by males only briefly for deposition of eggs. The smallest mature adults that I have seen are approximately nine inches in total length and are males; probably, maturity is attained in the third or fourth year of life in Kansas.

In the Ozark region, redhorses have long been the object of a substantial "gig-fishery." Practiced at night, from boats, the spearing of these fish is an exciting sport demanding alertness and skill. Redhorses and some other suckers can be caught on hook-and-line, using natural bait. They contribute an important measure of diversity and interest to the recreational angling that is available in Kansas. Although bony, redhorses are otherwise excellent food-fishes, superior to many game-fish in the flavor and texture of their flesh.

River redhorse

Moxostoma carinatum (Cope)

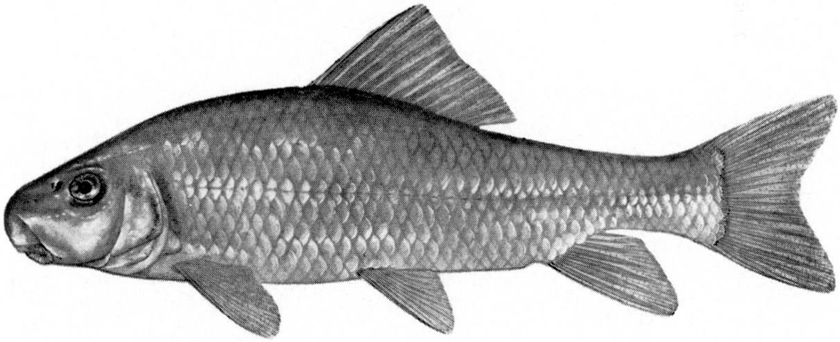

Placopharynx carinatus, Breukelman (1940b:379).
Moxostoma erythrurum, Breukelman (1940b:379, misidentification, in part).
Moxostoma breviceps, Breukelman (1940b:383).
Moxostoma aureolum, Jennings (1942:364, in part).
Moxostoma carinatum, Schelske (1957:39); Clarke, Breukelman, and Andrews (1958:167); Metcalf (1959:393,394, 1966:143); Breukelman (1960:24,25,33).

Body stout, resembling *Moxostoma erythrurum;* head length 3.6-4.2 in standard length; mouth large, lips full and plicate; upper lip not expanded medially, lower lip nearly straight along posterior margin; caudal peduncle deep (as in *erythrurum*); dorsal fin with 13-15 rays; anal rays 7; pelvic rays 9; lateral-line scales 41-44; pharyngeal arch strong, with knobby, molariform teeth (Fig. 9B); air bladder three-chambered; vertebrae 43.

Olivaceous brown dorsally, yellowish or golden laterally, with obscure dark spots on scale-bases; fins (especially caudal fin) red in life; thin black line of melanophores outlining terminal scales on base of caudal fin.

Maximum size 29 inches, 10½ pounds, possibly larger (Trautman, 1957: 260). Largest Kansas specimens 18 inches long.

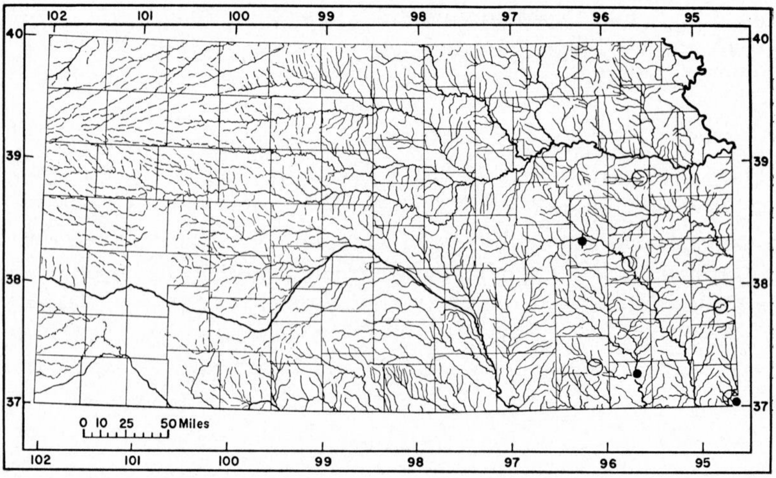

The river redhorse is now rare. All recent records are from the Arkansas River System, but *M. carinatum* formerly inhabited other drainage basins in eastern Kansas. Data on all known specimens are given below, because most records of the river redhorse have been published under names other than *carinatum.* Data are lacking in support of the reported occurrence (Clarke, Breukelman, and Andrews, 1958:167) of the river redhorse in the Cottonwood River in Lyon County.

Kansas River System—Wakarusa River, Shawnee County, one adult (KSU 2732), "presumably collected in 1886 or before, probably before 1885" (Jennings, 1942:364, as *M. aureolum*).

Osage River System—Marmaton River, Bourbon County, two juveniles (KU 1755, 1757) obtained on 28 June 1911; listed by Breukelman (1940b:383) under the name *Moxostoma breviceps,* from card-catalogue in University of Kansas Museum of Natural History, but specimens not seen by him; specimens subsequently relocated in KU collections.

Arkansas River System—Elk River, Elk County, one juvenile (KU 223) obtained on 11 July 1912; tabulated by Breukelman (1940b:379) as *M. erythrurum.* Verdigris River in Sec. 9, T. 31 S, R. 15 E, Montgomery County, one juvenile in collections of Kansas State Teachers College, Emporia, obtained on 16 April 1954; reported as *M. carinatum* by Schelske (1957:39). Neosho River, Coffey County, six juveniles (KU 244-249) collected on 27 June 1912; tabulated by Breukelman (1940b:379) as *Placopharynx carinatus.* Spring River, Cherokee County, two juveniles (KU 215-216) collected on 11 July 1911; tabulated by Breukelman (1940b:379) as *M. erythrurum.* Unnamed tributary of Shoal Creek in Sec. 36, T. 34 S, R. 25 E, Cherokee County, one juvenile (KU 4210) obtained on 11 May 1958.

Northern redhorse

Moxostoma macrolepidotum (LeSueur)

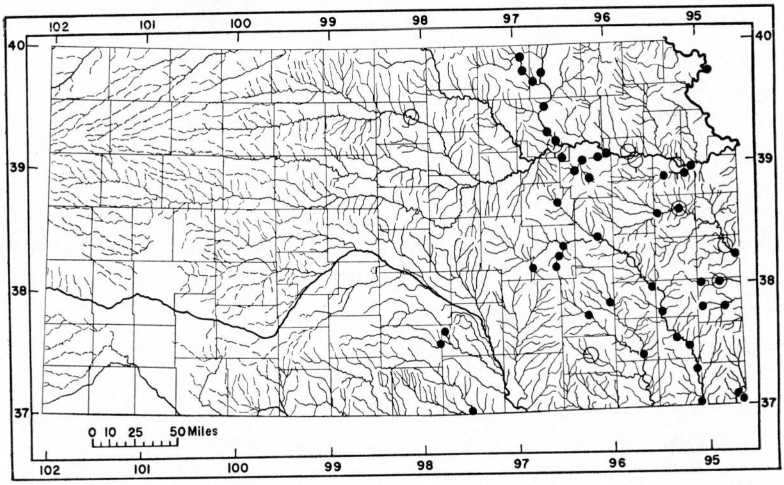

Moxostoma macrolepidotum, Gilbert (1885b:98); Cragin (1885b:108); Graham (1885a:4, 1885b:72); Evermann and Fordice (1886:185, probably erroneously); Metcalf (1966:143).

Moxostoma aureolum, Breukelman (1940b:379); Jennings (1942:364, in part); Cross and Hastings (1956:86); Minckley (1959:418); Breukelman (1960:24, 25, 33); Deacon and Metcalf (1961:316).

Moxostoma aureolum pisolabrum Trautman and Martin (1951 [orig. descr.]); Cross (1954:307-308); Moore and Buck (1955:21); Schelske (1957:39-41); Metcalf (1959:364, 393); Minckley and Cross (1960); Deacon (1961:378, 410).

Moxostoma aureolum aureolum, Minckley and Cross (1960).

Moxostoma erythrurum, Jennings (1942:364, misidentification, in part).

Body slender; head shorter than in other redhorses, length usually 4.5 or more in standard length except in young (4.0 or more in standard length in young-of-year); mouth small, lips thick and plicate, plicae of lower lip broken posteriorly (Fig. 16D); hind edge of lower lip straight or rounded (convex);

dorsal fin with 12 or 13 rays; anal rays 7; pelvic rays 9; lateral-line scales 41-46, most often 43; pharyngeal teeth thin, comblike; air bladder three-chambered; vertebrae 42-44.

Color of adults olivaceous dorsally, with golden (usually) to silvery sheen laterally, white ventrally; dorsolateral scales with diffuse dark spots near bases; all fins red, orange, or yellow, caudal and anal fins usually bright red. See Plate 1.

Breeding males bearing large tubercles on rays 1-6 of anal fin, and on lower lobe of caudal fin; head and scales lacking tubercles.

Length 18 inches or less in Kansas; elsewhere reported to attain length of more than 24 inches and weight of 4-6 pounds (Trautman, 1957:253).

The northern redhorse is represented by two subspecies in Kansas, one of which (*M. m. pisolabrum*) is mainly Ozarkian in distribution. The other (*M. m. macrolepidotum*) is widespread in the upper Mississippi Basin, the Hudson Bay Drainage, and the Atlantic Drainage of the northern United States and southern Canada. In *M. m. pisolabrum*, the upper lip is thickened medially and forms a prominent knob (accounting for the vernacular "pea-lipped northern redhorse," a name sometimes applied to this subspecies), whereas the upper lip is uniformly thin in *M. m. macrolepidotum*.

Like several other Ozarkian fishes, *M. m. pisolabrum* ranges westward commonly to the Neosho and Marais des Cygnes drainages in Kansas. West of the Flint Hills the abundance diminishes greatly, although this subspecies occurs southwestward to the Ninnescah and Chikaskia rivers. No specimens have yet been found in the Caney or Walnut rivers in Kansas. A record by Evermann and Fordice (1886:185) from Sand Creek near Newton, Harvey County, is tentatively referred to *M. erythrurum*, with which the name *macrolepidotum* was often associated (erroneously) in the late 19th century.

Moxostoma macrolepidotum is not a common fish in the Kansas River Basin, but seems to occur more widely there than does any other redhorse. Most records antedate 1900, and some may be referable to *M. erythrurum*. Only in Mill Creek, Wabaunsee County, have many redhorses been taken in recent years. Northern redhorses are caught rarely by commercial fishermen in the Missouri River. Most specimens from the Kansas Basin have the upper lip somewhat swollen, thicker than in *M. m. macrolepidotum* elsewhere, and are regarded as intergrades (Minckley and Cross, 1960).

The northern redhorse prefers larger streams than does *M. erythrurum*. Deacon (1961:378) stated that *M. m. pisolabrum* "typically occurs in riffles, most commonly at the uppermost end where the water flows swiftly and is about two feet deep" in the mainstreams of the Neosho and Marais des Cygnes. Riffles having rubble or gravel-bottoms may be required by *pisolabrum* both as feeding-areas and spawning-grounds. The presence of such riffles usually implies also that the water is relatively clear, another possible requirement of this species. The upper parts of the Ninnescah and Chikaskia rivers, where *M. m. pisolabrum* occurs rarely, have generally sandy bottoms and high summer temperatures (99° F. on August 2, 1964) but both streams have continuously flowing, clear water.

Specimens of *pisolabrum* in breeding condition have been taken from early April through early May in Kansas. Several aspects of the ecology of *M. macrolepidotum* in Iowa have been reported by Meyer (1962).

Hogsucker

Hypentelium nigricans (LeSueur)

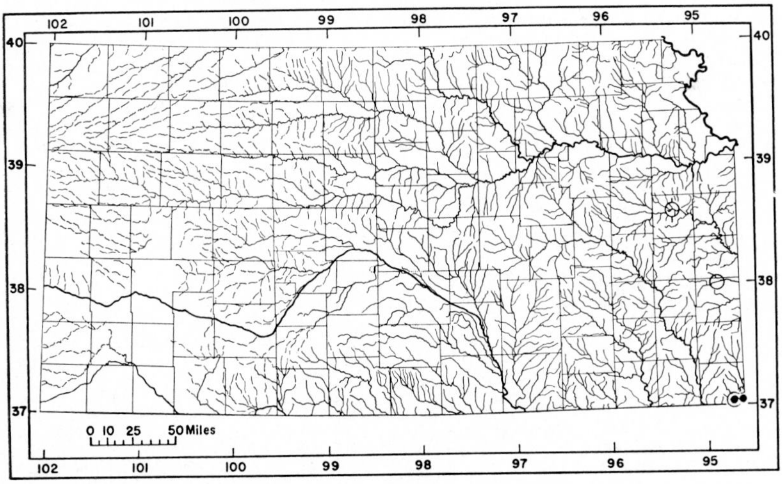

Hypentelium nigricans, Wheeler (1879:33); Breukelman (1940b:380, 1960: 22-23, 33); Metcalf (1959:393, 1966:163).
Catostomus nigricans, Cragin (1885b:108); Graham (1885b:72).

Body slender, terete; head large, flat or concave between orbits; snout long, eye small; distance from back of eye to upper end of gill cover (opercular cleft) 2.0 or more in snout length; mouth large, lips thick and strongly papillose; dorsal fin with 10-12 rays; anal fin with 7 (or 8) rays; pelvic rays usually 9; lateral line well-developed, scales usually 45-50; air bladder two-chambered; vertebrae 43-46.

Dark, olivaceous brown; young having dark brown dorsal saddles extending downward and forward (diagonally) onto sides; caudal fin with dark band crossing rays near base; tip of dorsal fin dark; pectoral and pelvic fins with much dark pigment near bases; anal fin clear.

Breeding males with large tubercles on rays of anal fin; numerous smaller tubercles on rays of pectoral fins, pelvic fins, and lower lobe of caudal fin; head densely clothed, dorsally and laterally, by microscopic tubercles.

Maximum size 24 inches, 5 pounds (Trautman, 1957:266), usually much smaller.

The hogsucker is rare in Kansas, having been found only in the Spring River Drainage, Cherokee County, in the past 15 years. Wheeler (1879:33) reported the species from the Marais des Cygnes River at Ottawa, and a specimen caught in 1911 from this stream-system is extant at The University of Kansas. Graham (1885b:72) stated that hogsuckers were "Common; Kansas and Neosho rivers", but only one specimen caught by Graham is now in collections at Kansas State University (KSU 2978), and that one lacks data as to the locality of capture.

Hogsuckers may have been eliminated from some streams that they occupied prior to settlement in Kansas. Cultivation of the tall-grass prairie probably increased the rate of siltation, and incidence of intermittency, on riffles required by this species. Hogsuckers normally inhabit the deeper riffles and adjacent parts of small or moderate-sized, clear streams that have rocky bottoms. The bulky head, expansive pectoral fins, tapering trunk, slender caudal peduncle, and small caudal fin of the hogsucker are clearly adaptations to life on the bottom of turbulent, relatively swift riffles. The species forages by sucking organisms off the exposed surfaces of stones, or overturning them to obtain insect larvae that live in crevices within the loose rubble.

Hogsuckers reproduce in April or May, at water-temperatures of 60° to 70° F. When ready to deposit eggs, the female moves onto a riffle, selects a spawning-site in shallow water, and is joined in the spawning act by several males. The fertilized eggs settle into the gravelly substrate, which is considerably disturbed [and cleaned of sediment] by the activities of the breeding fish. Spawning is repeated after intervals of rest in which the female retires to deeper water, accompanied by her group of males (Raney and Lachner, 1946). The eggs and young receive no parental attention. Male hogsuckers mature at lengths of 5 to 7 inches, females at lengths of 6 to 8 inches.

White sucker

Catostomus commersoni (Lacépède)

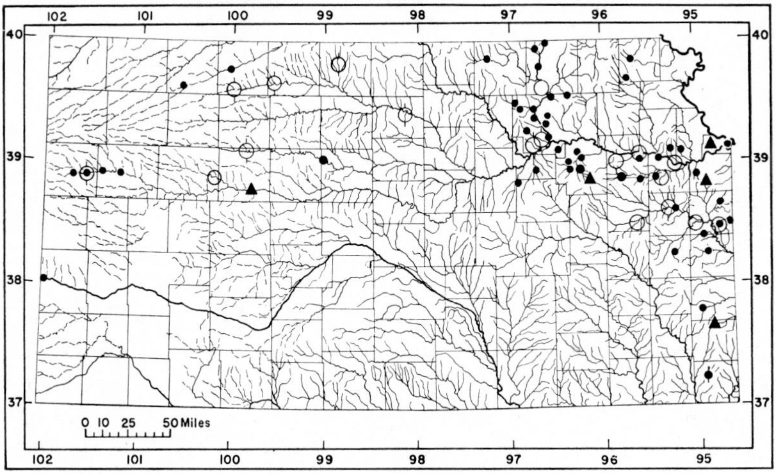

Catostomus chloropteron Abbott (1860a:473-474 [orig. descr. based on two specimens collected by Wm. A. Hammond, "Habitat: Kansas"]).

Catostomus chloropterum, Cope (1865b:85).

Catostomus teres, Wheeler (1879:33); Gilbert (1884:10, 1885:98, 1886: 210, 1889:40); Cragin (1885b:107); Graham (1885a:4, 1885b:72); Hay (1887:247, 250, 251, 253).

Catostomus commersonnii, Hall (1934:230); Breukelman (1940b:383, 1960: 22, 23, 33); Jennings (1942:364); Minckley (1956:253, 1959:418).

Catastomus commersonnii, Breukelman (1940b: 377, 380).

Catostomus commersonnii sucklii, Breukelman (1940a:369, 1940b:377).

Catostomus commersonnii commersonnii, Breukelman (1940b:377); Deacon and Metcalf (1961:315).

Catostomus commersoni, Clarke, Breukelman, and Andrews (1958:167); Kilgore and Rising (1965:139); Metcalf (1966:144).

White sucker—Snow (1875:141).

Body slender, nearly terete; head moderate in size, distance from back of orbit to upper end of opercular cleft much less than 2.0 in snout length; mouth ventral, lips thick and papillose (Fig. 15C); dorsal fin with 11-13 rays; anal rays 7 or 8; pelvic rays 9-11, usually 10; lateral line well-developed, with 65-74 scales; air bladder two-chambered; vertebrae 44-48.

Uniformly dark dorsally (olivaceous or bronze) fading to greenish-yellow laterally and creamy-white ventrally, without conspicuous markings; caudal and dorsal fins dusky, lower fins often yellowish; young mottled or tesselated dorsally, mid-sides with three oval dark blotches; breeding males having lateral sheens of pink, purple, and orange.

Breeding males with large tubercles on rays of anal fin, lower lobe of caudal fin, and scales on lower surface of caudal peduncle; minute tubercles on dorsal surface of head, on distal (branched) parts of rays of pectoral, pelvic, and dorsal fins, and on many scales.

Maximum size 6 or 7 pounds (Keleher, 1961), rarely more than 3 pounds.

White suckers have been reported from numerous localities in the Kansas River Basin, and may have occurred throughout that basin prior to 1900. Western populations have since been decimated, except in a few tributaries of the Smoky Hill and Republican rivers. In northeastern Kansas white suckers remain common in small, rocky, upland brooks. *Catostomus* is found occasionally in warm, muddy, intermittent creeks in the northeast, and in the mainstream of Kansas River. These streams seem less suitable for white suckers than do some streams in the eastern part of the Arkansas River Drainage where the species is not found. Records of *C. commersoni* in the Arkansas Basin in Kansas are few. Graham (1885b:72) implied occurrence there by reporting the species as "Common over State." Hall (1934:230) listed it from Cherry Creek and a small impoundment thereon in Cherokee County; but, his indication that this species was common, coupled with his failure to report other suckers that occur in the area he studied, suggests the possibility of misidentification. Breukelman (1940b:383) based a record from the "Cottonwood River, Florence, August, 1912" on a card-index reference not supported by extant specimens at The University of Kansas. Cards having the same data were listed by Breukelman for several other species: shovel-nosed sturgeon, long-nosed gar, gizzard shad, carp, black (or brown) bullhead, and drum. That combination of species might more likely have been taken at Lawrence (in the Kansas River) than at Florence (in the Cottonwood River).

White suckers occur commonly in the Arkansas River Basin in Colorado and New Mexico, and young individuals have been taken recently in the mainstream in western Kansas (Kilgore and Rising, 1965:139). Because the species also inhabits Ozarkian tributaries of the Arkansas River in Missouri, Arkansas, and Oklahoma, records from southeastern Kansas can be expected.

Perhaps the persistence of white suckers in marginal habitat in the Kansas River System reflects a continuing, gradual decline of the species under sustained deterioriation of habitat. Small populations found in muddy, intermittent creeks may be maintained by strays from nearby streams that still provide habitat continuously suitable for *Catostomus*. Several artificial lakes on upland streams in the Kansas Basin have an abundance of white suckers, and escapement from these lakes may reinforce populations in streams. In the Eskridge City Lake, Wabaunsee County, the abundant adults utilize short, rocky tributaries for spawning. Although these tributaries are highly intermittent, springs normally feed them while vegetation is dormant, there being no loss of ground-water due to transpiration; such seepage normally sustains a flow in these clear brooks well past the spawning-time of *Catostomus*. Subsequent drying of the tributaries strands some young, but many move downstream to the lake, and some escape to the streams below at times of spillway-overflow.

White suckers spawn in spring (April or early May in Kansas), over clean rocky bottoms. Spawning sites are most often in streams, in shallows swept by currents, but spawning on gravelly shoals of lakes has been reported. Males arrive first on the spawning grounds. No nest-preparation or defense of a stable territory is apparent. Individual females, when ready to deposit eggs, enter the spawning area from deeper water and are pursued across the shallows by one to several males. Normally two males move alongside the female, then converge against her as eggs and sperm are discharged simultaneously. Sand and gravel are dislodged from the bottom by the spawning fish, and gravel partly covers the eggs. Females then move to deeper water, but return at intervals to the spawning area until their complement of eggs (often 20,000 or more) for that season has been deposited. The eggs adhere to the substrate and develop without parental attention. At temperatures of about 50° F., hatching occurs in two to three weeks (Stewart, 1926:154); the larvae are 8 mm. long or slightly longer when hatched.

Larval white suckers (12-25 mm. long) have oblique mouths and short intestines. They feed near the surface on protozoans, diatoms, small crustaceans, and bloodworms brought by currents into areas occupied by the schools of fry. As the young grow, the mouth becomes ventral, the intestine elongates, and the fish seek food mainly on the bottoms of streams or lakes. Adults are almost omnivorous, but aquatic insects predominate in their diet (Stewart, 1926).

Catostomus grows larger in lakes than in streams of Kansas. Many suckers 17 to 19 inches long, weighing 2 pounds or more, have been netted from the Eskridge City Lake, Leavenworth and Wyandotte County State lakes, and Lone Star Lake in Douglas County. These sizes are attained in the fourth or fifth year of life in Eskridge City Lake, but Minckley (1959:418) reported that white suckers of the same ages in Blue River were only 8 to 9 inches long.

Catfishes

FAMILY ICTALURIDAE

KEY

1. Caudal fin deeply forked 2
   Caudal fin not forked 3
2. Anal rays 24-29 (Fig. 6A), margin of anal fin curved, channel catfish, *Ictalurus punctatus,* p. 205
   Anal rays 32-35, margin of anal fin nearly straight, blue catfish, *Ictalurus furcatus,* p. 209
3. Adipose fin completely separated from caudal fin (Fig. 17A) 4
   Adipose fin joined to caudal fin (Fig. 17B) 7
4. Anal rays 14-17 (Fig. 6A); premaxillary band of teeth continuous backward along sides of jaw (Fig. 18A), flathead, *Pylodictis olivaris,* p. 213
   Anal rays usually more than 17; premaxillary band of teeth confined to front of jaw (Fig. 18B) 5
5. Anal rays 24-27; chin barbels white, no darker than underside of head; caudal fin usually rounded . . . . yellow bullhead, *Ictalurus natalis,* p. 203
   Anal rays 17-24; chin barbels pigmented, darker than underside of head; caudal fin slightly notched 6

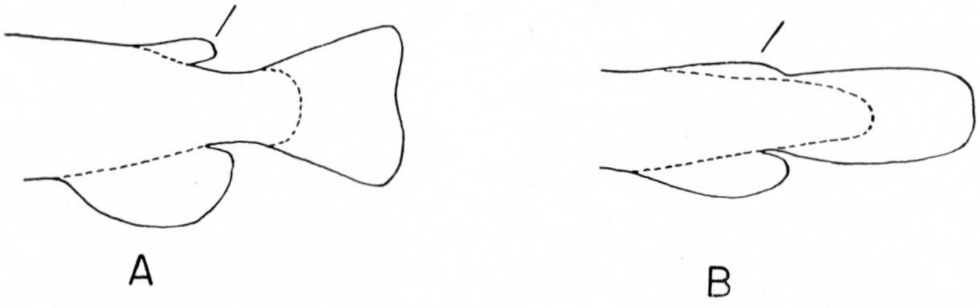

FIG. 17. Adipose fins of catfishes. A. Adipose free, as in genera *Ictalurus* and *Pylodictis.* B. Adipose adnate (joined) to caudal fin, as in genus *Noturus.*

6. Anal rays 17-21; pectoral spine nearly smooth posteriorly; body and anal fin not mottled, belly yellowish,
black bullhead, *Ictalurus melas,* p. 198

Anal rays 21-24; pectoral spine saw-edged posteriorly; body and anal fin often mottled or barred, belly white,
brown bullhead, *Ictalurus nebulosus,* p. 201

7. Body conspicuously mottled; caudal fin vertically banded or with dark basal bar; posterior end of dorsal-fin base about equidistant from tip of snout and base of caudal fin (central rays), or nearer the latter 8

Body color plain or nearly so; caudal fin without vertical dark bars; posterior end of dorsal-fin base nearer tip of snout than base of central caudal rays 9

8. Dark blotch on adipose fin extending to fin-margin; dorsal and caudal fins black-tipped; least depth of caudal peduncle contained about 3.0 times in distance from adipose notch to posterior end of dorsal fin-base .... Brindled madtom, *Noturus miurus,* p. 224

Dark blotch on adipose fin not extending to fin-margin; dorsal and caudal fins with dark bands medially, not black-tipped; least depth of caudal peduncle contained 3.5 or more times in distance from adipose notch to posterior end of dorsal fin-base,
Neosho madtom, *Noturus* species, p. 222

9. Upper and lower jaws approximately equal 10

Lower jaw shorter than upper jaw (snout projecting beyond mouth) 11

10. Notch at juncture of adipose and caudal fins much nearer tip of depressed dorsal fin than end of caudal fin; body stout; fins evenly pigmented (not dark-edged) .. tadpole madtom, *Noturus gyrinus,* p. 216

Notch at juncture of adipose and caudal fins nearer tip of caudal than tip of depressed dorsal fin; body slender; dorsal, caudal, and anal fins dark-edged, pale basally .... slender madtom, *Noturus exilis,* p. 219

11. Teeth on upper jaw confined to narrow band without backward extensions (Fig. 18B); pectoral spine nearly smooth anteriorly; caudal fin uniformly dark or narrowly white-edged,
freckled madtom, *Noturus nocturnus,* p. 218

Band of teeth on upper jaw with backward extension on each side of jaw (Fig. 18A); pectoral spine saw-edged anteriorly; caudal fin light dorsally and ventrally, with central dark band from base to tip,
stonecat, *Noturus flavus,* p. 221

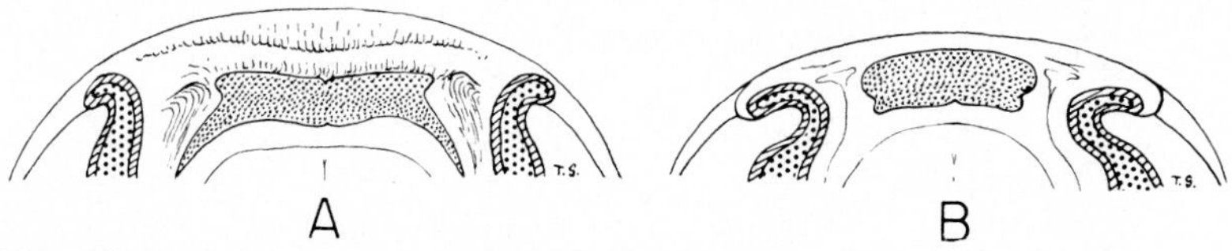

FIG. 18. Upper jaws of two kinds of madtoms, illustrating differences in form of premaxillary toothpatch (central stippled area, above letter A and letter B).
A. Stonecat, having backward extensions of toothpatch along each side of jaw.
B. Slender madtom, lacking backward extensions of toothpatch.

Black bullhead
Ictalurus melas (Rafinesque)

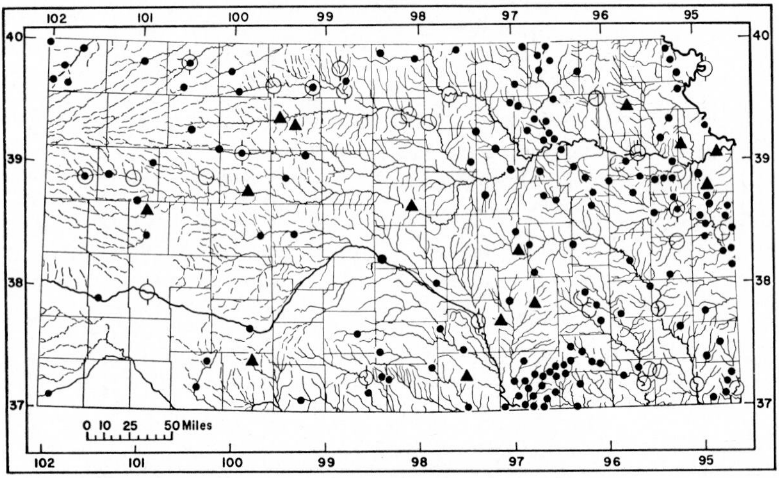

Amiurus atrarius, Snow (1875:141); Wheeler (1879:34).

Amiurus cragini Gilbert (1884:10 [orig. descr.], 1885a:512).

Amiurus melas, Gilbert (1884:10, 1885b:97, 1886:210, 1889:38, 40); Cragin (1885b:107); Jordan and Meek (1885:13); Graham (1885a:4, 1885b:71); Evermann and Fordice (1886:185); Hay (1887:242, 247, 248, 251, 253).

Ameiurus melas, Jordan (1891:17); Hall (1934:231); Breukelman (1946:61); Minckley (1956:355); Schelske (1957:46).

Ameiurus melas catulus, Hubbs and Ortenburger (1929a:40); Hall (1934:231); Breukelman (1940b:381); Jennings (1942:365); Cross (1954:311); Moore and Buck (1955:24).

Ameiurus melas melas, Breukelman (1940a:372, 1940b:381); Jennings (1942:365).

Ameiurus nebulosus, Breukelman (1940b:383, "probably *A. melas catulus*").

Ictalurus melas, Greer and Cross (1956:360); Clarke, Breukelman, and Andrews (1958:168); Cross, Deacon, and Ward (1959:163); Minckley and Cross (1959:212); Metcalf (1959:377, 391-392, 1966:148); Minckley (1959:427); Harms (1960a:262, 1960b:295); Breukelman (1960:34); Deacon (1961:391-392); Deacon and Metcalf (1961:317); Hastings and Cross (1962:8); Fisher (1962:428).

"Bullhead catfish"—Schoonover and Thompson (1954:178).

Form stout; caudal fin slightly notched, almost square-tipped; adipose fin separate from caudal; anal fin rounded, with 17-21 rays; pectoral spine almost smooth (sometimes rough posteriorly, but not conspicuously toothed); premaxillary tooth-patch without backward extensions; jaws equal in length or the upper protruding slightly; vertebrae 39 or 40.

Young black, adults variably brownish-yellow to black, never mottled light-and-dark; membranes of anal fin uniformly dark, rays light; belly yellowish; chin barbels pigmented, always darker than skin on underside of head.

Size usually less than one pound, rarely attaining weights of two pounds or more; State record "bullhead" (species not designated) weighed 4 pounds 3½ ounces, length 17 inches [Kansas Fish and Game, 23(1):11, December, 1965].

The black bullhead occurs throughout Kansas so commonly that the map above would be nearly saturated with records if farm ponds and small lakes were taken into account.

The habitat of the black bullhead is characterized by soft bottoms and high turbidity, in quiet backwaters, oxbows, the mouths of creeks, and pools of small, intermittent streams. The species is not abundant in large streams where bottoms are rocky or sandy, nor in small streams that have a permanent flow of clear water. In the headwaters of the Neosho River, Deacon (1961:408-418) found that 7 to 32 per cent of all fish in large, quiet pools having muddy bottoms were black bullheads, whereas they comprised 2 per cent or less of the fish in adjacent areas having rocky bottom and current. The relative abundance of bullheads declined from 1956, a year when the Neosho was ponded, through 1959, following three years of semipermanent flow. Farther downstream in the Neosho River, black bullheads were not found by Deacon but were abundant in oxbows adjacent to the channel. Metcalf (1959:390-392) indicated that black bullheads comprised 29 to 100 per cent of the fish in the uppermost pools of three intermittent streams that he studied in southeastern Kansas; farther down these three stream channels, bullheads were less prevalent.

On the basis of short-term movements by marked specimens in the upper Neosho River, Deacon (1961:418) considered the black bullhead to be a vagile species.

The high vagility and predilection for headwater pools account for the presence of bullheads in most farm ponds in Kansas. Bullheads rapidly invade formerly-dry drainageways after rains, and gently-sloping spillways allow access of bullheads into many ponds while they overflow.

The reproductive habits of the black bullhead make it unlikely that eggs of this species are carried into ponds by waterbirds. The nests of black bullheads usually are concealed beneath some protective cover; at least, the nests are so concealed in clear water where observations of them are possible. All nests that I have seen were located partly or wholly beneath matted vegetation or woody debris. A small area of bottom beneath the vegetation (or debris) was cleaned of sediments by the attendant fish. The eggs adhere to one another in a large, golden-colored mass. An adult bullhead hovers continuously over the egg-mass and occasionally disturbs it by gentle swimming movements or tight turns above it. Eggs like these, adhering in masses, shielded above by some cover, and guarded by the parent fish, seem less likely to be picked up on the feet of wading birds than do eggs of many other kinds of fish that rarely or never occur in farm ponds.

Subsequent to hatching, the young remain in compact schools for several days—probably for two weeks or longer in most cases. The conspicuous "balls" of black young move slowly, near the surface in moderately deep water. Although the school itself may remain in one place for several minutes, the individual young circle constantly and rapidly within the dense, swirling swarm. I have often seen one or two adult bullheads accompanying the schooled young, beneath and slightly to one side of the "ball." Forney (1955: 159) reported that more than two adults sometimes accompanied the young in a lake in Iowa. He believed that adults desert the young after they attain a length of about an inch, when the compact schools begin to disperse. The young then move to shallow water and spread out over the bottom. Prior to that dispersal, the schools are easily captured by seining, because the fish tend to remain together and those missed in one dip of the net quickly regroup. After their habit changes to a loose, horizontal aggregation in shallow water, the fish are much less vulnerable to seines because they scatter when disturbed; the larger, stronger young are also more elusive than are balled young.

Growth to maturity is accomplished in the second, third, or fourth summer, depending on the population density and the available food supply. Some bullheads reproduce at sizes too small to have value as sport fish. Their reproductive season is long, extending from late May through August in Kansas. In many ponds—especially in muddy ponds having few bass or other predatory species —few if any bullheads attain usable size, although their total weight often exceeds 200 pounds per acre.

Black bullheads are omnivorous. They rely extensively on aquatic insects as food, but also consume some vegetation, and are efficient scavengers. Bullheads are attracted to places where dead fish (or the heads and viscera of dressed fish) have been discarded. Bullheads undoubtedly consume many fish that die naturally in lakes and streams, partly accounting for the infrequency with which dead fish are seen in nature.

Black bullheads respond well to supplemental feeding of pelleted rations, as do channel catfish. In ponds under study by the State Biological Survey, black bullheads have grown to lengths of six inches or more in the year that they hatched, and to weights of one pound or more as yearlings, when they were fed daily. A disadvantage of this species, compared with channel catfish, is that the black bullhead reproduces so abundantly that most young must be removed to prevent overcrowding and to obtain satisfactory estimates of the amount of feed needed each day to maintain rapid growth.

Brown bullhead

Ictalurus nebulosus (LeSueur)

Amiurus nebulosus, Cragin (1885b:107); Graham (1885a:4, 1885b:71).
Amiurus vulgaris, Graham (1885b:71).
Ameiurus nebulosus, Breukelman (1946:61).
Ictalurus nebulosus, Metcalf (1966:149).

Form stout; caudal fin shallowly notched, nearly square-edged; adipose fin separate from caudal; anal fin rounded, with 21-24 rays; pectoral spine toothed along posterior edge; premaxillary tooth-patch without backward extensions at sides of jaw; jaws nearly equal in length; vertebrae usually 39.

Color of young black, of adults yellowish-brown, usually indistinctly mottled (variegated); anal fin slightly mottled, rays not lighter than membranes; belly usually white; chin barbels dark.

Weight to two pounds or more; seldom exceeding one pound.

Although the brown bullhead was reported by some early students of fishes in Kansas, I doubt that the species is native to this State. Confusion in identifications of catfishes is apparent in the multiplicity of names used by Wheeler, Snow, Graham, Cragin, and other writers in the late 19th century. Perhaps the inclusion of

I. nebulosus in lists of Kansas fishes at that time resulted from misidentifications of black bullheads; or, early reports may have been anticipatory, based on an assumption that brown bullheads, common east of the Mississippi, should occur in Kansas as well.

Brown bullheads have been introduced in Kansas from several sources. In the 1950's, the species was propagated and distributed by the Federal Fish Hatchery at Farlington, Crawford County, in the hope that brown bullheads would prove to be a desirable pond-fish here. The effort was not notably successful and was abandoned. Many of the "fee-fishing" lakes in eastern Kansas are stocked with brown bullheads, along with carp and black bullheads, that are brought periodically from other states.

To my knowledge, *I. nebulosus* has not become established in streams of Kansas, despite survival and some reproduction by the species in ponds.

The brown bullhead differs little from the black bullhead in its habits and the size it attains. In the eastern United States, brown bullheads are abundant in many clear, weedy lakes, but also live in muddy pools of intermittent drainageways. A preference for ponded waters and tolerance of pollution are emphasized by some authors. The species spawns from May to July. Nest-sites are commonly but not invariably adjacent to stones, logs, or other shelter. A shallow excavation is cleared of silt as a "floor" for the nest, which is constantly attended by at least one parental fish. Some reports state that both the male and the female care for eggs. The diet of the brown bullhead is varied, but aquatic insects contribute a major part of its food supply.

Yellow bullhead

Ictalurus natalis (LeSueur)

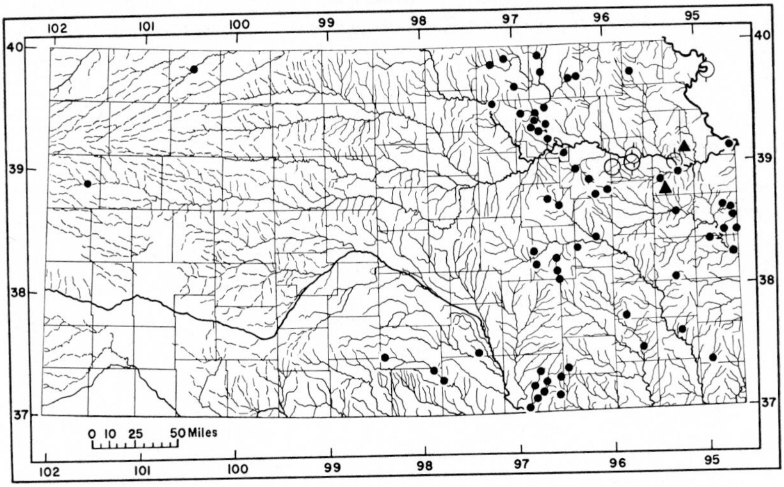

Amiurus albidus, Wheeler (1879:34) (see, also, Cragin, 1885b:107).

Amiurus natalis, Cragin (1885b:107); Jordan and Meek (1885:13); Graham (1885b:71); Gilbert (1886:207).

Ameiurus natalis, Hall (1934:231); Breukelman (1946:61).

Ameiurus natalis natalis, Breukelman (1940a:372, 1940b:381); Jennings (1942:365); Cross (1954:311).

Ictalurus natalis, Clarke, Breukelman, and Andrews (1958: 169); Metcalf (1959:377-378, 393, 1966:148); Minckley (1959:427); Harms (1960a: 262, 1960b:295); Breukelman (1960:34); Deacon (1961:390-391); Deacon and Metcalf (1961:317); Hastings and Cross (1962:8).

Form rather slender, caudal peduncle deep; margin of caudal fin rounded, slightly notched above mid-point of its distal edge; adipose fin separate from caudal; anal fin long, low, with 24-27 rays; pectoral spine saw-edged posteriorly; premaxillary tooth-patch without backward extensions at sides of jaw; jaws nearly equal in length; vertebrae 42-45.

Color of young black, adults variably yellowish-brown to black, never mottled; fins dark; belly white; chin-barbels unpigmented (white), matching underside of head.

Weight usually less than one pound, rarely as heavy as six pounds.

The yellow bullhead is principally a stream-fish, and is most common in clear, permanently-flowing tributaries that have rocky bottoms. Thus its distribution complements that of the black bullhead, which seems best adapted to ponds and muddy intermittent creeks. These habitats are not fully discrete, however; both species are found at many localities.

Nearly all records of *I. natalis* are in eastern Kansas, where the species seems most abundant in small streams of the Marais des Cygnes (Osage) System. Records from western Kansas are few, and some are problematical. One of the mapped records represents specimens caught in 1958 below the dam at Decatur County State Lake, and may result from introduction of the species in that impoundment. Metcalf obtained several young yellow bullheads in headwaters of the Smoky Hill River, Wallace County, in 1961. Earlier, Breukelman (1940a:372, 1940b:381) reported the species from the Saline River (locality not specified), on the basis of one specimen that he found in collections at the University of Kansas, and six other specimens that he caught from that river in 1938. No specimens of *I. natalis* that were caught prior to 1940 are now extant at the University of Kansas.

Channel catfish

Ictalurus punctatus (Rafinesque)

Pimelodus hammondii Abbott (1860b:568-569 [orig. descr.]).
Pimelodus notatus Abbott (1860b:569 [orig. descr.]).
Ictalurus simpsonii Gill (1862:43-44 [orig. descr.]).
Ictalurus notatus, Cope (1865b:86).
Ictalurus caerulescens, Snow (1875:141); Cope (1865b:85).
Ictalurus lacustris, Cragin (1885b:107).
Ictalurus furcatus, Graham (1885b:71); Hall (1934:231); [probable misidentifications].
Ictalurus punctatus, Wheeler (1879:33); Gilbert (1885b:97, 1886:210, 1889:40); Cragin (1885b:107); Jordan and Meek (1885:13); Graham (1885a:4, 1885b:71); Hay (1887:242, 247, 251); Jordan (1891:17); Dyche (1914:77-81); Doze (1925); Hall (1934:231); Cross (1954: 311); Cross and Hastings (1956:86); Greer and Cross (1956:360); Schelske (1957:46); Clarke, Breukelman, and Andrews (1958:168); Cross, Deacon, and Ward (1959:163); Davis (1959); Metcalf (1959: 377, 1966:147); Minckley (1959:427-428); Minckley and Deacon (1959:346); Harms (1960a:262, 1960b:295); Breukelman (1960:34); Tiemeier and Elder (1960); Deacon (1961:385-390); Deacon and Metcalf (1961:317); Hastings and Cross (1962:8); Fisher (1962:428); Tiemeier (1962); Tiemeier, Deyoe, and Weardon (1965); Simco and Cross (1966).
Ictalurus lacustris punctatus, Breukelman (1940a:372, 1940b:381); Jennings (1942:365).
Ictalurus Lacustrus Punctatus, Brown (1942).
Channel catfish—Schoonover and Thompson (1954:177-178).

Form slender, not humpbacked before dorsal fin; caudal fin deeply forked; anal fin with 24-29 rays, its margin rounded; jaws unequal, upper jaw protruding; teeth of upper jaw in broad transverse band without backward extensions; in specimens 10 to 24 inches long, length of dorsal spine less than distance from tip of snout to back of eye, and length of dorsal spine 2.5-5.0 in predorsal length of fish; maxillary (longest) barbels much longer than head (except in breeding males, which sometimes have barbels shortened by wear); vertebrae usually 48 or 49. Breeding males with enlarged heads; lips thickened and fleshy, increasing apparent width of mouth; head with low rounded pads above and behind eyes ("chucklehead"); fin-membranes thickened, especially those investing spines.

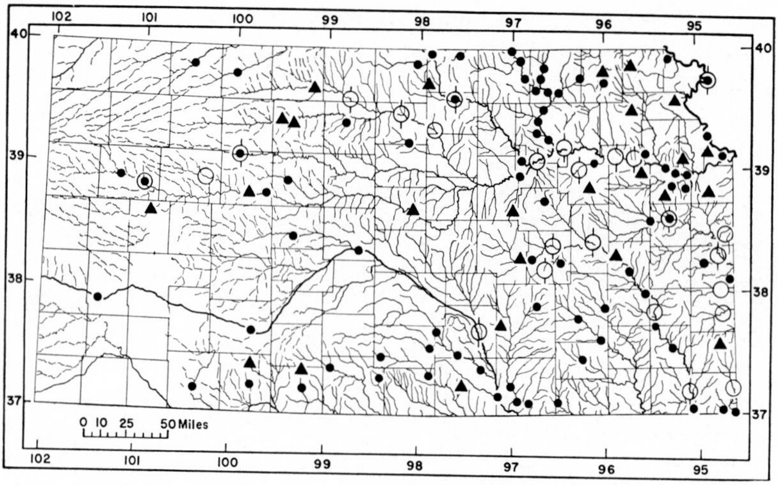

Color bluish-gray dorsally, fading to white ventrally; sides usually with scattered dark flecks (spots often lost in large adults); breeding males gray to blue-black, darker than non-breeders.

Largest Kansas specimen 40½ inches long, weight 32 pounds.

The channel catfish is common in most streams of Kansas, and has been stocked in lakes and farm ponds throughout the State. Some evidence indicates that its abundance has increased within the last few decades, especially in southwestern Kansas.

The size attained by channel catfish varies greatly, but rarely exceeds five pounds in streams. Some lakes produce much larger fish, the current record being a 32-pound specimen (KU 7268, skull only) that was caught from Gardner City Lake by Mr. E. S. Dailey on August 14, 1962. In a study of the growth-rates of channel catfish throughout Kansas, Davis (1959:12-13) reported an average length of approximately 13 inches (weight ¾ pound or less) for channel catfish at an age of five years; but, the average size at that age varied in different lakes from 8.7 inches (weight less than four ounces) to 19.3 inches (weight more than two pounds). Stunted fish that were tagged and transferred to lakes having few channel catfish grew rapidly. For example, a fish 11 inches long that weighed six ounces when tagged and released in Wyandotte County Lake in August, 1954, at a probable age of 5 years, was 26 inches long and weighed 7 pounds, 2 ounces when recaptured in July, 1957. Four- and five-year-old channel catfish that weighed approximately five ounces when stocked in a ¾-acre pond in 1954 weighed about 1¼ pounds two years later, and 4¼ to 5¾ pounds seven years later, when the last of the stocked fish were recaptured. The age attained by those fish (11 or 12 years) is unusual; few channel catfish live longer than seven or eight years in Kansas waters, although individuals as old as 14 years were found by Davis (*loc. cit.*).

Deacon (1961:385-390), Davis (1959) and others have discussed habits of the channel catfish, which can be summarized as follows: In streams, most adults retreat in daytime to pools where they lie adjacent to log-drifts, undercut banks, or other cover if available. The fish often move at night onto the stronger, deeper riffles for feeding. Channel catfish are said to be omnivorous, but staple items in their diet are aquatic insects, crayfish, small mollusks, and fish.

Reproduction occurs from late May to early July. The male catfish locates a suitable dark cavity or crevice in stream-banks, beneath debris lodged in the stream, or under ledges where rock-strata outcrop in the channel. Abandoned burrows of muskrats and beavers may be adapted as spawning-sites by channel catfish. Deacon (1961:389) found that shallow holes which he dug into steep clay-banks were occupied and enlarged by channel catfish in their breeding season.

The optimal temperature for spawning is approximately 80° F. Each female probably spawns but once each year, depositing her eggs in the form of a flattened, gelatinous mass that Doze (1925: 173) likened to a generous gob of tapioca. The male remains with the eggs; his presence probably protects them from most predators, from fungus-infections, and from oxygen-depletion within the nest-chamber. If the eggs are removed from a nest, the attendant male may accept a second and third female. The fry stay in or near the nest for several days after hatching, until their yolk-sacs are fully absorbed. The young then disperse to shallow water, generally in rocky riffles of streams, where they appear in abundance in late June or July and remain until autumn. In winter, the young leave riffles for deep water, but return in early spring. As their growth proceeds, the yearlings occupy progressively deeper water on riffles and gently-sloping gravel-bars, until they disappear from such areas altogether (except at night, when feeding) before the next generation of young appears on riffles.

Neither current nor a rocky substrate is essential for spawning, or for normal development of young channel catfish. The species often spawns in lakes and ponds; subsequently, the extent of survival and the growth-rate of the young vary with clarity of the water and with predation. Most muddy impoundments provide suitable dark nest-sites for channel catfish and have few large bass or other sunfish. Reproduction and survival of catfish often are excessive, resulting in "stunted" populations. Most clear lakes and ponds provide few dark nest-sites for channel catfish, and support more bass and other sunfish than do muddy ponds. The number of young channel catfish that survive in clear ponds is minimized, perhaps because the young, in avoiding light, seek sheltered places in deep water where they are especially vulnerable to predation. Total failure of reproduction in ponds usually indicates an absence of acceptable nest-sites, which can be corrected by placement of a few 10-gallon milk cans in the pond. Large wooden boxes staked to the pond-bottom, and sections of clay tile as large as milk cans, make excellent nest-sites also.

Scant reproduction by channel catfish in clear ponds has definite advantages in management of these ponds for sport-fishing. Overcrowding is prevented, insuring that the catfish present can be raised to sizes desirable for angling purposes. It is usually easier, and cheaper, to restock ponds depleted of catfish than to reduce populations (where excessive) to levels that permit satisfactory growth by the fish.

Because channel catfish readily accept artificial rations, their production in small ponds can be increased by supplemental feeding (Simco and Cross, 1966). Dry, pelleted rations containing 20 to 30 per cent protein are suitable, and are available from most feed stores. In experimental work by the State Biological Survey in ponds at Lawrence, productions of 1000 to 2000 pounds per acre per year have been obtained at a cost of 10 cents per pound of catfish produced. "Fingerling" channel catfish can be raised to average sizes of ½ pound or more in one year, and 2 pounds or more in two years, if stocking rates are not excessive. Feeding was done at a daily rate of two or three per cent of the (estimated) total weight of catfish in each pond. When daily feeding rates exceed three pounds of feed per 100 pounds of fish, gains in fish-production do not compensate for increased costs of feed. Feeding-costs also become excessive if the fish are not harvested after the pond contains 1200 or more pounds of catfish per acre.

Blue catfish

Ictalurus furcatus (LeSueur)

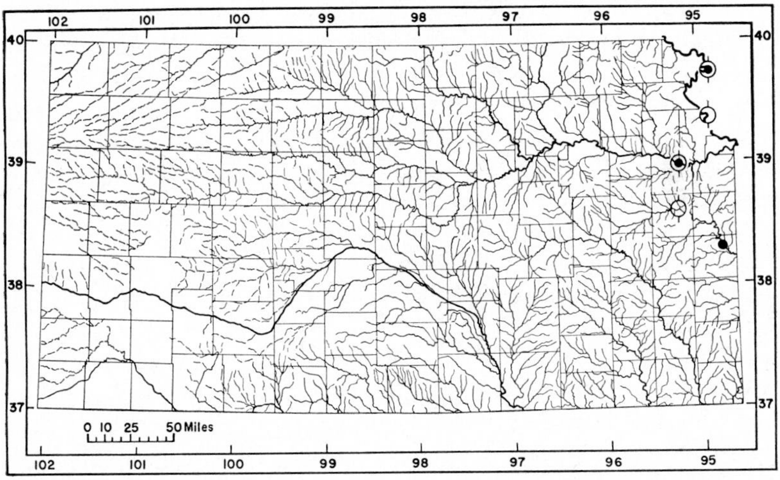

Ictalurus furcatus, Snow (1875:141); Cragin (1885b:107); Jordan and Meek (1885:13); Gilbert (1886:207); Dyche (1914:76); Doze (1925:167); Hall (1934:230, erroneously); Davis (1959:5); Breukelman (1960:34); Metcalf (1966:148).

Ictalurus nigricans, Snow (1875:141); Graham (1885b:71) [identity uncertain; possibly referable instead to *I. punctatus*].

Amiurus nigricans, Wheeler (1879:34) [identity uncertain; possibly referable instead to *I. punctatus*].

Form stout, adults prominently humped before dorsal fin; caudal fin deeply forked; anal fin long, with 30-35 rays, its margin straight; jaws unequal, upper jaw protruding; teeth in upper jaw in broad transverse band, without backward extensions; in specimens 10 to 24 inches long, length of dorsal spine greater than distance from tip of snout to back of eye, and length of dorsal spine 2.1-2.8 in predorsal length of fish; maxillary (longest) barbels scarcely exceeding head length; vertebrae 51-53.

Color plain, unspotted, gray dorsally, nearly white laterally and ventrally; generally paler than *I. punctatus,* but coloration of breeding males unknown to me, possibly dark as in breeding channel catfish.

The blue catfish, which is more often called the "fulton," "white fulton," or "white cat" in the Kansas region, occurs fairly commonly in the Missouri River but only rarely in the lower Kansas River. To my knowledge, the only specimen extant from the Kansas River (KU 7488, head only) was caught at Lawrence in July, 1942. I have heard subsequent reports from anglers of fish from the Kansas River that probably were *I. furcatus,* but have not been able to verify their identity by examination of specimens. The species still inhabits the lower Marais des Cygnes River also.

Although some of the reports mentioned below may apply to *I. punctatus* rather than *I. furcatus,* considerable evidence points to a marked decline in local populations of the blue catfish. Snow (1875:141) considered it "the most valuable species in the river [Kansas River at Lawrence], since it is quite abundant. . . ." Dyche (1914:76) called it "quite common" in large streams. Doze (1925:167) stated that it was "common in some Kansas streams."

More interesting than the formr abundance of *furcatus* is the almost incredible size attributed to the species by early writers. Snow (*loc. cit.*) wrote that he had seen a blue catfish, caught at Lawrence, which "weighed 175 lbs." and, "Tradition is positive that in the days of 1856 a fish of this species was captured, weighing 250 lbs." Another competent naturalist, L. L. Dyche, stated (1914: 76), "Specimens are not infrequently taken that weigh from 50 to 100 or even more pounds. Mr. J. C. Saunders of Lawrence, Kan., caught three of these fish several years ago that weighed 128, 133, and 147 pounds, respectively. The writer [Dyche] saw the 133-pound fish when it was taken. At another time Mr. Saunders caught in one net at one time twelve of these fish that weighed from 35 to 85 pounds each. Other specimens taken below the milldam at Lawrence have been reported as weighing from 150 to 177 pounds." The Lawrence *Daily Journal and Evening Tribune,* issue of June 25, 1895, contains a brief note near the bottom of page four that ". . . Dan Kimberlin a few evenings since captured a fish weighing a hundred and eighty pounds down the river near the city limits." Such a catch in 1965 would command front-page attention, with a photograph enabling identification of the fish.

I have a photograph of a 120-pound blue catfish, reported to have been caught just east of Lawrence in 1915 by Mr. Doug Smith. Doug Smith's son, Roy, now resident in Lawrence, told me that his father fished commercially out of Eudora and Lawrence from 1887 until the 1920's. In his youth Roy fished with his father. Roy recalls that four other blue catfish were taken in D-nets on the same day that the 120-pound specimen was caught. He stated that relatively few blue catfish were being caught in those years (about 1910-1920), and then only in June, when the river was high. He thought that the blue catfish were spawning-migrants, perhaps from the Mississippi River. Most of them were much smaller than the fish photographed—perhaps 30 pounds and upward, though live-weights were seldom gotten. The fish were unloaded and gutted at the foot of New York Street, near the Santa Fe Depot, and sent by rail to markets in Kansas City or Topeka.

Elsewhere in the range of *I. furcatus* there is evidence that it attained immense size. The journal of H. P. Hoy, a naturalist who traveled across Missouri in 1854, records under date of May 14 that "A lad caught on a hook to-day a catfish weighing 136 pounds" from the Grand River near Chillicothe, Livingston County, Missouri. Mr. Herbert J. Fisher, biologist for the Missouri Conservation Commission, called to my attention the quotation that follows, from a report of the 40th Meeting of the Missouri River Basin Inter-Agency Committee (May 15, 1950); Fisher wrote me (letter dated December 12, 1963) that Captain William L. Heckman probably provided the information about these two fish from localities on the Missouri River in Missouri:

> "Of interest to fishermen is the fact that the largest known fish ever caught in the Missouri River was taken just below Portland. This fish, caught in 1866, was a blue channel cat and weighed 315 pounds. It provided the biggest sensation of those days all through Chamois and Morrison Bottoms. Another 'fish sensation' was brought about in 1868 when two men, Sholten and New, brought into Hermann a blue channel cat that tipped the scales at 242 pounds."

In his book, *Steamboating Sixty-five Years on Missouri's Rivers*, Heckman (1950:136-146) wrote of several other large catfish, including one that "must have weighed over four hundred pounds," and he recalled a former time ". . . when it was common to catch catfish weighing from 125 to 200 pounds" in the channel of the Missouri River.

In 1879, Dr. J. G. W. Steedman of Saint Louis, Chairman of the Missouri Fish Commission, received from S. F. Baird of the U. S. Fish Commission a request for a "large Mississippi Catfish." On the day that Baird's letter was delivered to him, Steedman visited a Saint Louis fish-market and "luckily found two"—weighing 144 and

150 pounds. The larger fish was sent to the U. S. National Museum, where Bean (1880) described is as *Amiurus ponderosus* (new species). Steedman's use of the word "luckily" in his response to Baird (as quoted by Bean, *loc. cit.*) indicates that it was not a daily possibility to obtain specimens of the size sent. Steedman reported that the fisherman involved "assures me that the largest Mississippi Catfish he has met . . . weighed 198 pounds. (He says he has *heard* of Catfish weighing 250 and 300 pounds, but he does not believe the stories.)"

To my knowledge, no blue catfish approaching the size attributed to this species in the accounts above were taken anywhere for at least four decades prior to 1960. In that interval, the largest blue catfish mentioned in literature that has come to my attention are ones reported by Harlan and Speaker (1956:109), "Several specimens weighing in excess of 50 pounds have been observed by the writers," and by Fisher (1954:12), "A blue cat weighing 79 pounds was taken near Malta Bend [Missouri] in late 1948." Interestingly, several large blue catfish have been caught in the Missouri River System within the past three years, indicating a possible resurgence by the species. The available data for four fish are as follows:

90 pounds, 55 inches total length, Osage River southeast of Warsaw, Benton County, Missouri, August 25 or 26, 1963.

100.5 pounds, 65 inches total length, Missouri River in South Dakota, May, 1964.

117 pounds, Osage River west of Warsaw, Benton County, Missouri, May, 1964.

88.2 pounds, 52 inches total length, Lake Ozark, Benton County, Missouri, October 30, 1965 (KU 11343).

Regarding the habitat of *I. furcatus*, Heckman (1950:146) stated that it was "hardly ever caught any other place but in the channel of the [Missouri] River." Trautman (1957:413) cited fishermen on the Ohio River to the effect that blue catfish fed mostly "in swiftly-flowing chutes or rapids, and over bars or elsewhere in pools wherever there was a good current . . . When not feeding in winter it apparently retired into deeper waters . . . sometimes in depths of more than 30 feet. It seemingly avoided the silted bottoms of the most sluggish pools."

Harlan and Speaker (1956:109) stated that blue catfish spawn in June and early July, at temperatures of 70° to 75° F., after constructing nests similar to those of the channel catfish. Those authors and Brown and Dendy (1962) report that the food of blue catfish includes fish, crayfish, aquatic insects, and other items. The blue catfish has increased in abundance in several reservoirs, recently-constructed on the largest rivers in its range. The species is now (1965) being propagated in Arkansas, where its commercial use as a pondfish is being tested.

Flathead

Pylodictis olivaris (Rafinesque)

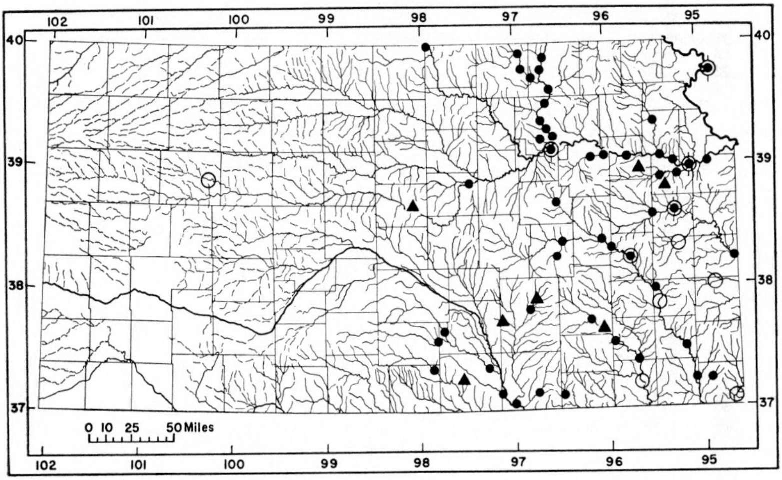

Amiurus cupreus, Snow (1875:141).
Hopladelus limosus, Snow (1875:141).
Hopladelus olivaris, Wheeler (1879:34).
Leptops olivaris, Jordan and Meek (1885:13); Cragin (1885b:107); Graham (1885b:71).
Loptops olivaris, Hall (1934:231).
Pilodictis olivaris, Breukelman (1940a:372, 1940b:381); Jennings (1942:365); Cross (1954:311); Cross and Hastings (1956); Greer and Cross (1956:360); Schelske (1957:46).
Pylodictis olivaris, Clarke, Breukelman, and Andrews (1958:168); Metcalf (1959:377, 1966:151); Minckley (1959:428); Minckley and Deacon (1959:344); Breukelman (1960:34); Deacon (1961:392-395); Deacon and Metcalf (1961:317); Hastings and Cross (1962:10).
Flathead catfish—Schoonover and Thompson (1954:177).

Form depressed, head extremely broad and flattened; caudal fin notched, not forked; anal fin short, rounded, with 14-17 rays; lower jaw protruding; band of teeth in upper jaw with backward extensions at sides of mouth; adipose fin large, separate from caudal fin; pectoral spine saw-edged both anteriorly and posteriorly; vertebrae usually 50 or 51.

Color variable with size and habitat—young black with white patch on upper lobe of caudal fin; juveniles mottled, with progressively less black and more olivaceous-brown pigment, white tail-patch disappearing; mottling diminishes with further growth, largest specimens more or less yellowish-brown, darkest in clear water, pale in muddy water.

Largest Kansas specimen weighed 86 pounds, 3 ounces (caught by Mr. Ray Wiechert in the Neosho River near St. Paul [Neosho Co.], on 24 August, 1966).

The flathead is a common fish in rivers of eastern Kansas. Perhaps the distribution is statewide, but the species is scarce in western streams, and its occurrences there may vary in relation to weather-cycles and stream-levels.

Adult flatheads generally occupy deep holes in the river-bed, created by swirling currents. Many such pools now exist below concrete aprons of low dams, and adjacent to bridge-supports that trap driftwood. Such obstructions in the channel disrupt the streaming flow of the current, leaving deep pockets in the otherwise shallow, sandy beds of most Plains rivers. These pools, often partly covered by tangled timber, seem ideal for large flatheads.

Flatheads mature at a size of about 18 inches, and an age of four years. They spawn in June or early July, in cavities similar to those used by channel catfish. Deacon (1961:393) found that flatheads entered and enlarged artificial holes that he dug into a steep clay bank of Neosho River. One bank-nest that Deacon described was about 14 inches in diameter at its entrance, but widened to 32 inches inside the nest-chamber. The bottom of the nest was clean (silt-free) and there was a ridge of clean gravel at the entrance.

Probably flatheads pair-off, as do channel catfish, and spawn but once each year. The eggs adhere in a single, large mass that is guarded by one of the parental fish, presumably always the male. A description of spawning by a pair of large flatheads in the Dallas Aquarium, several years ago, indicated that the male fish became intensely aggressive toward the female after her eggs were laid, and he alone tended the nest, which in this case was against a stump in the aquarium. The male hovered over the eggs, lifting, stirring, and rearranging them by means of his mouth and fins.

The young remain tightly schooled for several days after hatching. By mid-July they leave the nest, and are then found mostly on shallow riffles, beneath stones or other cover. Juveniles (yearlings) are more scattered, some near the larger stones on riffles, or beneath woody debris in shallow water, whereas others occupy pools. The adults reside almost exclusively in pools.

Young-of-the-year flatheads feed mainly on insects. As the fish grow larger, crayfish and fish enter their diet, and adults are mainly piscivorous. The flathead seems entirely carnivorous, unlike the channel catfish and the bullheads, all of which are partly scavenging in habit.

Minckley and Deacon (1959) have discussed several aspects of the biology of flatheads in Kansas.

Flatheads are not so easily propagated and raised in ponds as are channel catfish and bullheads. Mr. Seth Way, longtime hatchery superintendent for the Kansas Forestry, Fish and Game Commission, told me of his efforts to raise this species many years ago. Way succeeded in obtaining and hatching eggs, but the fry scattered in the ponds where they were stocked, concealed themselves beneath leaves, and did not utilize supplemental feed. Their survival was poor. I have had similar experience with one lot of flatheads in an experimental pond at Lawrence. The spawn of a pair of flatheads was placed in a 10-gallon milk-can, laid horizontally within a fine-meshed livebox in that pond. On hatching, the young left the interior of the can but remained near or beneath it. Once when the can was lifted the entire school of several thousand fry remained on the narrow outer rim of the recessed bottom of the can while it was raised entirely out of water. At this stage of life the tendency to aggregate, and the attachment to the nest, are strong.

These fish were released later in an open pond but were not fed. Only a dozen fish, four to six inches long, were found when the pond was drained in November of the year they were stocked. Some of the flatheads remained, well camouflaged against the soft mud-bottom, on the waterless floor of the pond rather than following the flow of water to the outlet. The fish were transferred to a large concrete tank containing clear water, where they could be observed. Unlike channel catfish, which characteristically mingled in schools in the same tank (as well as in ponds), the little flatheads disposed themselves singly over the bottom of the tank, where they lay motionless for long intervals.

Some success in propagation of flatheads has been achieved by state and private hatcheries in recent years. Moen (1964) trained the fry to eat commercial feeds (dry meal) by holding the newly-hatched fish in troughs and feeding at frequent (2-hour) intervals, beginning when the young began swimming-movements as their yolk-material diminished.

Flatheads occur in many lakes in Kansas, as well as in streams. Some lakes, especially the most turbid ones, have an abundance of flatheads, attesting to their ability to reproduce under lenitic conditions. Several persons have stocked small numbers of flatheads in ponds, hoping thereby to prevent overpopulation and stunting of sunfish in those ponds; results of these efforts have been inconsistent.

The flathead is a good sport-fish. Its devotees, though few in number, are highly partial to their sport. Flatheads are not easily caught, especially in the convenient hours of daylight; but, the flathead offers greater possibilities for hooking a really big fish than does any other species in Kansas. Flatheads that weigh 40 pounds or more are caught in several lakes and streams each year.

Tadpole madtom

Noturus gyrinus (Mitchill)

Noturus gyrinus, Graham (1885b:71); Cross and Minckley (1958:106-107); Deacon (1961:395).

Form stout; adipose fin joined to caudal fin, its notch nearer base of dorsal fin than tip of caudal fin; tooth-patch on upper jaw without backward extensions at sides of mouth; jaws nearly equal (upper jaw not protruding); pectoral spine smooth; anal rays 14-16; pectoral rays 6 or 7; pelvic rays 8; caudal fin large and gently rounded; vertebrae 37-39.

Color plain (never mottled), yellowish-brown to gray dorsally, fading to creamy white ventrally; fins uniformly dusky; skin thin and translucent, revealing underlying musculature and horizontal septum (fine dark streak along midsides).

Longest Kansas specimen 2¾ inches.

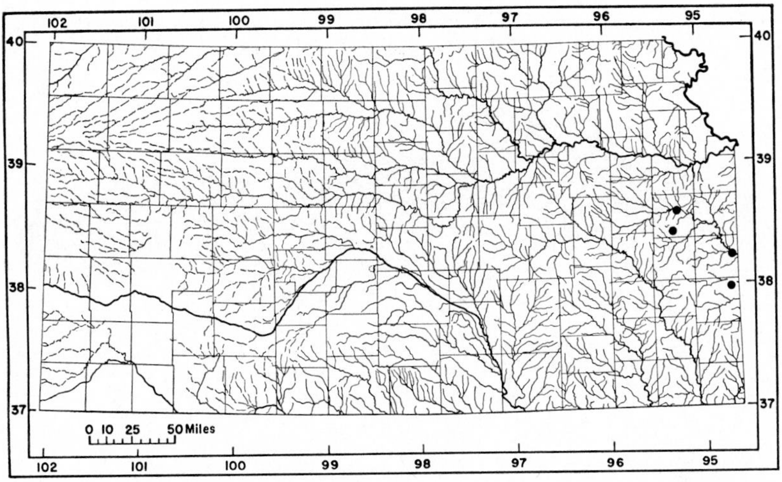

The tadpole madtom has been found only in the Osage River System in Kansas, although it is known from other tributaries of the Missouri River in Missouri. Graham (1885b:71) cited no localities of capture in listing this species from Kansas. *N. gyrinus* inhabits calm water, in oxbows and sluggish, lowland streams. Like other catfish, the tadpole madtom is most active nocturnally, seeking concealment by day beneath woody debris or in vegetation. I have found this species in both clear and turbid water, but only over mud-bottom. Other species of madtoms that are known from the Osage River usually occupy shallow riffles over rocky bottoms.

N. gyrinus is rare in Kansas, and no information is available on its life-history in this area. Elsewhere, the tadpole madtom is said to spawn in May or June, and to utilize foreign objects (tin cans, boards, pieces of crockery) as nest-sites (Adams and Hankinson, 1928:384). Some observers have found that madtoms adopt beer-cans as nest-sites. The egg-masses within the cavity are attended by at least one parental fish.

The food of madtoms consists mainly of larval insects and small crustaceans. Madtoms are excellent bait, and where they are abundant they contribute significantly to the food-supply of game fishes.

Freckled madtom

Noturus nocturnus Jordan and Gilbert

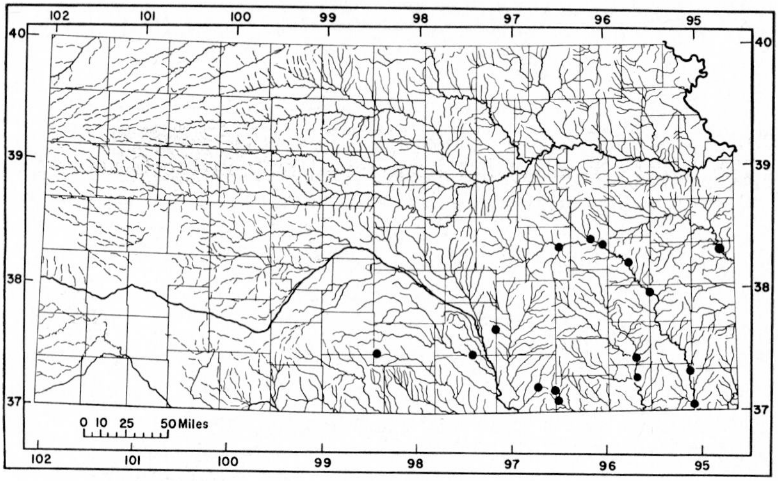

Schilbeodes nocturnus, Cross (1955:475-476).

Noturus nocturnus, Clarke, Breukelman, and Andrews (1958:168); Metcalf (1959:393); Minckley and Deacon (1959:348); Deacon (1961:395-396).

Form moderately stout; adipose low, its posterior notch nearer tip of depressed dorsal fin than tip of caudal fin; tooth-patch on upper jaw without backward extensions at sides of jaw; upper jaw protruding beyond front of lower jaw; pectoral spine rough posteriorly, not obviously toothed; anal rays 16-18; pectoral rays usually 9; pelvic rays 8 or 9; caudal fin rounded; vertebrae 38-41.

Color brownish-gray to black; dorsal, adipose, and caudal fins uniformly dark gray, caudal fin narrowly white-edged; anal fin dark-pigmented, most intensely near its margin; pectoral and pelvic fins heavily pigmented, not so dark as median fins; lower jaw gray, chin-barbels all dark-pigmented near bases; underside of head and belly freckled by dark pigment.

Longest Kansas specimen 4¼ inches.

The freckled madtom occurs mainly in streams having moderate or low gradients. Although *N. nocturnus* sometimes occupies riffles,

I have found it more often in leaves or other woody material where the current was sluggish and the bottom was muddy. Places where trash lodges against stream-banks, or where undercutting exposes roots of terrestrial vegetation, are more frequently occupied by freckled madtoms than are crevices beneath stones in mid-stream. This species seems scarce at all localities where it has been recorded in Kansas. I have never found *N. nocturnus* in the same places with *N. gyrinus* or *N. exilis,* the madtoms which *nocturnus* most resembles.

Slender madtom

Noturus exilis Nelson

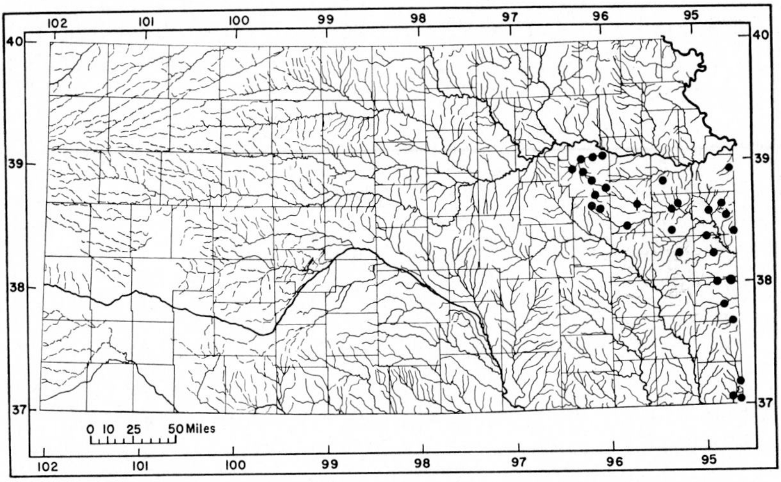

Noturus exilis, Jordan (1877b:100); Cragin (1885b:107); Graham (1885a: 4, 1885b:71); Clarke, Breukelman, and Andrews (1958:168); Metcalf (1959:393, 1966:150); Deacon (1961:396); Deacon and Metcalf (1961:317).

Schilbeodes exilis, Breukelman (1940b:381); Jennings (1942:365).

Schilbeodes insignis, Hubbs and Raney (1944:20, Map 1).

Form slender; adipose fin low, its posterior notch much nearer end of caudal fin than tip of dorsal fin; tooth-patch on upper jaw without backward extensions (Fig. 18B); jaws nearly equal; pectoral spine strongly toothed posteriorly; anal rays 18-21; pectoral and pelvic rays 9 or 10; caudal fin short, its tip rounded; vertebrae 41-43.

Color plain, brown or slate-gray dorsally, fading to creamy white ventrally; dorsal midline dark except for pale areas behind occiput and behind dorsal fin-base; adipose fin plain (not blotched); dorsal, caudal, and anal fins dusky, darkest along their margins (caudal usually black-edged); pectoral fins dark-pigmented basally; lower jaw dark-pigmented; outer pair of chin-barbels with sparse dark pigment.

Longest Kansas specimen 4½ inches.

The slender madtom occurs in all major drainage-basins in Kansas, but is restricted to small streams that seldom cease to flow. Usually, *N. exilis* inhabits shallow, gravelly riffles in the middle of the stream-channels, hiding by day beneath stones; but, it is sometimes found in deep leaf-litter of calm pools if their water remains clear and cool. Slender madtoms occur in only a few streams of the Kansas River Basin, but are abundant in Mill Creek, Wabaunsee County. *N. exilis* persists in the Wakarusa River also, most commonly in Washington Creek, Douglas County, where a limited population is sustained by continuous release of water from Lone Star Lake.

The absence of definite records of the slender madtom from the Neosho River System is surprising, because that river has many small tributaries that appear suitable for the species. Perhaps the lack of records reflects inadequate collecting in small streams of the Flint Hills; or, *N. exilis* may be excluded from that drainage by competition with the four other species of madtoms that occur there.

The slender madtom is an interesting, adaptable aquarium-fish. Despite its secretive nature in the wild, it is moderately active in captivity. Its loach-like form, serpentine swimming-motions, and odd poses when at rest add to its interest as a novelty in aquaria. In nature, *N. exilis* seems to be strictly a bottom-dwelling, insectivorous fish; but specimens that I have kept in aquaria soon learned to feed at the surface on dry rations, and often cruised about the tank in midwater.

N. exilis spawns in June, on riffles littered by large stones.

Stonecat

Noturus flavus Rafinesque

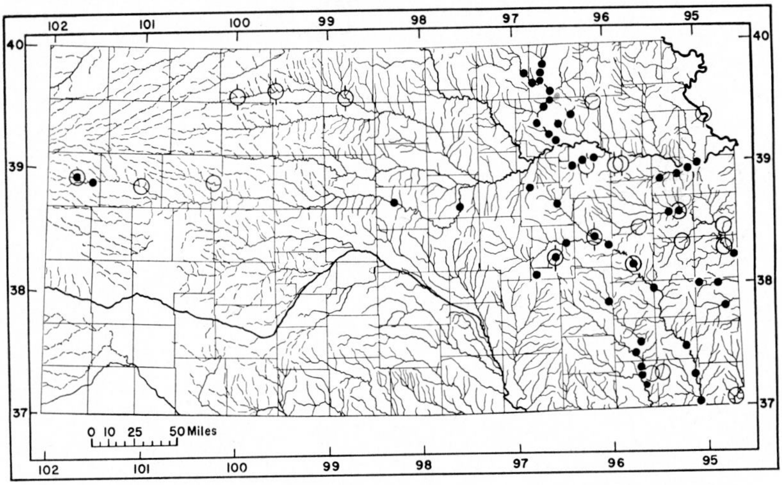

Noturus flavus, Cragin (1885b:107); Graham (1885a:4, 1885b:71); Gilbert (1886:207, 1889:40); Hay (1887:250, 253); Breukelman (1940a: 372, 1940b:381, 1960:34); Jennings (1942:365); Cross (1954:311); Schelske (1957:46-47); Clarke, Breukelman, and Andrews (1958:168); Minckley (1959:428); Minckley and Deacon (1959:348); Deacon (1961:395); Deacon and Metcalf (1961:317); Metcalf (1966:150).

Form slender; adipose fin low, its posterior notch much nearer tip of caudal fin than base of dorsal fin; tooth-patch on upper jaw extending backward on each side of jaw (Fig. 18A); upper jaw protruding beyond front of lower jaw; pectoral spine almost smooth; anal rays 15-18; pectoral rays usually 10; pelvic rays 9 or 10; caudal fin almost rectangular (square-tipped); vertebrae 41-44.

Coloration nearly plain, yellowish-brown dorsolaterally, creamy ventrally; indistinct dark brown areas behind operculum (above pectoral fin-base), narrowly continuous across occiput; base of dorsal fin darkened; behind dorsal fin, dark saddles vague or absent; adipose fin without dark blotch; caudal fin with broad, medial dusky band, narrowing distally (upper and lower edges of caudal pallid, yellowish); dorsal, anal, pelvic, and pectoral fins without dark pigment, yellowish to white; lower jaw and chin-barbels creamy white.

Longest Kansas specimen 8 inches.

The stonecat is the largest and most widespread of the madtoms in Kansas; seemingly, it is also the most adaptable madtom in terms of habitats occupied. *N. flavus* is found most commonly over rocky bottoms in currents of large streams, where it hides by day beneath slabs of shale or limestone. Such cover is not required, because stonecats are numerous in Blue River along bars composed of small gravel and sand, but devoid of large stones (Minckley, 1961:28). Rarely, stonecats are taken in the Kansas River on sandy bottom, beneath driftwood or other debris.

N. flavus formerly was more common in the western part of the Kansas River Basin than at present. Hay (1887) and Gilbert (1889) reported stonecats in several of their collections from northwestern Kansas, and additional records were obtained by the State Biological Survey in 1910-1912. But, Breukelman (1940a) failed to find this species anywhere in northwestern Kansas in the late 1930's, and *N. flavus* has seldom been taken in subsequent collections from that area. The western streams where stonecats persist are clear, permanent tributaries of the Smoky Hill River, such as Rose Creek in Wallace County; isolated populations of other fishes, notably *Notropis cornutus* and *Hybognathus hankinsoni*, occur in the same streams. Possibly the protracted drought of the early 1930's extirpated many western populations of these species.

Neosho madtom

Noturus species

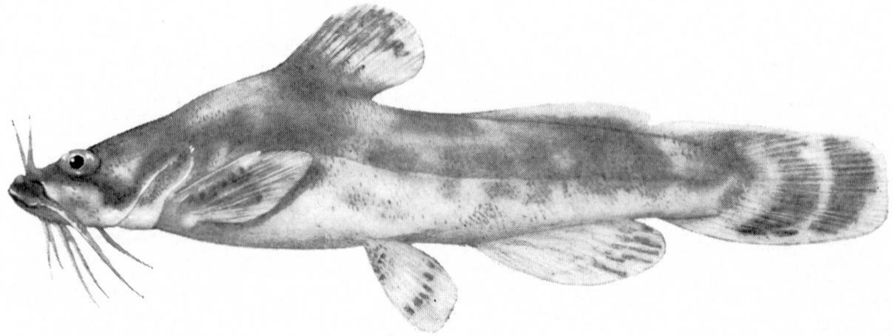

Noturus miurus, Gilbert (1886:207, probable misidentification, based on locality of capture).

Schilbeodes species, Cross (1954:311, 1955:475-476).

Noturus species, Clarke, Breukelman, and Andrews (1958:168); Deacon (1961:396).

Form moderately stout, strongly arched dorsally; adipose notch usually nearer tip of depressed dorsal fin than tip of caudal fin; tooth-patch on upper jaw without backward extensions; upper jaw protruding beyond front of lower

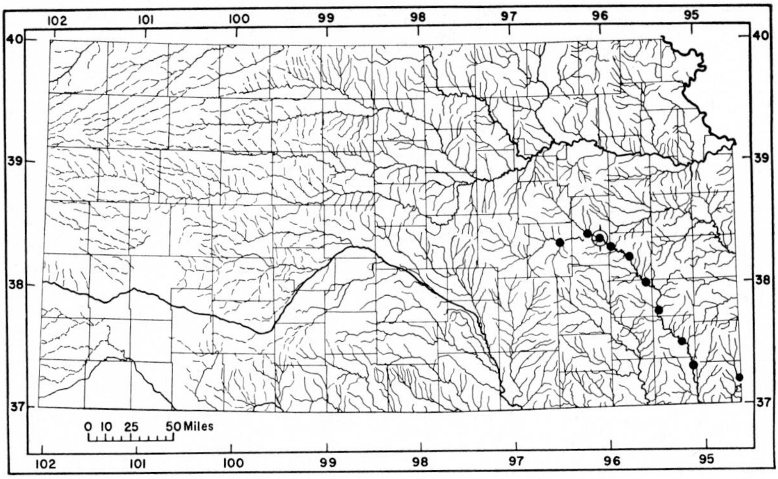

jaw; pectoral spine large, strongly toothed posteriorly, its length greater than distance between bases of maxillary barbels (snout and mouth narrow); anal rays usually 13-15; pectoral rays 7-9; pelvic rays 8 or 9; tip of caudal fin convex or nearly square; vertebrae 37 or 38.

Color mottled, brown on yellowish background, its tones less sharply contrasting than in *N. miurus;* four obscure dark saddles dorsally (across occiput, in dorsal fin-base, between dorsal and adipose fins, and near middle of adipose fin); dark blotch in adipose not extending vertically to fin-margin; in life, pallid area on nape prominent; belly unpigmented; dorsal fin with submarginal brown blotch; caudal fin with broad, nearly vertical dark bands through central and distal parts of fin; anal fin with small, submarginal dark blotch; pectoral fins with much brown pigment; chin-barbels white, outer pair sometimes sparsely pigmented.

Longest Kansas specimen slightly less than three inches.

The Neosho madtom lacks a scientific name, but has been recognized and described in manuscript by W. R. Taylor (doctoral dissertation, University of Michigan, 1955). The species is known only from the Neosho (Grand) River System and the lower part of the Illinois River (tributary to Arkansas River) in Oklahoma; its total range is smaller than the range of any other fish that inhabits Kansas.

This species has not been found in any of the smaller tributaries of the Neosho System, although many creeks in the Flint Hills have clear water and gravelly riffles that seem suitable for madtoms. *Noturus* sp. is confined to the mainstream of Spring River, Neosho River, and the lower course of the Cottonwood River, which is a larger stream than the Neosho above their confluence. Shallow gravel-bars that are swept by swift currents are the principal habitat of this madtom.

Because of its restricted distribution, the Neosho madtom is unusually vulnerable to the effects of drought and pollution. Large collections, sometimes comprising 100 or more specimens, were obtained from some localities in the Neosho and Cottonwood rivers in 1952, at the close of a cycle of abundant rainfall in eastern Kansas. In dry years that followed, the Neosho River became intermittent along most of its length for the first time since flow-records have been obtained on this river. Normal flow was restored in 1957, and has continued since. In 1957, Deacon (1961:396) was unable to find any Neosho madtoms in numerous collections at two localities where the species occurred in 1952. A few specimens were taken at one of Deacon's stations in 1958; and, in 1959, the third year of continuous flow in Neosho River, Deacon found this species frequently at both stations. His largest series, obtained in August of 1959, contains 29 specimens of three age-groups. The rate at which this species regained abundance was slow, by comparison with other riffle-dwelling fishes recorded by Deacon.

Brindled madtom

Noturus miurus Jordan

Noturus miurus, Graham (1885b:71); Metcalf (1959:393).
Schilbeodes miurus, Breukelman (1940b:381); Schelske (1957:47).

Form moderately stout, arched anteriorly; adipose fin high, its notch usually nearer tip of depressed dorsal fin than tip of caudal fin; tooth-patch on upper jaw without backward extensions; upper jaw protruding beyond front of lower jaw; pectoral spine moderately toothed, its length usually less than distance between bases of maxillary barbels (snout and mouth broad); anal rays usually 13-15; pectoral and pelvic rays 8 or 9; caudal fin rounded; vertebrae 38-40.

Color mottled; black blotches on light yellowish background, most prominent in young; dorsally, one dark saddle across occiput, another at origin of dorsal fin, third behind dorsal fin-base (before adipose fin), fourth on middle of adipose; adipose blotch extending vertically to fin-margin, where often elongated into anvil-shape; belly unpigmented; dorsal fin black-tipped anteriorly; caudal fin with broad dark band paralleling fin-margin, narrow basal band shaped

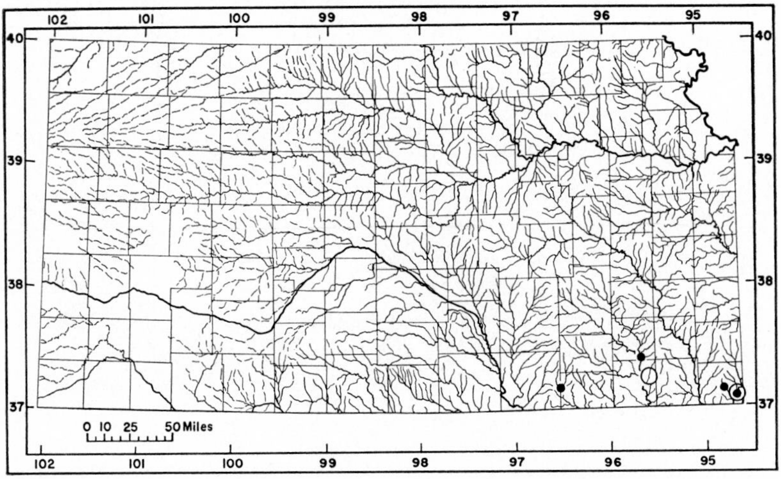

like question-mark, and (sometimes) having dusky area in central part of fin; anal fin with some dark pigment near margin; pectoral fins freckled anteriorly near spine; chin-barbels mostly white, outer pair with some dark pigment.

Longest Kansas specimen approximately three inches.

The brindled madtom barely enters Kansas, in the southernmost parts of streams tributary to Arkansas River, from the Caney River eastward to Spring River. I doubt Graham's (1885b:71) report of *N. miurus* from "Branches Missouri river" because this species has not been recorded elsewhere in the Missouri Basin.

In Kansas, I have found *N. miurus* only in leaf-litter on the floor of pools, never on riffles; but, the species reportedly inhabits riffles in other parts of its range. Brindled madtoms seem intolerant of high turbidity and intermittency, being recorded only from relatively clear, large streams.

Trautman (1957:441-442) gave evidence of a pronounced decline in the abundance of *N. miurus* in Ohio during the first half of this century. He attributed the decline to deterioration of habitat through siltation. In Kansas, *N. miurus* is now rare, its populations few and isolated.

Trout-perches

FAMILY PERCOPSIDAE

Trout-perch

Percopsis omiscomaycus (Walbaum)

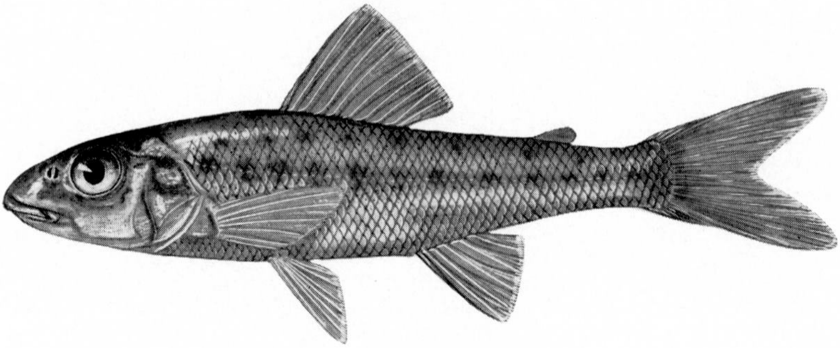

Percopsis Hammondii Gill (1864:151 [orig. descr.]).
Percopsis hammondii, Cope (1865b:85).
Percopsis Hammondi, Cragin (1885b:109).
Percopsis guttatus, Graham (1885b:75); Evermann and Cox (1896:416).
Percopsis omiscomaycus, Hubbs and Lagler (1958:98); Bailey and Allum (1962:102); Metcalf (1966:163).

Body slightly compressed, thick anteriorly; head scaleless, large, length about 3¼ in standard length; mouth large, scarcely oblique; upper jaw non-protractile; maxillary excluded from gape, hinged as in sunfishes; scales in lateral line about 52; nape partly naked; adipose fin present; dorsal fin with two weak spines, usually 10 soft-rays; caudal fin forked; anal fin with 1 spine, 6 soft-rays; pelvic fins with 1 spine, 7 or 8 soft-rays; pectoral rays 13; vertebrae usually 33 or 34.

Coloration pallid, body translucent; 9-12 small dark blotches along lateral line; another longitudinal line of blotches, less well-developed, on upper sides; dorsal midline with obscure dark blotches; fins nearly plain, colorless or with faint dark pigment along rays.

Maximum length 6 inches, usually less than 4½ inches.

Many writers besides those cited above have ascribed trout-perch to Kansas, mentioning this State in delimiting the range of the species southwestward. All reports seemingly stem from the original description of *P. hammondii* Gill, based upon a specimen "obtained by Surgeon General Hammond in Kansas". Hammond was stationed temporarily at Fort Riley. The fishes that he collected were delivered from that base to the Academy of Natural Sciences of Philadelphia, but the precise localities of their capture are uncertain. Many were taken on an expedition in 1856, through areas now within the states of Nebraska and Wyoming (see Olund and Cross, 1961:331-332). But, the trout-perch has not since been found in those states, so I assume that Gill's specimen may in fact have come from Kansas. None has since been reported from this State.

Over most of its present range, the trout-perch occupies glacial lakes, often in relatively deep, open water. Southern populations inhabit streams, especially the sandy ones in the loess-area of southwestern Iowa and northern Missouri.

Trout-perch seem mainly nocturnal, moving into shallows to feed at night, principally on aquatic insects and crustaceans.

In an analysis of factors that influence growth-rates and abundance of this species in Lower Red Lake, Minnesota, Magnuson and Smith (1963) found that few trout-perch survived more than three years. The reproductive season extended from late May through August, with one or more peaks of spawning-activity in June and early July. Spawning occurred a few inches below the surface, where the water was less than 3½ feet deep along the sandy beaches of Lower Red Lake or in tributaries to the lake. Eggs sank to the bottom and adhered to the substrate. Seemingly, survival was reduced by windy weather, which may have increased losses among eggs and fry through molar action of shifting sand on the beaches.

Codfishes

FAMILY GADIDAE

Burbot

Lota lota (Linnaeus)

Lota maculosa, Cragin (1885b:11); Breukelman (1940b:384).
Lota lota maculosa, Gilbert (1886:210).
Lota lota, Breukelman (1960:34); Fisher (1962:428); Metcalf (1966:153).

Body elongate, terete; scales minute, embedded (body appears naked); fins long and low with thick and turgid membranes; first dorsal fin with 9-15 soft-rays, second dorsal fin with 61-81 rays; anal fin-rays 52-72; pelvic fins jugular (inserted farther forward than pectorals); pelvic rays 7 or 8; pectoral rays 17-22; one median chin-barbel; anterior nares with long, barbellike flaps; vertebrae about 60.

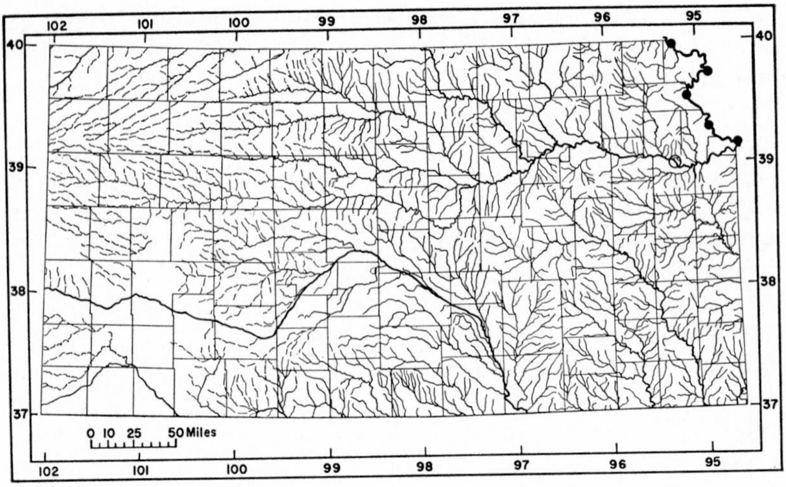

Mottled brown and olivaceous; fins (except pelvics) dark in adults, mottled or outlined by dark pigment in young; pelvics white or nearly so; belly pallid, lightly freckled with dark pigment.

Maximum weight 60 to 75 pounds (Keleher, 1961). Specimens from Kansas 10 to 20 inches long.

The burbot occurs in the mainstream of the Missouri River, having been recorded near Kansas City, Leavenworth, Atchison, St. Joseph, and White Cloud. Possibly Graham's reference (1885b:71) to *Amia calva* from "Branches of Missouri river, Osage river, etc." was based on reports of burbots by fishermen, whose descriptions were misinterpreted; Graham omitted *Lota* from his list in recording the bowfin.

Former occurrences of burbots in the Kansas River are indicated by two specimens in the University of Kansas Museum of Natural History: one, 12.5 inches long, labeled "Kaw River, 1903" and another, 14 inches long, labeled "Kaw River at Lawrence, Kansas, 1906." The Kansas (= Kaw) River was unusually high in the years when these fish were caught. Floods in 1903 exceeded any on record except those of 1951, and flooding occurred in 1906 also. I suspect that the burbots obtained then were migrants from the Missouri River, about 40 miles distant from Lawrence. Another species that is normally confined to the Missouri mainstream, *Scaphirhynchus albus* (the pallid sturgeon), temporarily occupied the lower Kansas River after floods in 1951. That species seems to be more common than the burbot in the Missouri River at the present time. To my knowledge, no burbots were caught in the Kansas River following the floods of 1951.

Burbots that are caught on hook-and-line nowadays attract notice in local newspapers as oddities, indicating their rarity in the lower Missouri River. A few are taken also in hoop nets by commercial fishermen. Interestingly, this species is called the "mother eel" by some fishermen in this area.

The habitat of the burbot is described by Robins and Deubler (1955:7) as "areas of rock slides [as along riprapped dikes and levees], collapsed bridges, fallen trees and where erosion has honeycombed the bottom with tunnels. The important feature is the presence of shelter of sufficient size for an adult to hide itself completely." Warm water-temperatures probably limit the southward extent of its range; the species seems to prefer temperatures lower than 70° F. at all seasons.

Burbots spawn in winter. In New York State, Robins and Deubler (1955) reported that adults in small streams migrated in late fall to larger rivers for spawning. The adults returned to creeks between March and May. Young inhabited weed-beds on rocky or gravelly bottom in swiftly moving water of the larger rivers.

According to Cahn (1936) and Simon (1946), burbot spawn communally in shallow water (depth 4 feet or less) over gravelly or sandy bottom. The eggs, fertilized as extruded by compact groups of adults, are scattered over the substrate and abandoned. Each female that is 2 feet long or longer may lay more than 1,000,000 eggs. Spawning is thought to occur only at night, the adults retreating to deep water by day.

The food of burbots consists of fish and aquatic insect-larvae.

Simon (1946) stated that burbots have value as a sport fish in Wyoming, where they are caught in winter; minnows are used as bait. Burbots are not considered good food-fish.

Topminnows

FAMILY CYPRINODONTIDAE

KEY

1. Dorsal fin with 9-11 rays (total count), originating behind origin of anal fin; scales fewer than 40 in lengthwise series 2

   Dorsal fin with 13-16 rays (total count), originating over or in front of origin of anal fin; scales more than 40 in lengthwise series 3

2. Sides with broad black lateral band, continuous around snout; caudal peduncle slender, its least depth 7.5 or more in standard length.
   black-striped topminnow, *Fundulus notatus*, p. 232

   Sides plain, without dark lateral band; caudal peduncle deep, its least depth 6.5 or less in standard length.
   plains topminnow, *Fundulus sciadicus*, p. 231

3. Sides with 12-20 dark vertical bars; lateral scales partly embedded, in more than 50 rows; gill membrane joined to body wall below upper end of opercle, opposite upper end of pectoral fin base,
plains killifish, *Fundulus kansae,* p. 235

Sides plain or with fine longitudinal streaks; lateral scales exposed, in 40-45 rows; gill membrane joined to body wall at upper end of opercle, above upper end of pectoral fin base,
studfish, *Fundulus catenatus,* p. 230

Northern studfish

Fundulus catenatus (Storer)

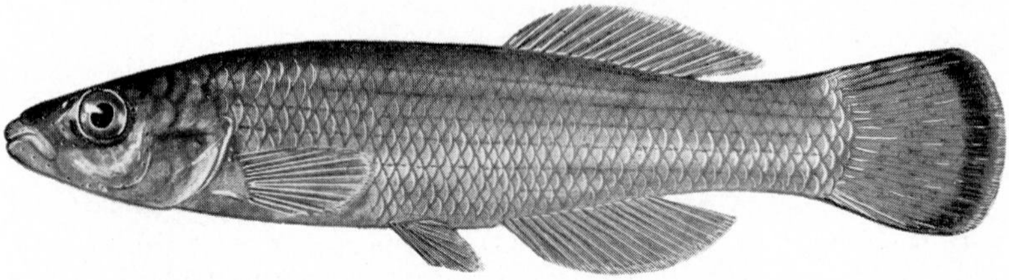

Fundulus catenatus, Miller (1955:9); Branson (1964:746).

Body slender, moderately compressed; head large, flattened dorsally, plated by large scales, its length 3.1-3.4 in standard length; gill membranes free from isthmus; scales moderately large, in about 45 rows from opercular cleft to base of caudal fin, none pored; dorsal fin rounded, with 13-16 rays, originating approximately over origin of anal fin; caudal fin rounded or nearly square; anal fin rounded, with 15-18 rays, most often 16; pelvic rays 6; intestine looped forward (S-shaped) but not convoluted, peritoneum black; vertebrae 35-37.

Olivaceous; sides with 8-10 fine, lengthwise dark lines, often interrupted; juveniles with irregular dark blotches dorsally, vertical bars posteriorly on sides, becoming obscure in adults; fins nearly plain, dorsal and caudal dusky and flecked by minute dark spots near bases; anal, pelvic, and pectoral fins usually unpigmented. Sides of breeding males iridescent blue with yellow-orange longitudinal lines; caudal fin orange-tipped and with submarginal black bar; rays of anal fin tuberculate, especially distally.

Maximum length approximately 5 inches.

Miller's reference to the studfish in Kansas is based on one specimen, 75 mm. long, in the University of Michigan Museum of Zoology; the associated data indicate that this fish was caught by D. Jennings in July, 1941, from Black Jack Creek at St. George, Pottawatomie County (letter from R. R. Miller to F. B. Cross, October 24, 1960). Dr. W. R. Taylor of the U. S. National Museum has informed me of his belief that the record is erroneous, having resulted from accidental transfer of the single studfish into a series of plains killifish, *F. kansae,* which is deposited at UMMZ and which has the same collection-data as the specimen of *F. catenatus*. These two species occupy strikingly different habitats and have not been found together at any other locality. I agree with Taylor in rejecting the record from Pottawatomie County as valid evidence of the existence of *F. catenatus* in Kansas.

Nevertheless, the studfish probably has occurred in Kansas in recent times, and Branson (1964:746) has predicted that future records will be obtained. He reported *F. catenatus* from Shoal Creek in Missouri, near the place where that stream enters Kansas. Studfish are abundant in southern tributaries of the Osage River in Missouri, and in direct tributaries of the Missouri River north of the Osage River System. Thus, *F. catenatus* has been found at several localities less than 100 miles east of Kansas. All of these localities are in Ozarkian streams, where studfish constitute one of the dominant faunal elements. Disregarding the record from Kansas, the western limit of the known distribution of *F. catenatus* corresponds closely to the western boundary of Ozarkian terrain, even where that boundary cuts across present drainage-patterns. The studfish inhabits clear streams having permanent flow and rocky bottoms.

Plains topminnow
Fundulus sciadicus Cope

Fundulus sciadicus, Branson (1964:745-746); Metcalf (1966:152).

Body stout, compressed; head flattened dorsally, plated by large scales, its length usually 3.3-3.5 in standard length; gill membranes free from isthmus; caudal peduncle deep, least depth 6.5 or less in standard length; scales large, 33-36 in lengthwise series, none pored; dorsal fin rounded, with 9-11 rays, originating behind origin of anal fin; caudal fin rounded; anal fin 12- to 15-rayed, its base sheathed anteriorly in females; intestine looped forward (S-shaped), peritoneum black; vertebrae 31-34.

Coloration plain, olivaceous dorsally fading to white ventrally, without dark stripes or bars; fins somewhat dusky but unspotted, red or orange in breeding males.

Length 2½ inches or less.

Although known as the "plains topminnow," *F. sciadicus* is not widespread in the prairie region south of the Platte River. Specimens (KU 7444) have been taken at only one locality in Kansas. Dr. Branley A. Branson of Kansas State College of Pittsburg, who obtained this record in 1963, described the habitat as a small, weedy pool alongside the channel of Shoal Creek in Cherokee County. Farther up Shoal Creek (in Missouri), this species has been collected frequently, as it has in other Ozarkian streams of the Arkansas River Basin in Oklahoma and the Missouri River Drainage in Missouri.

The only other record near to Kansas is from Frenchman Creek, a tributary of Republican River in Hitchcock County, Nebraska. There, I obtained numerous specimens (KU 4856) immediately below Enders Dam in September, 1959. An introduction of the species at this locality is suspected, because it is the only place in the Kansas River Basin where *sciadicus* has been found, and because many of the bait-minnows used in Enders Reservoir are brought from the Platte River, where *sciadicus* is common locally. The plains topminnow may spread from Enders to tributaries of the Republican River in Kansas.

The habitat of *F. sciadicus* is described by Branson (1964:746) as "spring-fed pools and backwater situations with abundant aquatic vegetation", and by Miller (1955:10) as "small to medium-sized, clear, sandy to rocky streams, in moderate to rapid current." I have found the species abundantly only in small spring-runs having sandy bottom and luxuriant growths of aquatic vegetation in the Platte River Basin (Nebraska).

Black-striped topminnow
Fundulus notatus (Rafinesque)

Zygonectes notatus, Graham (1885b:75); Evermann and Fordice (1886: 185); Gilbert (1886:209).

Fundulus notatus, Hall (1934:231); Moore and Buck (1955:25); Schelske (1957:47); Clarke, Breukelman, and Andrews (1958:169); Metcalf (1959:376-377); Deacon (1961:396).

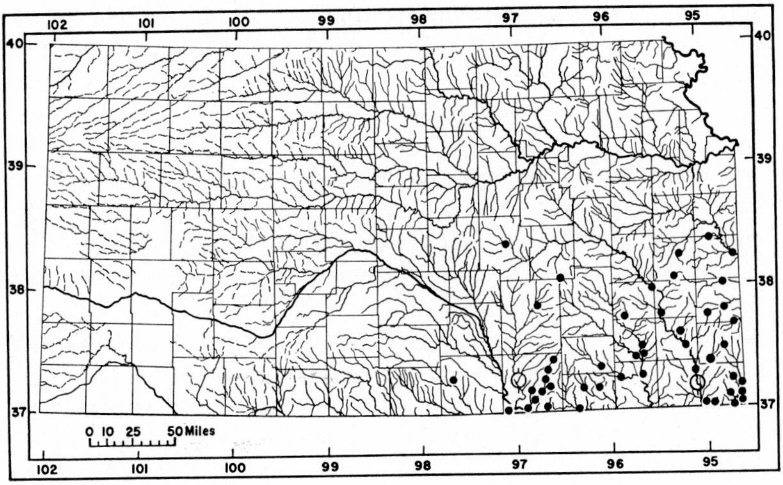

Body slender, nearly terete; head flattened dorsally, plated by scales, its length usually 3.4-3.8 in standard length; gill membranes free from isthmus; caudal peduncle slender, least depth 7.5 or more in standard length; scales large, 32-34 in lengthwise series, none pored; dorsal fin rounded, usually 9-rayed, originating behind origin of anal fin; caudal fin rounded; anal fin usually 12-rayed, with base slightly sheathed anteriorly in females; anal and dorsal fins larger (longer) in males than in females; pelvic rays 6; intestine short and straight or with single forward loop, peritoneum partly silvery; vertebrae 32-35.

Green dorsally, white or yellowish ventrally; sides with intense black longitudinal stripe, nearly straight-edged in females, broken by cross-bars in males; fins yellowish; dorsal and caudal fins flecked by dark dots, more numerous in males; pectoral and pelvic fins plain or dusky, without prominent spots; chin of males blue, lower sides with bluish reflections. See Plate 1.

Length 3 inches or less.

The black-striped topminnow inhabits clear small streams, in southeastern Kansas, that have rocky or muddy bottoms. Its distribution is bounded westward by the sandy mainstream of the Arkansas River, except for single records of occurrence in the Chikaskia River and in a spring that discharges into the Arkansas River in southwestern Cowley County. Northward, *F. notatus* occurs in the southern part of the Osage River System, possibly as a result of introductions there. Thus the range of the black-striped topminnow almost exactly complements that of the plains killifish, *F. kansae*, which is the only other common cyprinodontid in Kansas. Because of striking differences in the preferred habitats of these two species, they rarely occur together.

Fundulus notatus normally avoids strong currents, being found mainly in pairs or small groups alongshore, especially where leaf-litter and other organic sediments accumulate. The species is made conspicuous by its surface-dwelling habit and by a striking pale blotch (parietal spot) on its head; it is easily sought out for selective collection.

Carranza and Winn (1954) have described the reproductive habits of *F. notatus*. The spawning season extends from May to mid-August, and the fish tend to remain paired. Eggs are deposited singly in vegetation, to which they adhere during development. Within the span of a few minutes, several eggs are deposited by a female, which will spawn again after other eggs have ripened several days later. There is no parental attention to eggs after their deposition, and occasional predation on the eggs was noted among specimens of *notatus* that were confined in aquaria by Carranza and Winn.

The black-striped topminnow is a handsome aquarium-fish that can be propagated by providing a substrate suitable for attachment of the eggs. One of my students, John Vandermeer, used a string-type floor-mop for this purpose. After spawning has occurred the mop can be removed to another aquarium to avoid predation on the eggs and young.

The usual food of *F. notatus* consists of surface-dwelling insects, crustaceans, and their larvae. The species will accept commercially-prepared fishfood in aquaria.

After the above account was prepared, I had opportunity to examine three specimens of *F. notatus* in the U. S. National Museum (USNM 93671) that are labeled as having been taken two miles east of Callista, Kingman County, on May 25, 1934, by C. E. Burt and L. Hoyle. That locality is approximately 30 miles west and 12 miles north of the westernmost record shown on the distribution-map for this species.

Plains killifish

Fundulus kansae (Garman)

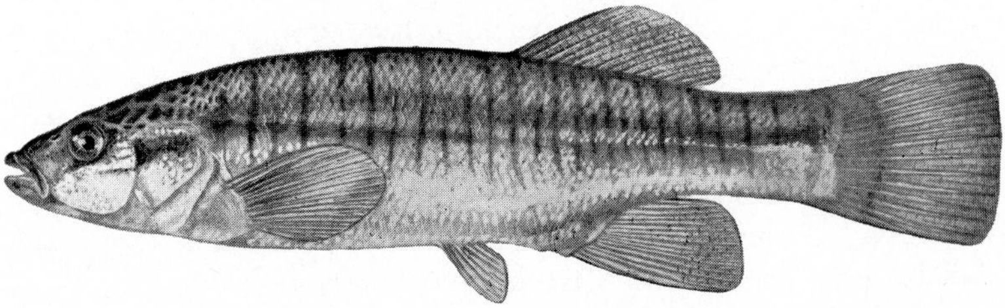

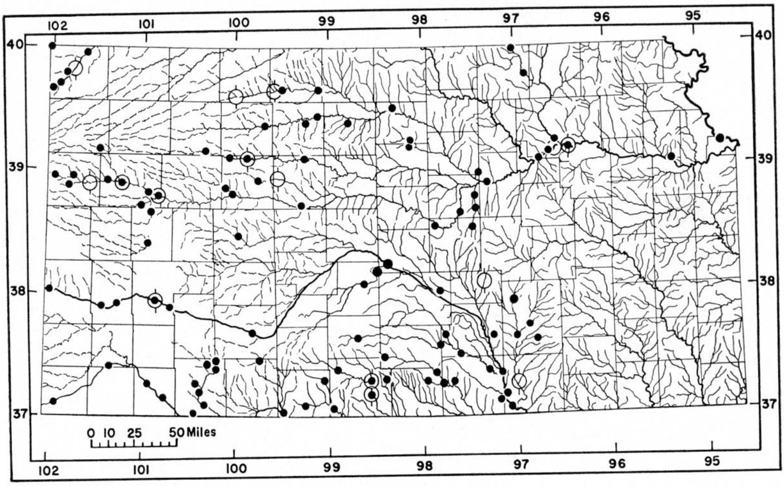

Fundulus zebrinus, Gilbert (1884:15, 1885:99, 1886:211, 1889:39,40); Cragin (1885b:110); Graham (1885b:75); Evermann and Fordice (1886: 185); Hay (1887:249, 250, 252).

Fundulus diaphanus, Cragin (1885b:110).

Fundulus diaphanous, Graham (1885b:75).

Plancterus kansae, Breukelman (1940a:372, 1940b:382); Jennings (1942: 365).

Fundulus kansae, Moore and Buck (1955:25); Metcalf (1959:376, 1966: 151); Minckley (1959:428); Kilgore and Rising (1965:141).

Body moderately robust, thick anteriorly; head large, broadly flattened dorsally, length 3.2-3.6 in standard length; head with large platelike scales, dorsally and on gill-covers; gill membranes free from isthmus; scales small, 55-60 in lengthwise series, none pored; dorsal fin rounded, with about 15 rays, originating slightly anterior to origin of anal fin; caudal fin square-tipped; anal fin with 13 or 14 rays, with basal sheath in females; pelvic rays 6; intestine long and convoluted; vertebrae 32-36.

Light brown to olivaceous dorsally, sides with 12-28 dark vertical bars, interspaces yellowish or white; bars fewer, wider, and more prominent in males than in females (female illustrated above); dorsal fin dusky; caudal, anal, pelvic, and pectoral fins pallid or yellowish in females, bright orange in breeding males.

Length 4 inches or less.

The distribution of the plains killifish is unique, among Kansas fishes, in that the species occurs throughout the western part of the State but is absent from most eastern streams. Evidence from early fish-collections indicates that there has not been appreciable change in this distributional pattern since the time of settlement. Interesting, in this regard, is the report of *F. diaphanus* by Cragin (1885b:110), who stated, "Taken at Neosho Falls by Col. N. S. Goss and identified by Cope." In the same year, Graham listed *F. diaphanous* (*sic*) from the "Kansas river" without further comment, and subsequently several authors have mentioned "Kansas" in statements of range of *diaphanus.* That species superficially resembles *F. kansae* (hence its inclusion in the synonymy above) but its present range terminates far to the north of Kansas. Inasmuch as *F. kansae* is an unlikely inhabitant of the upper Neosho River, where Goss reportedly took *diaphanus,* the basis for inclusion of *diaphanus* in the Kansas fauna may lie in faulty locality-designations as well as in misidentifications. No specimens are extant. Misidentification seems probable in the case of Graham's record, erroneous locality-data in the case of Cragin's—especially since Goss was credited also with taking bowfin (*Amia calva*) in Neosho River (Cragin, 1885b:106). The latter species is an associate of *F. diaphanus* in northeastern states, but its occurrence in the Neosho River is not corroborated by any recent evidence.

Fundulus kansae inhabits shallow streams that have sandy bottoms and are highly alkaline or saline. The species can be found abundantly either in rapid current or in backwaters, but rarely in water more than six inches deep.

Salinity higher than that tolerated by most freshwater fishes may be preferred by *F. kansae,* limiting its range eastward. In the Arkansas River System, the only tributary east of the mainstream in which I have found plains killifish is the Walnut River. That river is naturally salty in part of its headwaters (Whitewater River), and is sometimes unduly saline downstream as a result of pollution by the petroleum industry. In the Kansas River System, as in the Arkansas System, the general level of dissolved solids (salts) diminishes eastward. The Kansas River differs from the Arkansas River in Kansas in that several of its eastern tributaries (as well as the mainstream) are shallow and sandy. Nevertheless, the only plains killifish that I have taken in the eastern part of the Kansas Basin was caught from an isolated pool in the flood-plain, near Lawrence, in the autumn of 1951; presumably, this fish was swept downstream by unprecedented floods earlier in 1951. Plains killifish are scarce in the Missouri River, although they have been taken at several localities in the mainstream in Kansas and Missouri. The easternmost locality of occurrence is a salt spring in Howard County, Missouri (Miller, 1955:11).

According to Koster (1948), the plains killifish spawns in summer, at water-temperatures of about 80° F. Because temperatures vary greatly during each 24-hour period in the shallow, exposed streams that are occupied by *F. kansae*, its reproductive activity may be restricted to a short interval each day. The breeding season in Kansas probably is three months or more long.

The sites selected for spawning are "pools" that are a few inches in depth and have slight current. Males congregate in these spawning-areas and, as described by Koster, defend "elbow room" (moving territories) by "deferred combat ceremonial"; the latter activity involves parallel-swimming by rival males, together with maximal expansion of their brightly-colored fins. Matings of individual males with receptive females follow brief courtship activity. Eggs are deposited in coarse sand on the stream-bottom and are left unattended.

The food of plains killifish is diverse, but includes surface-insects and other aquatic invertebrates. Because *F. kansae* occurs abundantly where other fishes are few, its role in reducing populations of larval mosquitoes may be significant. This killifish is unusually hardy—one attribute of a good bait-minnow—but is otherwise considered poor bait by most anglers.

Livebearers

FAMILY POECILIIDAE

Mosquitofish

Gambusia affinis (Baird and Girard)

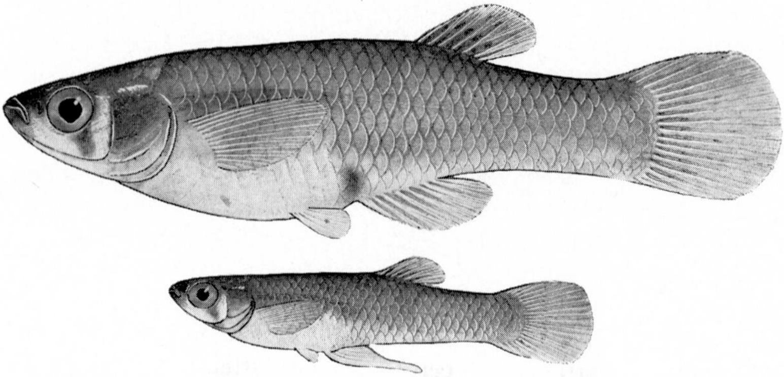

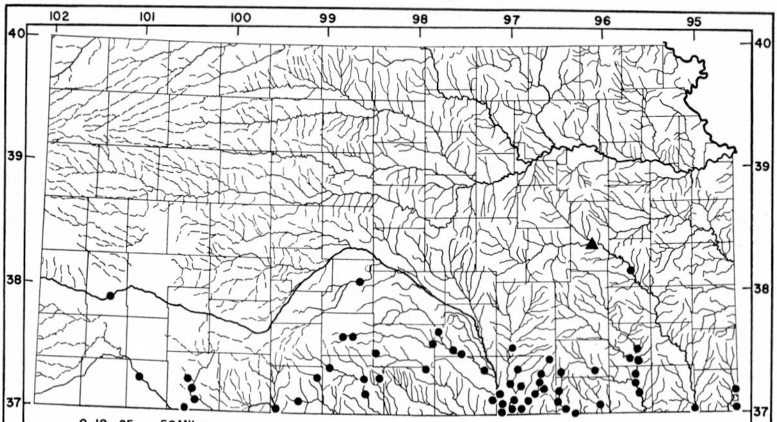

Gambusia affinis, Cross (1954:476); Schelske (1957:47); Clarke, Breukelman, and Andrews (1958:169); Metcalf (1959:376); Kilgore and Rising (1965:141).

Body stout; head small, flattened dorsally, with platelike scales; gill membranes free from isthmus; dorsal fin small, rounded, originating behind origin of anal fin; caudal fin rounded; dorsal rays 7; anal rays usually 7; (6 branched rays plus 3 unbranched rays anteriorly); anal fin of male rodlike (modified as a slender intromittent organ); pelvic rays 6; scales large, 29-32 in lengthwise series, none pored; intestine short, with single forward loop, peritoneum dusky or silvery; vertebrae usually 32 or 33.

Coloration plain olivaceous, scales outlined by dark pigment; predorsal dark stripe (on midline of back) usually present; dorsal, caudal, and anal fins with minute flecks along rays, tending to form 1 to 3 dark streaks across fins.

Length of males 1 inch, of females 1¾ inches or less.

The mosquitofish probably is not native to Kansas, although it occurred naturally in the Arkansas River Basin near Fort Smith, about 110 miles (airline) southeast of the southeastern corner of Kansas (Jordan and Gilbert, 1886:8). The first published records from Kansas were by Cross (1954:476), but Alice Elliott found *Gambusia* in the Ninnescah River in 1944-1946 (M. S. dissertation, Kansas State Univ., 1947). Elliott stated that mosquitofish escaped from the hatchery of the Kansas Forestry, Fish and Game Commission on the upper Ninnescah River, after having been brought there for use as a forage fish. Additional introductions undoubtedly facilitated its rapid dispersal throughout southern Kansas. One such introduction in 1954, into Lake Wooster on the campus of Kansas State Teachers College at Emporia (Clarke, Breukelman, and Andrews, 1958:169), is plotted as the northernmost locality of record on the map above. Since that map was prepared in 1965, mosquitofish have been found in the Cottonwood River in Chase County and the Kansas River at Lawrence. I have no records from the Marais des Cygnes Drainage in Kansas, but assume that the species occurs there now; specimens have been taken from several streams in that drainage in western Missouri.

The mosquitofish prefers calm, shallow waters, where it feeds near the surface on many kinds of aquatic insect-larvae and on crustaceans. The foods eaten are those kinds that happen to be most abundant (hence most available) at any given time and place. There is little reason to suppose that this species is more effective in control of mosquito-larvae than are various native minnows and topminnows (*Fundulus*) where the latter fishes occur.

The mosquitofish is the only Kansas fish that gives birth to young rather than depositing eggs. "Litters" of as many as 30 active, independent young are produced repeatedly during the warm months. I think that many females produce 3 or 4 groups of young each year in Kansas, but definite evidence on this point is lacking.

Mosquitofish have limited tolerance of cold weather, so overwinter mortality is high. The species is scarce at most localities in spring but increases rapidly as successive generations are produced and enter the reproductive cycle during summer. In autumn, the mosquitofish is abundant in pools and backwaters of many streams in southern Kansas.

Silversides

FAMILY ATHERINIDAE

Brook silverside

Labidesthes sicculus (Cope)

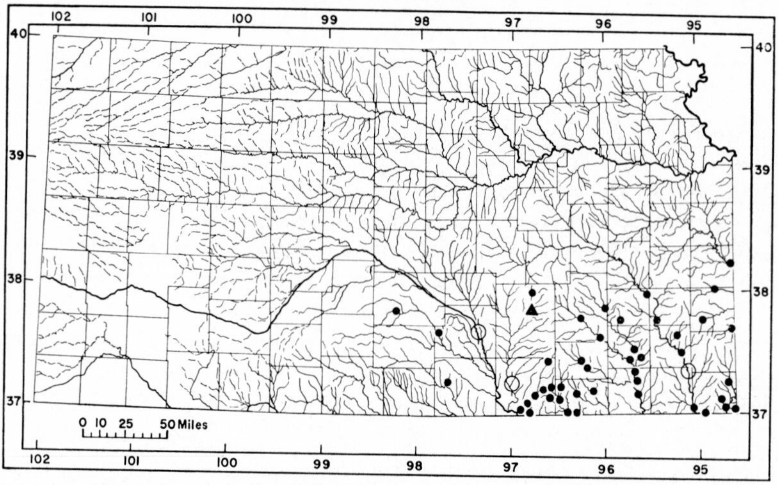

Labidesthes sicculus, Graham (1885b:74); Evermann and Fordice (1866: 185); Jordan (1891:18); Moore and Buck (1955:25); Greer and Cross (1956:362); Schelske (1957:47); Clarke, Breukelman, and Andrews (1958:169); Metcalf (1959:378, 393); Deacon (1961:396).

Body slender, terete; head scaled, conical, small, length less than ¼ standard length; mouth terminal, strongly oblique; jaws elongate, protractile, and toothed; scales small, about 75 in longitudinal series, no pored lateral-line row; first dorsal fin inconspicuous, with 4 or 5 weak spines, far forward of 11-rayed soft-dorsal fin; caudal fin forked; anal fin long and low, with one weak spine and more than 20 soft-rays; pelvic fins with 1 spine and 5 soft-rays; pectorals emerging high on sides, with 12 rays; intestine short, peritoneum silvery; vertebrae 40-42.

Coloration pallid, greenish but translucent; narrow, bright-silvery lateral stripe; dorsal scales moderately outlined by melanophores; head dusky; parietal spot conspicuous; lower jaw pigmented; spinous dorsal fin black-tipped, other fins colorless, except for microscopic dark flecks along rays.

Length 3½ inches or less.

The brook silverside has been found commonly in the eastern part of the Arkansas River System, and occasionally in streams of the Osage (Marais des Cygnes) System, but never in the Kansas River Basin.

Labidesthes prefers calm, clear water, but inhabits many small streams that have considerable current. Metcalf (1959:378) found silversides to be most numerous in pools having rocky bottoms. This species has become abundant in many reservoirs in the first few years after impoundment. Traveling in schools, brook silversides feed mainly on small crustaceans and insects on or near the water-surface. *Labidesthes* is attracted by lights, and collections at night sometimes yield many more specimens than do daytime-collections from the same sites.

According to Hubbs (1921), *L. sicculus* spawns from May to July. Male fish in streams congregate over gravel-bottom, where they are joined by females that enter the breeding area (repeatedly) when ready to spawn. The eggs are extruded singly. Each egg has an adhesive thread that anchors it on contact with a stone, vegetation, or debris. In Kansas, the young usually appear in collections for the first time in June or early July. Hubbs (*op. cit.*) indicated that most of the young inhabit the surface-zone over deep water during their early development, but move into shallows alongside as large juveniles or adults. Brook silversides mature as yearlings, and most live only one year.

Sculpins

FAMILY COTTIDAE

Banded sculpin

Cottus carolinae (Gill)

Uranidea richardsoni, Graham (1885b:74).
Cottus carolinae, Metcalf (1959:393).

Body scaleless, depressed and almost wedge-shaped (bluntly rounded anteriorly and tapering posteriorly); head large, nearly as broad as long, length 3.0 or less in standard length; mouth large, terminal, lips protractile; preopercle having short, sharp spine; gill membranes broadly united to isthmus; first dorsal fin supported by 8 weak spines; second dorsal with 16-19 soft-rays; anal fin having 12-14 soft-rays, no spines; pelvic fin with 1 spine and 4 soft-rays, the spine and first soft-ray enveloped by single turgid membrane; pectoral fin with 15 or more rays, base long; rays of all fins except caudal unbranched, their tips often free, margins of fins scalloped; lateral line complete, evident as low ridge on thickened epidermis from head to base of caudal fin; vertebrae 32-34.

Mottled brown, with four dark brown or black saddles: one in anterior part of spinous-dorsal fin-base, one in anterior and one in posterior part of soft-dorsal fin-base, and one immediately anterior to caudal fin-base; saddles extending downward as dark bars across sides, last two saddles expanded ventrally; ventral surface pallid, sparsely flecked by melanophores; all fins yellowish to brownish-orange, coarsely flecked by melanophores.

Length to 6½ inches, rarely more than 4 inches.

Although Graham (1885b:74) reported cottids from the "Neosho river," banded sculpins have since been taken only in Shoal Creek, Cherokee County, where they are rare. *C. carolinae* inhabits swift riffles over rubble-bottom, in clear, permanent streams having high gradients.

The banded sculpin is abundant in suitable habitats in southwestern Missouri and northeastern Oklahoma, but its range terminates abruptly along the western Ozark border. Only this species is present in the Arkansas River System exclusive of the White River Basin, where a second kind (currently referred to *C. bairdi* Girard) occurs with *carolinae.* I doubt that any sculpin other than *carolinae* will be found in Kansas, and doubt that the banded sculpin occurs west of the Spring River Drainage.

The food of banded sculpins consists mainly of larval insects (stoneflies, mayflies, caddisflies) and amphipods, according to J. E. Craddock (unpublished doctoral dissertation, University of Louisville, 1965). Small mollusks are eaten also. Large sculpins consume crayfish and some small fishes.

I know nothing of the reproductive habits of the banded sculpin in Kansas, other than that breeding occurs early in spring; young-of-the-year have been obtained in April and May. Males of *C. bairdi,* and probably also of *carolinae,* establish territories in crevices beneath stones. Females enter the nests only to deposit eggs, which are attached to the underside of the stone. The eggs are protected during their development by the guardian male (Adams and Hankinson, 1928:512).

Sea Basses

FAMILY SERRANIDAE

White bass

Roccus chrysops (Rafinesque)

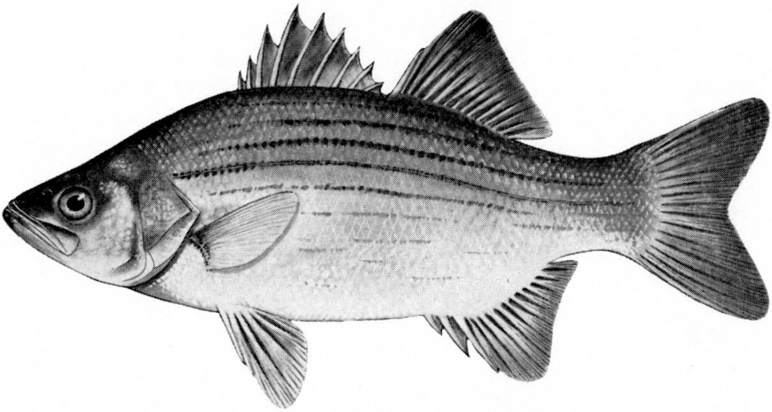

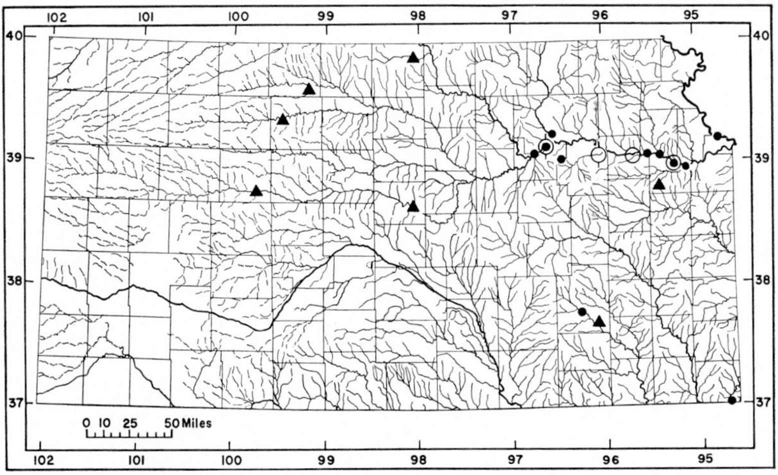

Labrax chrysops, Snow (1875:140).

Roccus chrysops, Cragin (1885b:111); Graham (1885a:4, 1885b:77); Minckley (1959:428-429); Breukelman (1960:34); Metcalf (1966:154).

White bass—Schoonover and Thompson (1954:175); Cross, Deacon, and Ward (1959:164).

Body compressed; head small, snout acute; preopercle strongly serrated; pseudobranchium present; supramaxilla absent; all fins except spinous dorsal scaled basally; first dorsal fin with 9 strong spines, second with 1 spine and 13 soft-rays; anal fin with 3 short spines (second spine distinctly shorter than third) and 11-13 soft-rays; second dorsal and anal fins triangular; pelvics with 1 spine, 5 soft-rays; pectoral fins rounded, with 15-17 rays; lateral line complete, nearly straight, with 50-55 scales; vertebrae 25.

Gray dorsally; sides silvery, with 6-9 brownish longitudinal stripes (stripes variably interrupted); fins uniformly dusky gray, unspotted. See Plate 2.

Largest Kansas specimen 20¾ inches long, its weight 4 pounds 11½ ounces.

Records in the nineteenth century attest that white bass are native to Kansas, but few were seen by anglers prior to introductions of the species in reservoirs within the past 20 years. According to a report in Kansas Fish and Game Magazine (Vol. 20, No. 1, p. 18, 1962), the first substantial stock of white bass was placed in Fall River Reservoir, Greenwood County, in 1950. Since that time, self-sustaining populations have been established in most mainstream-impoundments in Kansas, and in some small lakes that are not fed by permanent streams. I found more white bass in the Kansas, Verdigris, and Spring rivers in the 1960's than in the 1950's. Young white bass occurred abundantly alongshore in the dredged channel of the Missouri River at Wolcott (Wyandotte County) in 1965; interestingly, Fisher (1962) did not obtain this species at any of his 11 collection-sites on the Missouri River in 1945. Adult white bass now are caught sporadically in streams by angling.

White bass are highly mobile fish that travel in large schools. They seem migratory in rivers, appearing temporarily (often in autumn, or in early spring) at localities far from those where white bass occur continuously. In lakes, the schools roam pelagically, feeding on other schooling fishes such as gizzard shad (*Dorosoma cepedianum*).

An abundance of gizzard shad seems almost requisite to sucessful establishment of the white bass in reservoirs of the southern plains region. Dense populations of *Dorosoma* develop naturally in most large reservoirs in Kansas; whether white bass eventually would have appeared in the same lakes without stocking is problematical. *R. chrysops* failed to appear in the Kanopolis Reservoir until the species was introduced there several years after impoundment, despite early records of occurrence of white bass in the Kansas River Basin, and despite the abundant occurrence of shad in Kanopolis Lake throughout the years before the introduction of white bass. I think that the interval preceding stocking of white bass in Kanopolis was long enough to indicate that none occurred in the Smoky Hill River upstream from Kanopolis Dam. Perhaps the original (native) stocks in rivers of Kansas were extirpated soon after settlement of this area. Recently, numerous impoundments have greatly increased the amount of habitat suitable for white bass, enabling reestablishment of populations that probably are larger and more widespread than those which originally occupied streams in the State.

White bass are short-lived fish that usually grow to a size of one to three pounds in three or four years. Larger and older fish are rare. The 4-pound, 11½-ounce specimen that holds the State Record (as recognized by the Forestry, Fish and Game Commission) was caught in Fall River Reservoir on April 12, 1964, by Mr. Ray Cleghorn of Eureka. Cleghorn's fish weighed only 6½ ounces less than the current World Record for the species.

White bass spawn pelagically, in spring, over shoals in lakes. Reproduction occurs in rivers also, in shallow water where currents remove sediments and expose a firm, clean stream-bed. Groups of fish spawn together, without preparation of specific nesting-sites and without parental attention to the eggs after their deposition.

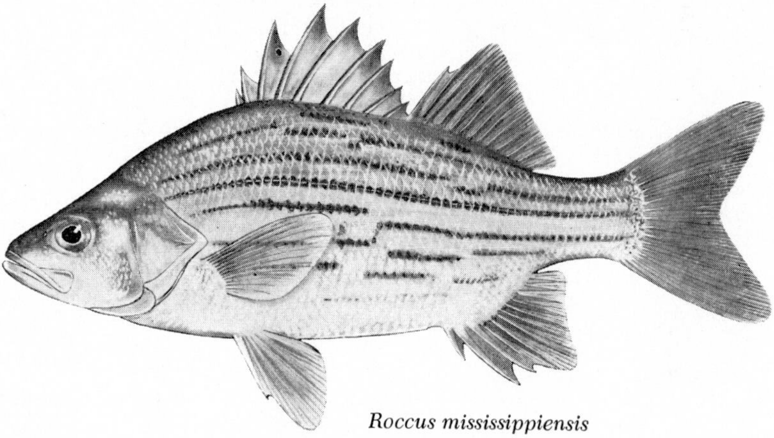

Roccus mississippiensis

Roccus mississippiensis (Jordan and Eigenmann): Graham (1885b:78) and Cragin (1885b:11) reported the yellow bass (as *Roccus interruptus* Gill) as well as the white bass in their lists of Kansas fishes. But, neither of the reports is clearly indicative of naturally-occurring populations. Graham (*loc. cit.*) stated that yellow bass were "planted . . . by the State Fish Commission." Cragin (*loc. cit.*) attributed his record to F. H. Snow, presumably on the basis of personal communication; Snow did not mention this species in his (1875) accounts of fishes in the Kansas River at Lawrence. I know of no other reports of yellow bass in Kansas, but occasional introductions of the species seem likely. *R. missis-*

sippiensis differs from *R. chrysops* in having: second and third spines in anal fin large, almost equal in length; 10 anal fin-rays; dorsal fins slightly connected; 12 rays in soft-dorsal fin; preorbital (lacrymal) bone large and broad, enveloping upper half of maxilla (preorbital narrow in white bass, scarcely overlapping maxilla); green dorsally, silvery to yellowish laterally, with six bold, dark longitudinal stripes, those ventral to lateral line abruptly broken or offset posteriorly.

Sunfishes

FAMILY CENTRARCHIDAE

KEY

1. Anal spines 5-7 2
   Anal spines 3 4
2. Dorsal spines 11 or 12 .... rock bass, *Ambloplites rupestris*, p. 272
   Dorsal spines 5-8 3
3. Dorsal spines 5 or 6; length of dorsal fin-base less than distance from origin of dorsal fin to eye ...... white crappie, *Pomoxis annularis*, p. 274
   Dorsal spines 7 or 8; length of dorsal fin-base equal to or greater than distance from origin of dorsal fin to eye, black crappie, *Pomoxis nigromaculatus*, p. 277
4. Greatest depth of body usually less than ⅓ standard length; lateral-line scales more than 55 5
   Greatest depth of body more than ⅓ standard length; lateral-line scales fewer than 55 7
5. Dorsal fin deeply notched, shortest posterior spine less than ½ length of longest spine; anal and soft-dorsal fins scaleless; scales on cheeks large, in 9-12 rows .... largemouth, *Micropterus salmoides*, p. 252
   Dorsal fin slightly notched, shortest posterior spine more than ½ length of longest spine; anal and soft-dorsal fins with small scales between rays near fin-bases; scales on cheeks minute, in more than 12 rows 6
6. Dorsal soft-rays 12; sides having dark lateral band, sometimes broken into blotches; lower sides usually with rows of dark dots anteriorly, spotted bass, *Micropterus punctulatus*, p. 250
   Dorsal soft-rays 13-15; sides plain greenish-brown, or with indistinct vertical bars .... smallmouth, *Micropterus dolomieui*, p. 248
7. Opercle stiff along its posterior edge, within dark "earspot" (only the narrow, transparent marginal membrane flexible; Fig. 19A) .. 8
   Opercle attenuated into flexible dark "earspot" (Fig. 19B) 10
8. Upper jaw shorter than highest dorsal fin-spine; pectoral fins long and pointed; gill rakers short, knoblike (Fig. 7D), redear, *Lepomis microlophus*, p. 261
   Upper jaw longer than highest dorsal spine; pectoral fins short and rounded; gill rakers slender (Fig. 7C) 9

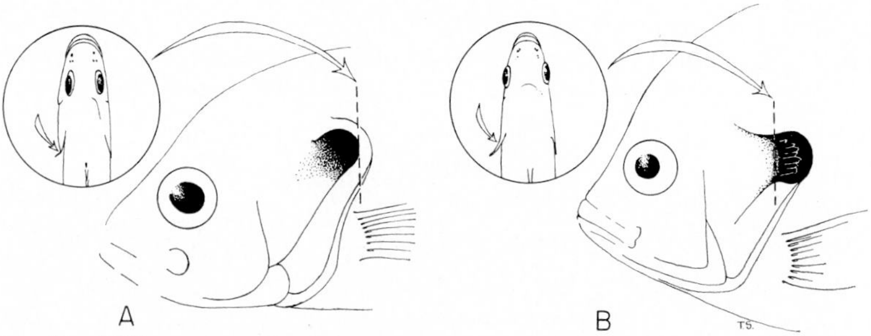

FIG. 19. Differences in flexibility of opercles in sunfishes.

A. Opercle inflexible posteriorly, its bony edge sharply defined where joined by the marginal gill-membrane (as in the warmouth, green sunfish, and redear).

B. Opercle flexible posteriorly, attenuated as a thin, fimbriate, cartilaginous extension into the gill-membrane (as in the bluegill, longear, and orange-spotted sunfish).

9. Tongue having central patch of sandpaperlike teeth; lateral-line scales fewer than 45; supramaxilla well-developed,
warmouth, *Chaenobryttus gulosus*, p. 256

No teeth on tongue; lateral-line scales usually more than 45; supramaxilla weak, inconspicuous . . green sunfish, *Lepomis cyanellus*, p. 258

10. Gill rakers short and knoblike (Fig. 7D); pectoral fins short and rounded, less than 4 times length of pectoral fin base, and less than twice least depth of caudal peduncle; reddish streak on midline of back, before dorsal fin, in life (pallid in preserved specimens),
longear, *Lepomis megalotis*, p. 269

Gill rakers slender (Fig. 7C), longest when depressed extending to base of second raker below; pectoral fins pointed, their length at least 4 times length of pectoral base, and at least twice depth of caudal peduncle; no reddish predorsal stripe 11

11. Supraorbital canals (two pit-like depressions atop head between eyes) wider than bony space between them; anal soft-rays usually 9; length of upper jaw much more than ⅓ length of pectoral fin; opercular projection large in adults and brilliantly white-edged,
orange-spotted sunfish, *Lepomis humilis*, p. 266

Supraorbital canals narrower than bony space between them; anal soft-rays usually 10-12, rarely 9; length of upper jaw less than ⅓ length of pectoral fin; opercular projection short, dusky to its margin,
bluegill, *Lepomis macrochirus*, p. 263

Smallmouth

Micropterus dolomieui Lacépède

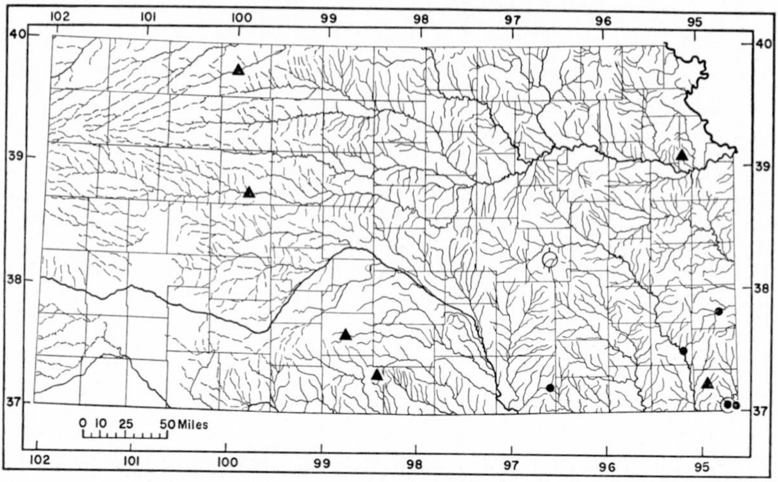

Micropterus dolomieu, Graham (1885b:76,78); Dyche (1914:43); Hall (1934:231, possibly misidentification of *M. punctulatus*).

Micropterus dolemieu, Breukelman (1946:61).

Micropterus dolomieui, Breukelman (1960:9,34); Deacon (1961:397); Metcalf (1966:154).

Micropterus dolomieui velox, Cross (1954:311).

Body moderately compressed, depth contained more than 3.0 times in standard length; spinous dorsal fin low, broadly joined to soft-rayed part of fin; dorsal spines 9 or 10, subequal in length, shortest (posterior) spine more than ½ length of longest dorsal spine; dorsal soft-rays 12-15; anal spines 3, soft-rays usually 11; pelvic fins with 1 spine, 5 soft-rays; pectoral rays 16-18; scales small, 68 or more in lateral line; cheeks with 14 or more rows of scales from eye to angle of preopercle (cheek-scales obviously smaller than those on opercle); membranes of soft-dorsal and anal fins scaled near bases; vertebrae 31-33.

Brown or olivaceous brown, either plain or mottled by diffuse dark vertical blotches; no dark longitudinal stripe; belly white; fins dusky; young with caudal fin orange basally, and with submarginal black band.

The smallmouth is probably native to streams of southeastern Kansas, but the extent of its original distribution has been obscured by introductions. Only in the Spring River Drainage of Cherokee County have I found smallmouths frequently, and I think that populations there may be the only native stocks that persist in Kansas.

Outside the Spring River System, few records of the smallmouth exist excepting those that are known to result from introductions. Deacon (1961:397) reported a single smallmouth (KU 4682, 41 mm. in standard length) from the Neosho River in Neosho County, and I caught a hybrid (KU 4682, smallmouth × spotted bass) in the Marmaton River, Bourbon County, in 1953. The westernmost record from a stream (and also the earliest record of the smallmouth from Kansas) is based upon a juvenile (KSU 2998, 77 mm. in standard length) caught in Rock Creek, Chase County, by I. D. Graham (Cross, 1954:311). The date of capture is unknown, but almost certainly was prior to 1886 (see Jennings, 1942:366). Even that specimen may not have been a native fish, because Graham (1885b:78) listed the smallmouth among "Fishes planted in the waters of Kansas by the State Fish Commission" before 1886. Dyche (1914:43) scarcely mentioned the smallmouth in his accounts of Kansas game-fishes, stating that it was "Rare in Kansas streams, and has not done well when introduced in this state. . . ."

The most recent introductions known to me have been in Otter Creek, tributary to Caney River (in Cowley and Chautauqua counties), repeatedly since 1957; in ponds in Barber County in 1962; and in Cedar Bluff Reservoir (Trego County), Norton Reservoir (Norton County), and the Leavenworth County State Lake in 1962-1964.

As a native fish in latitudes as far south as Kansas, the smallmouth originally occupied only clear, cool, upland streams that had relatively stable waterlevels. Natural populations remain in many Ozarkian streams in southern Missouri, northern Arkansas, and northeastern Oklahoma. The adults usually inhabit pools, especially those having undercut banks, boulders, or fallen trees as cover. The principal food of the species consists of crayfish, aquatic insects, and fish, obtained from gravelly riffles and shallows peripheral to the pools.

The reproductive season of the smallmouth usually begins in April and extends through May. Each male fans out a shallow depression in the bottom as a nest, most often over gravel or sand-bottom adjacent to a boulder or stump in shallow water. Probably, only one female deposits eggs in each nest. She is then routed by the male, which remains over or near the nest until the young have hatched and dispersed from it. Most smallmouths mature in their third or fourth year of life, at lengths of 9 to 12 inches. Some reports indicate that juveniles and adults are highly sedentary, tending to remain in the same pool throughout life—and to return to the "home" pool if displaced from it.

Spotted bass

Micropterus punctulatus (Rafinesque)

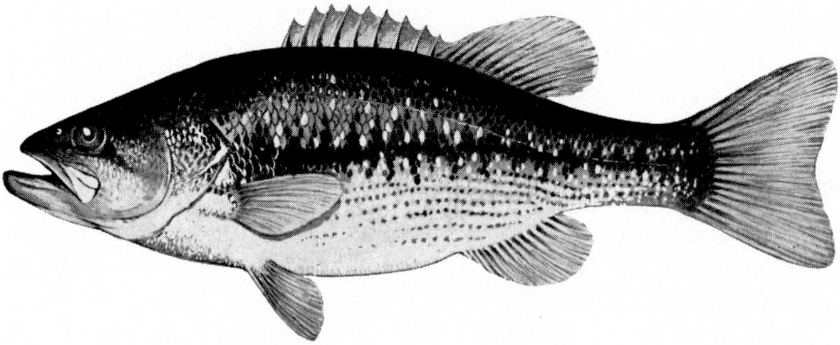

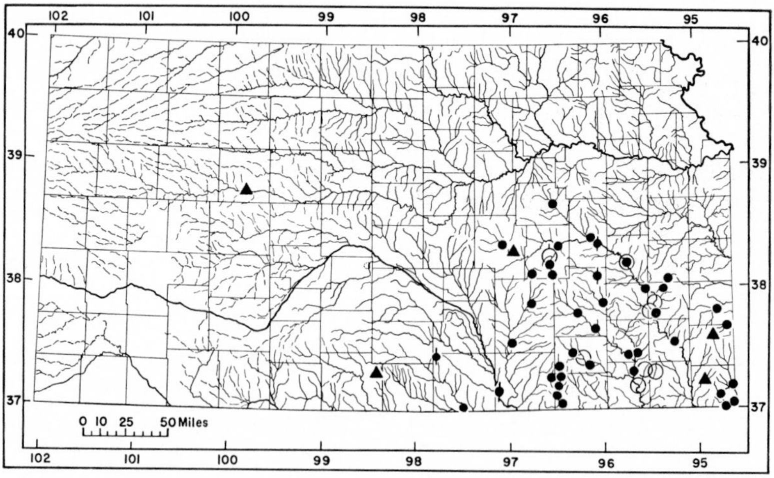

Micropterus punctulatus, Wall (1948:101-113); Moore and Buck (1955:26); Clarke, Breukelman, and Andrews (1958:169); Metcalf (1959:380, 393, 1966:154); Breukelman (1946:61, 1960:9,34).

Micropterus punctulatus punctulatus, Breukelman (1940a:373, 1940b:382); Jennings (1942:366); Cross (1954:312); Schelske (1957:48); Deacon (1961:397).

Huro salmoides, Jennings (1942:366, misidentifications in part).

Body moderately compressed, depth contained more than 3.0 times in standard length; spinous dorsal fin low, joined to soft-rayed part of fin; dorsal spines usually 10, shortest (posterior) spine more than ½ length of longest dorsal spine; dorsal soft-rays usually 12; anal spines 3, soft-rays usually 10, pectoral rays 15 or 16; lateral line with 60-68 scales; cheek-scales in 12 or more rows, obviously smaller than scales on opercle; membranes of soft-dorsal and anal fins scaled near bases; vertebrae usually 32.

Olivaceous dorsally, sometimes blotched or variegated; mid-sides with dark (black) blotches, usually merging in irregular longitudinal stripe; lower sides commonly lined anteriorly by lengthwise rows of dark dots; belly white; fins dusky; caudal fin orange basally in young, and dark near tip.

Largest Kansas specimen 17½ inches long, weight 3 pounds 12½ ounces (State record on hook-and-line, caught by John I. Waner in Marion County Lake in April, 1964).

The spotted bass is common in most streams of the Arkansas River System that drain limestone-uplands, and occurs also in the southernmost tributaries of the Osage River System. The streams inhabited are mostly small, clear, and spring-fed, but approach intermittency in late summer and fall.

Seemingly, the native range of *M. punctulatus* did not include the Kansas River Basin, and occurrences elsewhere in the Missouri River System may be the result of introductions. The absence of this species from north-flowing streams in the Flint Hills of Wabaunsee, Riley, Morris, and Pottawatomie counties contrasts sharply with its prevalence in nearby streams that discharge southward into the Neosho River. Wall (1948:104) correctly indicated that *M. punctulatus* is "the dominant species of black bass in the streams of the Flint Hills . . . of southeastern Kansas." Failure to recognize the spotted bass accounts for the lack of early records; several specimens exist among collections made by Graham in the 1880's and by the State Biological Survey in 1910-1912.

While spotted bass abound in the headwaters of the Cottonwood, Neosho, Caney, Verdigris, and Spring rivers, this bass yields to the largemouth in the lower mainstreams of those rivers. Spotted bass became common in the Neosho when that river was unusually low and clear during the protracted drought of 1952-1956, but declined in abundance during subsequent wet years (Deacon, 1961:397).

Crayfish and insects are the principal food of the spotted bass. Wall (1948:111) commented that "crayfish are always in abundance" in the habitat of spotted bass, and a close association of *M. punctulatus* with crayfishes (*Orconectes nais* or *O. neglectus* in Kansas) has been noted by others. Spotted bass readily strike artificial flies and small spinners.

Spotted bass have attracted surprisingly little attention from anglers in Kansas, perhaps because this fish and the streams that it occupies are generally small. Seldom do spotted bass exceed a pound and a half in weight, and the largest one on record from Kansas was barely ⅓ the size of the record largemouth. But, some of my own most satisfying hours of fishing have been spent in catching spotted bass and little long-eared sunfish from pools along the brooks that drain the open, untilled prairies of Chase County.

The reproductive habits of the spotted bass are generally like those described for the smallmouth. Examination of scales of spotted bass from Otter Creek, Cowley County, indicated that the species attained a length of 2.5 to 5 inches in the first year of life, 6.5 to 7 inches in the second year, and 8.6 inches in the third year (specimens and data obtained in 1957 by W. L. Minckley).

Largemouth

Micropterus salmoides (Lacépède)

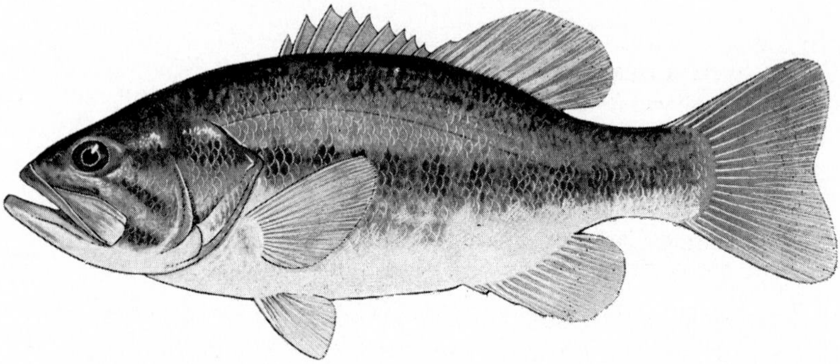

Micropterus nigricans, Wheeler (1879:33).

Micropterus salmoides, Cragin (1885b:110); Graham (1885a:4, 1885b:76); Jordan and Meek (1885:14); Gilbert (1886:211); Dyche (1914:42, 45-51); Maupin, Wells, and Leist (1954:168, 171); Moore and Buck (1955:26); Greer and Cross (1956:360); Clarke, Breukelman, and Andrews (1958:169); Cross, Deacon, and Ward (1959:163-164); Breukelman (1960:9, 34); Hastings and Cross (1962:10, 15); Kilgore and Rising (1965:141).

Aplites salmoides, Hall (1934:231).

Huro salmoides, Breukelman (1940a:373, 1940b:382); Jennings (1942:366 in part).

Micropterus salmoides salmoides, Cross (1954:312); Schelske (1957:48); Metcalf (1959:380, 1966:154); Minckley (1959:429); Deacon (1961:398); Deacon and Metcalf (1961:318).

Largemouth bass—Schoonover and Thompson (1954:173-174).

Body slightly compressed, greatest depth contained more than 3.0 times in standard length; dorsal fin deeply notched, shortest spine (in notch) less than ½

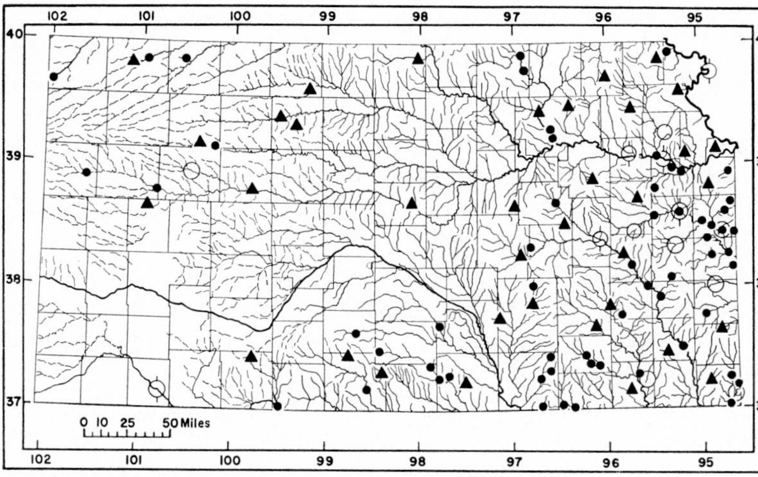

length of longest spine; soft-dorsal and anal fins not scaled near bases; scales on cheek in 9-12 rows, about as large as scales on opercle; lateral-line scales usually 60-65; dorsal fin usually with 9 spines, 12 or 13 soft-rays; anal fin with 3 small spines, usually 11 soft-rays; pelvic fins with 1 spine, 5 soft-rays; pectoral rays 14 or 15; vertebrae usually 32 or 33.

Plain olivaceous dorsally, fading to white ventrally; mid-sides with dark stripe of variable intensity, most prominent in young; lateral stripe often interrupted anteriorly, but continuous and almost straight-edged on caudal peduncle (not blotched as in spotted bass); lower sides never lined by dark dots; fins unspotted; caudal fin in young lacking orange pigment. See Plate 2.

Largest Kansas specimen 25 inches long, weight 11 pounds 3 ounces (State Record fish caught in Bourbon County by Mr. Charles Prewett in January, 1965).

The largemouth occurs throughout Kansas, partly as a result of construction in the last few decades of thousands of impoundments, most of which have been stocked with this species. It is native to Kansas, and is common in the Neosho and Marais des Cygnes rivers and their larger tributaries. Elsewhere populations in streams are small and sporadic.

The principal habitat of the largemouth in Kansas is in ponds and reservoirs, where the species does well regardless of the size of the impoundment, so long as the water remains clear. Many Kansas lakes and ponds are turbid in summer; hence, the success of their bass-populations, and of angling, is disappointing. Since 1950, I have noted changes in the abundance of bass in several lakes that seem to correlate with weather-cycles. In wet years from 1950 until 1952, small bass were not abundant in these lakes, but the number increased in subsequent dry years through 1956. From

1957 until 1962 (wet years), populations decreased again. Because turbidity (muddiness of water) is partly a function of the amount of runoff following rains, the higher populations in dry years may result from clearer water in the dry periods.

Deacon (1961:398) found evidence of change in the abundance of largemouths and spotted bass in the Neosho River, attributable to weather-conditions in the 1950's. That relationship is mentioned in my account of the spotted bass.

Weather-cycles and turbidity are not the only factors that affect the abundance of bass, nor do high populations always ensure good catches of fish. For one reason or another, a high abundance of bass seldom sustains itself; instead, the greatest number of young (strongest year-classes) usually are produced when adult bass are scarce, and weak year-classes are likely when large bass are abundant. Hatcherymen are aware of this relationship, recognizing that only a few brood-fish are needed to produce all the young that can be supported in rearing-ponds; an increase in the number of brood-fish reduces the production of young. This relationship may account, at least in part, for the decline in angling success in many reservoirs that provide excellent bass-fishing in the early years of impoundment but then taper off to low rates of catch. Most large impoundments on streams have a few adult bass that formerly occupied the stream or ponds in the area inundated. Young spawned by these few fish, supplemented by fingerlings that are stocked, generally enjoy good survival and rapid growth because this first year-class is almost free of predation and competition by older and larger fish. The young that are produced in the first year or two after the lake fills provide more bass for the creel than do subsequent year-classes, despite the fact that far more adults are available for spawning in later years.

The history of a bass-population in a 2-acre pond at Lawrence provides an extreme example of the principle discussed above. The pond had no fish in it for three years after it filled, and during that time an abundance of food-organisms developed naturally. Six bass, each about 10 inches long, were stocked in 1959 and spawned in that year. The young flourished, attaining lengths of almost six inches in their first year of life, and 8 to 11 inches in the summer of 1960. Approximately 500 bass were caught from the pond in 1960, and several more were taken as 1½-pound fish in 1961.

The second year-class of bass was less successful than the first. Possibly, as many young were spawned in 1960 as in 1959, but their growth was slow. At least 500 of these (1960) fish were caught in 1961—as many yearlings as were harvested from the preceding year-class—but few fish from the second spawn attained lengths of 8 inches by the fall of their second year. Few of them ever grew larger than 8 inches, even as late as 1964, when a careful estimate of the population indicated that about 280 bass remained in the pond. These small bass were mature, and some that were transferred to other ponds reproduced; but, no bass hatched in 1961, 1962, or 1963 were found in the 2-acre pond. Either the adult bass failed to spawn under the crowded conditions that existed after the spring of 1960, or all the young that were produced were eaten by larger bass. In 1964 and 1965, after further cropping had depleted the 1960 year-class, many young were produced again for the first time since 1960.

The largemouth is an obligate carnivore, and that fact limits the poundage of bass that any body of water can support. A diverse array of living organisms is eaten by bass, but I know of no instance in which bass-production has been increased substantially by the addition of supplemental food other than live animals. Bass differ in this respect from most kinds of catfish and trout, which readily accept artificial diets prepared from dry foodstuffs.

Few lakes and ponds can be made to support more than 100 pounds of bass per acre, including young fish as well as adults large enough to be vulnerable to angling; the average "standing crop" of bass is considerably less than 100 pounds per acre, even in good bass-lakes. Therefore, small lakes cannot reasonably be expected to yield numerous large bass to anglers throughout the year.

The most successful bass-fishermen are those who fish often, and who are thoroughly familiar with the waters being fished. Experience helps, because the precise spot where one large bass has been caught will yield others at later times. The most avid local fisherman on a given lake is likely to catch more bass there, through his knowledge of the sites where these fish "hang out," than is any visiting angler no matter how expert the latter may be in handling his tackle.

Warmouth

Chaenobryttus gulosus (Cuvier)

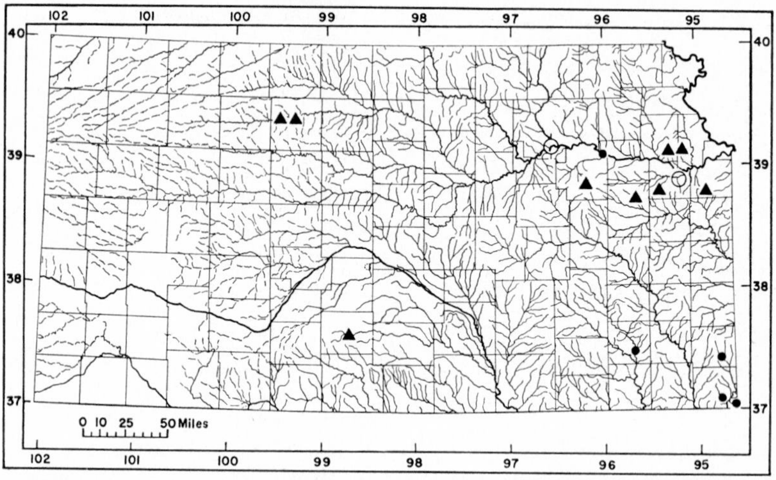

Chaenobryttus gulosus, Graham (1885b:75); Breukelman (1940b:382, 1960:12,34); Clarke, Breukelman, and Andrews (1958:169); Cross, Deacon, and Ward (1959:163); Deacon and Metcalf (1961:318); Metcalf (1966:155).

Chaenobryttus coronarius, Maupin, Wells, and Leist (1954:168, 171).

Body compressed; head and mouth large; supramaxilla well-developed; width of jawbone, posteriorly, about twice narrowest space between upper jaw and eye; dorsal fin with 10 or 11 short spines, usually 10 soft-rays; anal fin with 3 spines, 9 or 10 soft-rays; pelvics having 1 spine, 5 soft-rays; pectoral fins short and rounded, rays usually 13; lateral line complete, arched anteriorly, with 35-44 scales; opercle stiff to edge of dark opercular spot; gill rakers slender; scales on midline of breast and isthmus large, exposed, conspicuous; vertebrae 28-30.

Brown with obscure vertical bars or with lines of dark dots along scale-rows; sides of head with alternating brown and yellow bars radiating outward from orbit (bars never iridescent green); iris red or reddish-brown; fins dark or coarsely mottled; dorsal fin lacking distinct basal blotch posteriorly; pelvic fins white-edged.

Weight one pound, length 11 inches or less (Trautman, 1957:498; Larimore, 1957:62); seldom heavier than ½ pound.

The warmouth occurs mainly in impoundments in Kansas. Our records based on net-catches are mostly from the older State and County lakes such as Leavenworth (Tonganoxie), Lone Star (Douglas County), Wabaunsee County (Eskridge), and Crawford County (Farlington). Most or all "rock bass" caught in these and other Kansas lakes are *C. gulosus* rather than *Ambloplites rupestris.* The scarcity of warmouths in Kansas, except in impoundments, suggests the possibility that the species is not indigenous; but, Graham's (1885b:75) report of *C. gulosus* from the "Kansas River," and absence of this species from his list of fishes introduced prior to 1885, argues for its native status. The oldest extant specimens known to me (KU 8483, three specimens obtained in 1913) are from an oxbow lake in Douglas County. More recently, warmouths have been caught in streams tributary to the Arkansas River, and the species has been taken at one or more localities within all the major drainages in eastern Kansas. Probably warmouths are now more widespread than the mapped records indicate.

Larimore (1957) has written an excellent account of the life-history and ecology of *C. gulosus.* Its principal habitat is in ponded, often turbid water, where bottoms are soft mud and where dense weed-beds exist.

Adult warmouths do not form schools; they are sparsely scattered in Kansas lakes, in shallow water alongshore, usually adjacent to emergent vegetation or brush. The food of warmouths consists of larval insects (mayflies, damselflies, dragonflies, caddisflies, dipterans), crayfish, and a few small fishes (Larimore, 1957:14-15). The reproductive period in Illinois (*op. cit.*) extends from mid-May until August, but the peak of spawning is in early June. Nests (rounded depressions in the bottom) are excavated and attended by males, and are mostly in water less than three feet deep.

Most warmouths caught in Kansas lakes are six to eight inches long and weigh no more than six ounces. Their initial strike is spectacularly vicious, but my experience has been that the warmouth lacks stamina, turning on its side soon after its initial rush.

Green sunfish

Lepomis cyanellus Rafinesque

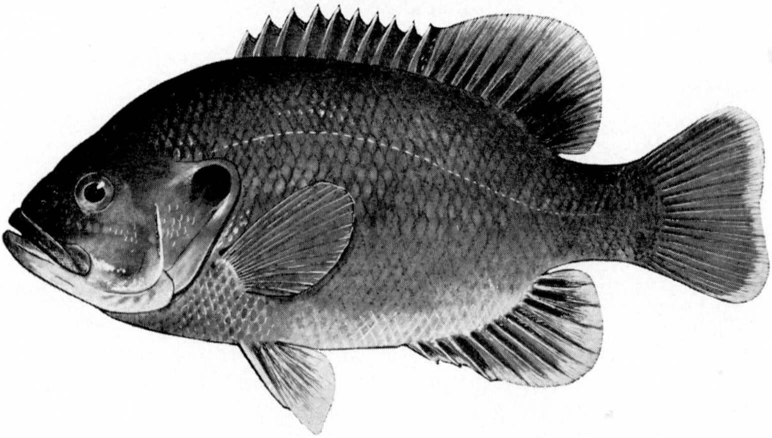

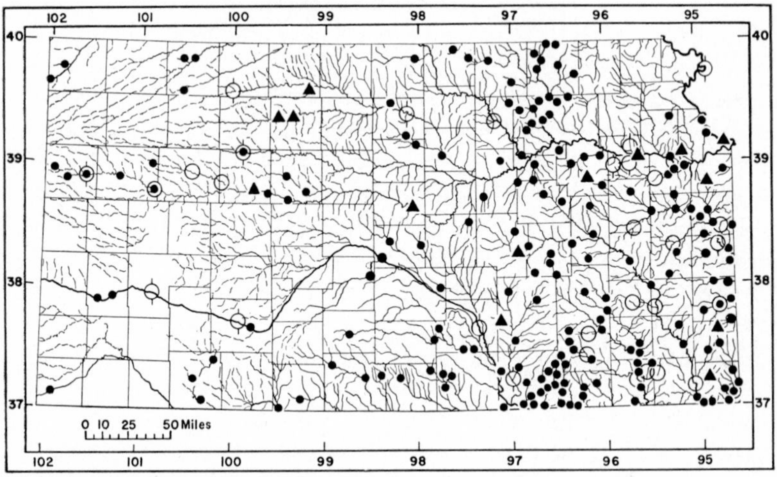

Bryttus longulus, Cope (1865b:85).

Lepomis cyanellus, Gilbert (1884:16, 1885:99, 1886:211, 1889:40); Cragin (1885b:110); Graham (1885a:4, 1885b:75); Jordan and Meek (1885: 14); Evermann and Fordice (1886:185); Hay (1887:243, 249, 250, 252); Jordan (1891:18); Dyche (1914:62, 115); Breukelman (1940a:373, 1940b:382, 384, 1960:12, 34); Jennings (1942:366); Maupin, Wells, and Leist (1954:168, 171); Cross (1954:312); Moore and Buck (1955:26); Minckley (1956:355); Schelske (1957:48); Clarke, Breukelman, and Andrews (1958:169); Cross, Deacon, and Ward (1959:163-164); Minckley and Cross (1959:212); Metcalf (1959:381, 1966:155); Minckley (1959:429); Deacon (1961:398); Deacon and Metcalf (1961:318); Hastings and Cross (1962:8, 18); Fisher (1962:428); Kilgore and Rising (1965:241).

Apomotus cyanellus, Hall (1934:231).

Green sunfish—Schoonover and Thompson (1954:174).

Body compressed, head and mouth large; supramaxilla thin, splintlike; width of jawbone, posteriorly, about equal to narrowest space between upper jaw and eye; dorsal fin usually having 10 short spines and 11 soft-rays; anal fin with 3 spines, 8 or 9 soft-rays; pelvics with 1 spine, 5 soft-rays; pectorals short and rounded, having 13 or 14 rays; lateral line complete, arched anteriorly, with 45-50 scales; opercle stiff to margin of dark posterior spot, membrane broad and pallid; gill rakers slender; scales on midline of breast and isthmus minute, inconspicuous, often partly embedded; vertebrae 28-30.

Adults dark olivaceous, breast and belly yellowish-orange; sides of head usually having iridescent green flecks or "worm-tracks"; dorsal and anal fins with dark basal blotch posteriorly. Breeding males with all fins dark; margins of pelvics, anal, and caudal fin lemon-yellow; young with closely-spaced, chain-like vertical bars on dark background. See Plate 3.

Largest Kansas specimen 12 inches long, weight 2 pounds 2 ounces (State record, caught by Mr. Lewis Ferlo of Scammon, from a strip-mine lake in Cherokee County on May 28, 1961).

The green sunfish is nearly ubiquitous, but its principal habitat seems to be small, muddy creeks that have temporary flow. Few other fish penetrate so far up minor drainageways during wet periods as do green sunfish, and few are so successful in surviving drought in residual pools.

L. cyanellus seems mainly solitary in habit, each adult occupying a small area in which it forages. The territories often are tiny and congested; usually they are near the water's edge, under cover such as rocks on dams (in large impoundments) or exposed roots on an eroded streambank. The food of green sunfish consists mainly of insects, of both aquatic and terrestrial origin. Fish are eaten also. I have found carp, bass, and many other kinds of fishes in the stomachs of green sunfish, which have the capacity to ingest fish half their own size.

Reproduction occurs throughout the warm months, most intensively in May and June. As in other centrarchids, males construct and guard nests. The nests are circular depressions formed by removal of the finer sediments, mainly by vigorous fanning action of the tail of the attendant male. The nests commonly occur in groups, in shallow places where the bottom is smooth, clean, and slopes gently away from the shoreline.

Because of their abundance and willingness to strike at natural or artificial baits, green sunfish are significant sport-fish in Kansas. In many lakes, they can be caught throughout spring, summer, and fall, at any hour of the day, by means of small hooks baited with worms or by casting wet-flies or poppers alongshore. The species is handicapped as a game fish, though, by small size and limited endurance. It strikes savagely but its subsequent fight is disappointing. Large green sunfish, weighing a half-pound or more, provide interesting angling, but *L. cyanellus* seldom attains that weight in Kansas. Green sunfish become so abundant in most farm ponds that few grow larger than six inches long, which is about the minimum usable size. Stunting is sometimes so severe that specimens three inches long are reproductively active. Under these conditions, the species is a nuisance rather than an angling resource.

Green sunfish occasionally hybridize with other species of *Lepomis* in Kansas, most commonly with the bluegill, *L. macrochirus*. Hybridization is thought to result from rarity of one of the parental species coupled with abundance of the other; scarcity of nesting sites may lead to hybridization also. Bluegill-green sunfish hybrids are males that probably are not reproductively functional, although they build and defend nests in summer. They exhibit "hybrid vigor" in the sense that they usually grow more rapidly than their parental species in ponds, and are more aggressive in taking anglers' lures than are the bluegills and green sunfish in the same ponds. This hybrid has some utility as a sport-fish. It can be produced in quantity by stocking a pond with a few male bluegills and a few female green sunfish, both of which are readily available as brood-stock. The young hybrids can then be seined and transferred to other ponds, in limited numbers to ensure their growth to large size. Ordinarily, enough young are produced in the brood-pond to provide stock for several other ponds, and for replacement of hybrids that are caught from those ponds. Both the brood-pond and the fishing-ponds should be free of other kinds of fish.

Redear

Lepomis microlophus (Günther)

Body compressed, rounded; mouth moderately small, oblique; dorsal fin with 10 high spines, 11 or 12 soft-rays; anal fin with 3 strong spines, 10 or 11 rays; pelvic fin with 1 spine, 5 soft-rays; pectoral rays usually 13; pectoral fin long, acutely pointed, usually extending to middle of anal-fin base when depressed, and extending beyond origin of dorsal fin when rotated upward; lateral line complete, scales usually 35-37; opercular flap short, stiff (edge of opercle thin and slightly flexible in juveniles); gill rakers short, the longest not reaching base of second raker below when depressed against gill-arch.

Adults pale olivaceous dorsally, silvery laterally or with faint brownish mottling; dark blotch on opercle bounded posteriorly by red crescent in life (membrane white in preserved specimens); dorsal fin uniformly dusky, without large, dark blotch on posterior membranes. Young-of-year marked by about 8 dark vertical bars, slightly narrower than interspaces (bars commonly interrupted); larger juveniles not barred, evenly mottled by dusky spots on silvery ground-color.

The redear has been introduced repeatedly in Kansas. One introduction of fish purchased in Georgia was made by Mr. Bill Schwartz into a pond at Topeka, and by Mr. Abe Cox into Lake Shawnee, in 1952. Mr. Roy Schoonover of the Kansas Forestry, Fish and Game Commission told me that redears formerly were raised at the Commission's fish-hatchery at Meade, but production of them there was discontinued several years ago. Other personnel of the Fish and Game Commission have informed me that redears have been stocked, and subsequently caught on hook-and-line, in many ponds in eastern Kansas in the 1960's.

The redear serves the same management-purpose in ponds as does the bluegill, in that its young provide forage for bass while the adult redears themselves afford angling catches. Substitution of redears for bluegills in initial stocks usually is based on an assumption that redears reproduce successfully but less prolifically than bluegills in ponds. If that assumption proves correct in the particular pond stocked, a troublesome problem of overpopulation and stunting by the forage-species is avoided or postponed. The pond may then yield redears that weigh a half-pound or more, and sustain production of such large fish for several years. This desirable result has not been achieved consistently in ponds that I have checked. In some of those ponds, redears "stunted" as quickly and as severely as do bluegills; in others, redears failed to establish self-sustaining populations and disappeared three or four years after release of the initial stock.

Redears are more difficult to catch than bluegills. One effective angling-technique involves use of a light line, fine leader, and minute hook generously loaded with worms. The bait should be fished without weight or bobber, on the bottom in deep parts of the pond. Redears often strike gently, and reject baits that offer resistance owing to lead weights or other encumbrances on the line.